PALMS OF THE WORLD

PALMS

Foreword by W. H. Hodge

President, The Palm Society

Illustrated with over 400 photographs

HARPER & BROTHERS, NEW YORK

OF THE WORLD

by James C. McCurrach

PALMS OF THE WORLD

1-16-61

CONTENTS

FOREWORD   vii

PREFACE   ix

ACKNOWLEDGMENTS   xi

INTRODUCTORY NOTES   xiii

Nomenclature
Economic Importance
Cultivation in the United States
Notes on Culture

ILLUSTRATED GLOSSARY   xix

PALM DESCRIPTIONS   2

APPENDIX   273

A List of the World's Valid Palm Genera
and Some Synonyms,
prepared by Max Burret and Eva Potztal

Lists of Palms to Be Found Growing Outdoors
in Certain Famous Botanical Gardens
(Reprinted from the various Garden lists)

To My Wife

Margaret M. McCurrach

FOREWORD
by W. H. Hodge

President, The Palm Society

To most people, palm trees and the tropics are synonymous. This is understandable, for the great family of the palms, whose species are almost legion, is almost exclusively tropical with representatives to be found in all equatorial regions of the world.

With but few species growing in temperate latitudes, it is but little wonder that palms are strangers to many of us who reside in temperate lands far from the warmth of the subtropics. This has been one reason why these attractive trees have remained relatively poorly known both to the layman and to the plant scientist.

This is not to say that man has had little to do with palms; for ages he has had much to do with them. The "Tree of Life" of the Bible was a palm, the date palm, whose culture was recorded as early as 3500 B.C. This species and hundreds of other palms continue to supply our civilization with some of its most important plant products. At the same time, other palms have been cloaking the vegetational regions of the tropics with a green elegance unmatched by many other plants. Fortunately, many palms have now made their horticultural mark as ornamentals and increasing numbers are to be found planted in tropical and subtropical gardens.

Growers of palms have long needed a ready reference to the species most frequently met with in cultivation. Up to now there has been no single volume purporting to present an illustrated treatment of this great family of plants. The keen interest of James C. McCurrach, an amateur plantsman and palm collector of the first order, has fortunately brought such a book into being. This detailed compilation has, according to the author, "been written in an effort to fill a void in the literature covering the family *Palmaceae*." It should certainly do all of that, for the wealth of illustrations alone will serve as a guide to all enthusiasts interested in one of the green world's most fascinating groups of plants.

vii

PREFACE

This book has been written by a palm collector in an effort to fill a void in the literature covering the family Palmaceae.

The palms are fascinating plants and deserve to be much better known to everyone interested in botany and gardening. This detailed compilation explains and illustrates the palm family as known today. The data were gathered from the written works of today's best-known authorities throughout the world and from personal observation of the living plants in many areas.

In assembling this information, I have sought to produce a reliable reference book, arranged in as convenient and efficient a form as possible. The descriptions of species appear close to the illustrations in order that the reader may observe as he reads. The genera are treated in alphabetical order. The object is to inform rather than to entertain. It is my hope that this volume will acquaint more palm lovers with the infinite variety available to them.

A certain amount of confusion exists concerning the nomenclature of palms and authorities are not always in agreement. I have taken no position on these differences of opinion. This would require much further study and research to resolve, but I have followed the practice of giving all the information that is available from reliable sources.

Only a few species of palms are indigenous to the United States. The various date palms that lend a tropical appearance to the landscapes of southern California and southern Florida were imported from India, Africa, and the Canary Islands. The royal palms[1] were brought in from Cuba, Puerto Rico, and South America. A few of Florida's beautiful coconuts may have floated in on the tides, but thousands were imported by man. These and a few other species (all rarities sixty years ago), are now familiar sights to residents and visitors in our warmer regions.

It is not generally realized that scores of other interesting species have been successfully grown for years in a few public or private gardens but have not yet become widely used or readily available. One of the most striking sights in Fairchild Tropical Garden in Coconut Grove, Florida, is a group of about thirty *Copernicia* palms. They are twenty years old and were raised in this garden from seeds imported from Cuba. Thousands of visitors must have been impressed by these spectacular and beautiful plants; yet, it would probably be hard to find fifty other copernicias in private gardens or nurseries in the whole state of Florida.

---

[1]One species of royal palm, *Roystonea elata*, is now believed to be indigenous to southern Florida.

The average nurseryman does not cultivate a large variety of palms. He confines himself, perforce, to the few popular species that are at present most familiar to landscape gardeners and homeowners. Those few nurserymen who have become interested in the more unusual palms have often been discouraged by the lack of public knowledge and appreciation. Having sent to some distant land for rare seeds and nursed a seedling through its first few, slow years of growth, they are dismayed to find that to many of their customers this precious plant is just another little palm.

The keen interest of some discriminating collectors is not so easily satisfied. Several such enthusiasts have private collections, some of which include over 400 species, ranging from small seedlings to young trees. These collections have been assembled by diligent searching among a few interested nurseries and by securing seeds through correspondence with friends and with botanical gardens in foreign countries.

I hope that this book will not only be of assistance to these collectors but that it will also add new enthusiasts to their ranks. The United States is fortunate in having within its borders climates suitable for palm trees, particularly those of southern Florida and southern California. The enterprising men and women who, fifty years ago, introduced so many new tropical palms have tremendously enhanced these areas. This book embraces several scores of species that can, and should, be added to the general scene, requiring only some enthusiastic pioneers to bring them to more general popularity.

The efforts of horticulturists interested in growing any but the most common palms will be greatly facilitated by membership in the recently formed Palm Society. Organized in April, 1956, the Palm Society[1] already has a membership spread over seventeen states and twenty-five foreign countries. It publishes a quarterly journal (under the direction of Dr. Harold E. Moore, Jr., today's prominent U.S. authority on palms) containing information not to be found elsewhere, and it has recently established a seed bank intended to supply members with seeds of uncommon trees.

JAMES C. McCURRACH

Palm Beach, Florida
October 1, 1959

[1]The Palm Society, 7229 S.W. 54th Avenue, Miami 43, Florida.

ACKNOWLEDGMENTS

This book would not have been completed in its present form without the aid of many persons who made available knowledge and resources essential to the subject as a whole. It is a pleasure to acknowledge my gratitude to those who have so generously helped me.

The Bailey Hortorium of Cornell University and its director, Dr. George Lawrence, were very helpful in permitting the author to go through Dr. Liberty Hyde Bailey's files and in lending from those files a number of photographs; Dr. Harold E. Moore, Jr., who is carrying forward Dr. Bailey's work on palms, was most patient in answering hundreds of questions.

Mr. and Mrs. A. C. Langlois added greatly to my knowledge during a visit to their estate, "The Retreat," in Nassau, Bahamas, where full sized specimens of many rare species could be seen and studied. Their enthusiasm toward a book of this nature helped strengthen my decision to continue with the work of compilation.

Harold F. Loomis spent many hours passing on the fruits of his invaluable experience as director of the U.S.P.I. Garden at Coconut Grove, Florida, and supplied some excellent photographs and necessary information on seed germination.

Dent Smith, founder and former president of the Palm Society spent many hours discussing the palms with me, amid his splendid collection at Daytona Beach, Florida; and gave of his time to read and check the final manuscript.

Edwin Johnston, of the Vero Beach Tropical Nursery, gave the full benefit of his many years' experience in germinating and growing uncommon palm varieties.

Nat De Leon, former treasurer of the Palm Society, not only served as an expert guide to Fairchild Tropical Garden, but shared his carefully kept records and information on seed germination.

Dr. David Keck, curator of the New York Botanical Gardens, read parts of my manuscript and offered encouragement and valuable suggestions.

Dr. Bruce Ledin, botanist at the Sub-Tropical Experiment Station of the University of Florida at Homestead, Florida, and Vice-President of the Palm Society, offered advice from his experience with palms and kindly consented to read carefully through the final manuscript, making many helpful suggestions and revisions.

Dr. Lawrence M. Simonson, an eminent horticulturist who has been raising all kinds of tropical plants, including palms, for over sixty years, permitted many hours of study in his garden in Lantana, Florida. I am particularly indebted to him for the encouragement he gave me at times when it was sorely needed.

For their assistance in various ways I am grateful to many others in the United States: Mr. E. J. Alexander of the New York Botanical Gardens; Mr. and Mrs. Mulford Foster for helpful information and several badly needed photographs; Mr. William Hertrich, curator emeritus of the Huntington Botanical Garden in San Marino, California, for copies of several photographs from his book, *Palms and Cyclads;* Mr. Theo K. Just, chief curator of the department of botany at the Chicago Natural History Museum in Chicago, Illinois, who offered to read parts of the manuscript in an early form; and Mr. Stanley Kiem, who often took time from his busy and active life at the Fairchild Tropical Garden to supply needed points of information.

I am greatly indebted to several good friends abroad who, through correspondence, supplied invaluable information on palms not available for study in these areas.

Dr. Max Burret, of the Berlin Botanischer Garten und Museum, one of the world's leading authorities on palms, was unable due to illness to correspond at any length, but I received helpful cooperation from his associate, Dr. Eva Potztal, who supplied a valuable list of palm genera of the world and several needed photographs.

Mr. Anwari Dilmy, director of the Herbarium Bogoriense in Bogor Gardens, Java, generously offered the results of his considerable experience with palms in one of the world's greatest botanical gardens. I am particularly grateful for the many photographs taken for him and for me by Mr. M. Jacobs.

Dr. João Angely, director of the Instituto Paranaense de Botanica, Brazil, sent me a complete list of all the palms in the famous Botanical Garden of Rio de Janeiro.

My gratitude is extended also to: Mr. T. Satake, president of the Satake Engineering Company of Tokyo, Japan, and a member of the Palm Society, for the use of his wonderful collection of photographs; Dr. R. E. G. Pichi-Sermolli, of the Instituto Botanico of the University of Florence, Italy, who forwarded several rare palm papers; Brother Alain of the Colegio De La Salle in Havana, Cuba, who sent copies of various papers and books on Cuban palms and several photographs from Brother Leon's files; Dr. C. X. Furtado of the Botanic Gardens, Singapore; Dr. E. G. G. J. Van Steenis, a former staff member of Bogor Gardens, Java; Dr. Armand Dugand of Barranquilla, Colombia; Professeur H. Humbert, of the National Natural History Museum, Paris, France; Mr. R. V. James, superintendent of the Royal Botanical Gardens in Jamaica, West Indies; and S. G. Saakov of the Botanical Institute Academy of Sciences of the U.S.S.R., Leningrad.

All have generously shared their knowledge, experience, and even records with me and I am deeply grateful to them for helping to make this book more all-embracing than it otherwise would have been.

No acknowledgment would be complete without a word of thanks to those who labored over details: Mrs. Marguerite C. Sweeney, my efficient and cheerful typist-secretary from June through October; and Mrs. Muriel S. Letsch who seemed tireless and ever enthusiastic during the long winter months that the book was in final preparation. Mrs. Letsch did the greater part of the typing during evenings and weekends, much of it from rough notes which required careful checking and often research. Many of her suggestions for rewording and rearranging were invaluable and are now a part of this volume.

J. C. McC.

INTRODUCTORY NOTES

NOMENCLATURE

The binomial system is today the accepted one for the naming of animals and plants. Under this system each plant receives two names, the first being the name of the genus to which it belongs, the second being the name of the species itself.

A *species* is a group of plants of the same ancestry, which possess in common certain characters distinguishing them from other similar groups, and which do, or may, interbreed, reproducing these same characters in their offspring.

A *genus* is a collection of closely related species.

Thus, a plant named *Cocos nucifera* is of the species *nucifera*, which in turn belongs to the genus *Cocos*.

Distinguishing characteristics between genera and species may have to do with structural parts, such as trunks, leaves, petioles, etc.; more often, they have to do with the details of the flowers and their reproductive parts. There may be varied opinions as to which common characteristics may properly be considered to hold certain species together in one genus.

The modern tendency is to restrict genera to much smaller and more closely related groups than the larger genera of the early naturalists, such as Linnaeus. Thus, the old and very large genus *Cocos* was broken up by Odoardo Beccari in 1916 into six genera: *Arecastrum, Arikuryroba, Butia, Cocos, Rhyticocos,* and *Syagrus.*

Although this division has been generally accepted and is now widely known, plants thus classified are still occasionally to be found under their old names. Some more recent changes of this kind in nomenclature, quickly recognized by botanical gardens, take many years to reach out to the smaller nurseries. *Adonidia merrillii* palms are still generally sold as adonidias, although their official name was changed to *Veitchia merrillii* by H. E. Moore, Jr. in August, 1957.

The estimates made by authorities vary considerably as to the actual total number of palm species. L. H. Bailey, in his *Hortus Second*, states there are probably "upward of 200 genera and perhaps 4,000 species." These figures, however, are likely to include many duplications, or certainly so many species that are so closely allied to others that their validity is a matter of opinion. In 1956 Max Burret, noted palm authority in Berlin, Germany, published in collaboration with his associate, Eva Potztal, a list that accounted for 235 valid palm genera in the world. This list was brought up to date for the author by Burret and Potztal and is published with their permission, on page 273.

This book describes all 235 of these genera, although descriptions of some of the more rare genera are necessarily brief. For some genera only one species is described; for others as many as a dozen species are described and many others mentioned.

The greater part of all palm species ever successfully introduced into the United States are included here. It is possible that a few rare importations have escaped notice. Included are all the palms grown in Fairchild Tropical Garden, the United States Plant Introduction Garden at Coconut Grove, Florida, and at Huntington Gardens in California.

It is impractical to attempt to describe all the species in botanical gardens throughout the world, but it has been possible to include all the genera to be found in the following famous botanical gardens: Botanical Gardens of Singapore; Royal Botanical Gardens in Trinidad; Atkins Garden at Soledad, Cuba; the famous Bogor Gardens (formerly Buitenzorg Gardens) at Batavia, Java, Indonesia; Hope and Castleton Gardens in Jamaica, the West Indies; Summit Gardens in the Panama Canal Zone; Botanical Garden of Rio de Janeiro, Brazil; the Botanic Garden, Adelaide, Australia; the Royal Botanic Gardens, Paradeniya, Ceylon.[1]

In deciding which species should be more fully described, preference was given to those widely known in several areas of the world. Species known only in one or two areas, and not to be found in public or private gardens elsewhere, are often briefly mentioned. Hundreds of little-known local species are necessarily omitted.

The nomenclature used in this book largely follows that of the late Liberty Hyde Bailey, noted American botanist and authority on palms, and of his successor, H. E. Moore, Jr., of the Bailey Hortorium, both of whom have published on palms in the many works mentioned in the Bibliography. Most of these works deal with palms that have been introduced into the United States. For other genera and species it was necessary to consult the works of authorities in various countries. These works are listed in the Bibliography.

Much additional information was found in the published works of the noted specialist Max Burret, of Berlin, and through correspondence with his associate, Eva Potztal.

ECONOMIC IMPORTANCE

Next to the grasses, the palm family is said to be the most important in its usefulness to man. It furnishes food, shelter, clothing, timber, fuel, building material, thatch, fiber, paper, starch, sugar, oil, wine, wax, dyes, and many minor supplies to natives of tropical islands and of some of our poor lands. The whole world still depends upon the palm family for certain few needed vegetable oils and waxes. The edible fruit yielded by the date palm, *Phoenix dactylifera*, is the staple food of some parts of North Africa. India is said to consume annually 800,000,000 pounds of palm sugar. Thirty million dollars' worth of betel nuts, the scarlet fruit of *Areca cathecu*, are chewed each year in India as a mild stimulant. To industrialized countries which have found better sources for most of the items mentioned, the economic importance of palms is more limited.

This book deals little with the commercial values of palms. The sugar palm, *Arenga pinnata*, may yield surprising amounts of sugar, but most palm fanciers are more interested in knowing that its shiny, brown, round seeds, hanging from the trees in solid 3-foot clusters, lend the scene an air of tropical luxuriance.

[1]For alphabetical lists of the various palms to be found in many of these gardens, see Appendix, page 280.

CULTIVATION IN THE UNITED STATES

Most of the species described or illustrated here are being successfully grown somewhere in the United States. A few species that are not actually known to have been grown in the United States are included because they are so well known elsewhere in the world, or in some cases simply because their striking appearance seems to warrant better acquaintance. In these few cases little information is available as to whether or not they can be successfully grown in this country. The country of origin is known, and its latitude may suggest that the species has not been subjected to temperatures as low as those to be encountered in the warmest regions of the United States. But this is not conclusive evidence that it will not grow here. *Phoenix reclinata* is native to tropical Africa, yet it seems to survive the coldest spells as far north as Pasadena, California.

No doubt there are some species so tropical in their requirements that they will not grow in the United States. Most species with stilt roots have been so far unsuccessful. Mr. Harold Loomis, formerly in charge of the United States Plant Introduction Garden at Coconut Grove, Florida, reports, after long experience, that *Cyrtostachys laka*, the beautiful sealing-wax palm, cannot be grown in Florida. This may be because it is native to Malaya which is equatorial. *Ceroxylon andicola*, the famous Andean wax palm, grows at high altitudes in the mountains of Colombia and Peru and should, therefore, be hardy to cold, yet repeated efforts to grow it in various parts of the United States have so far met with failure.

An asterisk (*) by the name of a genus in the pages following indicates that examples are to be found growing outdoors in one or both of the well-known botanical gardens in Florida: Fairchild Tropical Garden and the United States Plant Introduction Garden (unofficially known as Chapman Field), both located in Coconut Grove. A dagger (†) by the genus indicates that examples are grown outdoors in California at the Huntington Botanical Gardens, in San Marino. The Appendix at the back of the book contains complete lists of the palms to be found in each of those gardens.

The fact that a certain species can be grown and is grown in certain gardens of Florida should be encouraging to readers who are considering planting them in a similar subtropical climate. Plants growing outdoors in gardens of California have proved that they can stand a climate that is a little drier and considerably cooler. The absence of any certain species from these gardens, however, does not necessarily mean that they cannot be grown there, because they may not have been tried.

Palm enthusiasts are not easily discouraged. Each decade brings the introduction of some new species whose requirements have been finally discovered and supplied.

NOTES ON CULTURE

Certain palm species do not follow the general rules for palms but require very individual treatment. Information concerning these is given on later pages, whenever available. It appears under the caption, Cultivation, at the end of each genus discussion and is taken from the recent experiences and conclusions of several experienced growers.

A few general remarks, however, regarding the treatment of palms as a whole may be relevant at this point. Generally, palms do well with an abundance of water. They are unusually responsive to fertilizers. A coconut will grow without any special care; but with ample watering when needed and with large applications of organic fertilizer, it will really thrive.

Most mature palms must have full sunshine to achieve maximum growth. Before maturity they probably do better in partial sunlight or filtered sunlight, particularly during their first two or three years. Many mature palms are deliberately grown in partial shade, where their growth is slower[1] but their appearance greatly improved. The leaves are likely to be a darker, glossier green; and the plant often looks more rested and more elegant.

Little is known of their soil requirements but, as a whole, they are not believed to be particularly exacting. Plenty of fertilizer seems to overcome any soil deficiency. Experts believe that most people fertilize palms too carefully. Ten to twenty-five pounds of organic fertilizer is not too much at one time for a mature palm of any size. Organic fertilizer is believed by many to be safer than chemical fertilizer, but many experienced growers are very successful with the latter. Even with fertilizer, most palms grow very slowly. Some of the uncommon ones grow so slowly that few nurseries will plant them.

Palm seeds are generally slow, requiring from one month to two years for germination. Some figures on certain species are given under the heading, Cultivation, in later pages.

Seeds should be planted in flats filled with the best substance available. Opinions vary, but a recent favorite is equal parts of vermiculite, peat moss, sand, and fertile soil. The general rule has been to bury them as deep as their width. The United Fruit Company, after much experimenting, finds that oil-palm seeds germinate best in the tropics when set about ¼ inch deep in sand and completely covered with moist sawdust. These beds are set out in the full, tropical sun and kept continually moist. This procedure might prove effective with many palm seeds. The general object is to keep the ground warm and moist but not wet and sticky.

Several successful growers are convinced that germination can be hastened. One believes in soaking fresh seeds for two weeks in water kept hot by controlled electricity. When large seeds have heavy shells, he thins the shell with a file or grindstone. Another grower has made tests that convinced him that the most important thing is to heat the seedbed from beneath with a thermostatically controlled soil cable. The purpose of the heat is to stimulate the embryo into growth. The filing and soaking is to soften resistance.

Although the coconut can drift across oceans and still be viable, most palm seeds lose their viability very quickly. Success with palm seeds depends first on having fresh seed, and then on warmth and moisture.

When seedlings are potted, the pot should contain a soil mixture much like that mentioned above for seeds. Palms are not very subject to pests, and no attempt is made here to describe their control. The seeds of a few species throw a sinker straight downward for a considerable distance before growing leaves. These cannot be grown in flats or in a normal pot and are usually best planted in their permanent location in the ground.

Some palms may be propagated by dividing. Some species, such as *Phoenix dactylifera*, put out offshoots near the base of the trunk and these may be separated from the parent plant to form new plants. Others, such as *Chrysalidocarpus lutescens*, having several stems, may be divided into several plants when the plant is young by the division of root clumps.

Palms are comparatively easy to transplant, and in Florida they may even be moved in the winter, though the summer is safer. Root growth is much more active during the summer months, and when old roots are damaged in transplanting, new roots soon grow to take their place. The bigger the ball of earth taken with the plant, the better its chance for survival.

---

[1]This seems to be the opinion of the majority of growers and one with which the author's experience agrees. However, some experienced growers insist that certain species grow more quickly in partial shade.

Roots cut off never resume growing. In large plants with large root systems, it is safer to prune the roots, cutting off the ones that are beyond the intended ball of earth. A few months later, new, shorter roots will have grown. When the plant is moved, these new roots can go with it, undisturbed, ready to support it in its new home. Roots should never be exposed to sun and air but should be covered with burlap or a similar protection.

L. H. Bailey and Henry Nehrling were firm believers in the importance of digging a hole much deeper and wider than the ball of earth it is to receive and in filling it with rotted sod, rotted manure, and very fertile soil. Recent experiments have proved that trees planted with this care far outgrow others. Both Bailey and Nehrling advocated a square hole, 6 feet by 6 feet by 6 feet (an ambitious thought at today's labor costs). Nehrling even went so far as to dig his hole six months in advance, so that the mulch and other material placed in it would be decayed by planting time.

The reader will find special notes on recent experiences in growing palms from seed at the end of the description of each genus in the following pages. This information appears under the caption Cultivation. For much of this carefully collected information, I am deeply indebted to three friends. H. F. Loomis, formerly superintendent of the United States Plant Introduction Garden, at Coconut Grove, Florida, kindly supplied me with the information gleaned from the methodical records kept by his organization. Nat De Leon, former treasurer of the Palm Society and an enthusiastic collector of seeds from all over the world, supplied valuable records on seed germination from his experiences in Miami, Florida, during the last ten years. Edwin Johnston, of the Vero Beach Tropical Nursery, has been professionally germinating rare and common palm seeds for about ten years and was able to give me the benefit of his experiences. These three sources are referred to under Cultivation in the following abbreviated forms: U.S.P.I., De Leon, and Johnston.

ILLUSTRATED GLOSSARY

This book is written for the layman and the amateur collector. It deals with the outward appearance of palms, avoiding the detailed, botanical description of flowers. Palm flowers are usually tiny and insignificant and a technical description would be difficult for any but the trained botanist to follow. Instead, the descriptions offered are of the more obvious plant parts that are always available and are easily recognized.

In attempting to identify palm species, it is necessary to look for certain particular characteristics: dimensions of the trunks, petioles, leaves, leaflets, the spadices, and other parts. The following pages point out the type of variations that generally occur in all these parts. Most species can best be recognized by their particular combinations of these variations.

TRUNKS

The structure of palm trunks is quite different from that of our familiar timber trees in which a new ring, or layer of growth, is added to the trunk each year. In a palm tree there is only one main growing point—the terminal bud; and while the trunk enlarges, it does so from the inside by the deposit of new cells within the outer core of the expanding trunk.

The following illustrations show some of the varied characteristics to be found in palm trunks.

CROWNSHAFT

Although the crownshaft is not part of the trunk, it appears to be and requires explanation here.

Some species of both clustered- and single-trunk palms carry a glossy, green pillar at the top of the woody trunk which Bailey has named a *crownshaft*. This is not part of the trunk but is actually a tight package of the leafbases of all the leaves on the tree. To form this crownshaft, the leafbases are very erect, greatly expanded and lengthened, and so closely packed together that they lose their individual appearance.

xix

Fig. 1. *Mascarena lagenicaulis.*

Fig. 2. *Archontophoenix cunninghamiana.*

Figure 1 portrays one falling leaf, whose enlarged base is still the outside layer of the crownshaft. This is beginning to peel off and reveal the leafbase of the leaf beneath.

Figure 2 shows a crownshaft with flowerstalks beneath it. These flowerstalks are born within the crownshaft and are revealed only as the leafbases peel off.

Fig. 4. *Caryota mitis* (fishtail palm).

Fig. 3. *Cyrtostachys renda.*

CLUSTERED TRUNKS

Many palm species such as those shown in Figs. 3 and 4, produce suckers (offshoots) thereby forming clusters of multiple trunks.

SINGLE TRUNKS

Most palm species have single, unbranched trunks. A palm with 50 feet of trunk is considered tall. Still, quite a few reach 100 feet and the wax palm, *Ceroxylon*, has been known to grow to over 200 feet in height. Some species of the *Reinhardtia* genus have trunks no more than 2 feet high at maturity. Some palms are remarkable for their slender trunks, rising 30 feet in the air with a diameter of 1 or 2 inches; others are very stout with a diameter up to 6 feet (*Jubaea*). A few of the many variations in general appearance are illustrated here.

Fig. 5. *Copernicia.*

Fig. 6. *Corypha.*

Some species have smooth, uncluttered trunks like the two *Copernicia* specimens pictured in Fig. 5. In other species the trunks are covered for decades with adhering leafbases so that the trunk cannot be seen. Sometimes these leafbases are smooth, as in the *Corypha* picture in Fig. 6. Sometimes the leafbases are hairy or spiny and lend that appearance to the general mass.

Fig. 7. *Coccothrinax crinita.*

Fig. 8. *Arenga pinnata.*

Fig. 9. *Bactris plumeriana.*

Fig. 10. *Archontophoenix alexandrae* var. *beatricae.*

In some species the trunks are hairy as in *Coccothrinax crinita*, Fig. 7. Figure 8 shows the remarkable trunk of *Arenga pinnata*. Its trunk is enveloped by a thick mass of long, black fibers and sharply ascending strips which break into long spines. In both these cases, the

Fig. 11. *Pseudophoenix vinifera.*

Fig. 12. *Colpothrinax wrightii.*

hairs and fibers actually grow from the adhering leafbases whose tips can be seen protruding from the mass.

Figure 9 shows a very spiny trunk. These spines actually grow from the trunk itself. The rings of smooth trunk in between are actually scars left by leafbases that have fallen. Figure 10 shows the rings or scars left by fallen leafbases on a smooth trunk. These rings may be as little as an inch or as much as a foot apart, depending on the amount of growth of the trunk between each new leaf. The rings pictured in Fig. 10 are unusually prominent.

Many species have trunks that are enlarged or bulged at varying points and to varying degrees. The two specimens in Fig. 11 are *Pseudophoenix vinifera*. Figure 12 shows the tumor-like bulge of *Colpothrinax wrightii*. The placement and extent of these bulges usually varies considerably with cultural conditions.

Fig. 13. *Serenoa repens*.

Fig. 14. *Attalea cohune*.

Fig. 15. *Hyphaene*.

Fig. 16. *Sabal*.

TRUNKLESS SPECIES

Some species do not have any trunks above ground. In *Serenoa repens*, Fig. 13, the leaves seem to come right out of the ground though they are actually growing from an underground creeping trunk.[1]

Some species grow for many years and to a considerable height before showing any trunk. The *Attalea cohune*, Fig. 14, will eventually develop a trunk 30–40 feet in height. Often such species have been mistakenly described as trunkless because they appear so mature at this stage.

BRANCHING TRUNKS

There is only one genus, *Hyphaene*, Fig. 15, which naturally and normally has a branched or forking trunk. Palm trunks sometimes branch unnaturally after injury. Figure 16 shows a *Sabal* palm that has developed four heads after injury (or perhaps several injuries).

CLIMBING PALMS

There are over 400 species of palms, little known in the United States, that act as vines, climbing for hundreds of feet over nearby vegetation. In Fig. 17 a *Daemonorops* is ascending a tree; Fig. 18 shows another specimen of *Daemonorops* creeping through the treetops.

---

[1]In a few exceptional cases *Serenoa repens* has been known to form a short trunk above ground.

Fig. 17. *Daemonorops*.   Fig. 18. *Daemonorops*.

LEAVES

THE PARTS OF A PALM LEAF

A leaf is an outgrowth from the trunk. For botanical descriptions, it is divided into certain parts.

The *leafbase* (sometimes called the *leafsheath*) is that part which clasps the trunk. The *petiole* is the outward continuation of the leafbase. It is that part of the leaf between the clasping leafbase and the first point where leaflets are attached. It is that part of the stalk which is without leaflets.

In pinnate leaves an extension of the petiole continues through the leaf itself with leaflets attached. This extension is called the *rachis*.

The rachis is the outward continuation of the petiole. It is that part of the compound leaf to which leaflets are attached.

Palmate leaves do not have a rachis because the petiole dead-ends at the point from which all the segments of the leaf fan out.

In some palmate species, a narrow extension does protrude for some distance into the leaf; but this is not called a rachis, it is referred to simply as a *rib*. Such species are palmate but are also referred to as *costapalmate*.

The *blade* is all the leaf from the petiole outward. In pinnate leaves the blade consists of the rachis and the leaflets. In palmate leaves it consists of all the segments and any rib which may protrude into them.

The divisions of a pinnate leaf are called *leaflets*. The divisions of a palmate leaf are called *segments*.

LEAFBASES

A leafbase is that portion of the leafstalk which clasps the trunk. It may clasp the entire trunk, thus surrounding it, or it may clasp only half the trunk, or less. It may be hairy, spiny, toothed, or smooth.

In some species the leafbases are greatly enlarged and stretched out into a wide, thin, glossy layer. Packed closely together, they completely envelop the bud at the top of the trunk forming what is known as a crownshaft. See Figs. 1, 2, and 20.

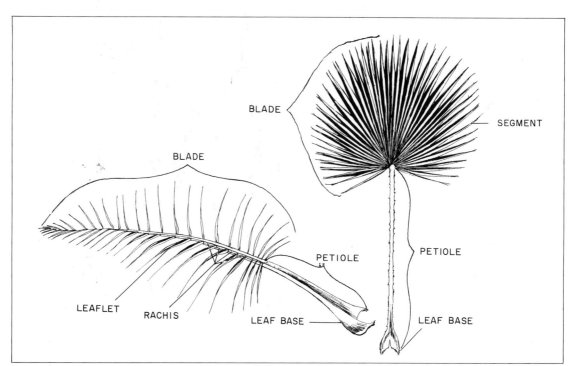

Fig. 19.

Fig. 20. *Veitchia merrillii.*

Fig. 21. *Pritchardia remota.*

PETIOLES

The petiole is that part of the leafstalk which is without leaflets. It is the bare portion between the trunk and the leaflets.

Petioles may be very short, as in *Veitchia merrillii*, Fig. 20. The leaflets begin almost at the leafbase, leaving a very short naked portion. The part to which the leaflets are attached is the rachis. In *Pritchardia remota*, Fig. 21, the naked portion (petiole) is very long.

Petioles often have teeth along their outer edges, as in *Borassus flabellifer*, Fig. 22. The upper surface is sometimes grooved or channeled, as in the petiole in the center foreground of Fig. 22. In the photograph of *Eugeissona*, Fig. 23, the petiole is covered with black spines.

LEAVES AND LEAFLETS

Palm leaves can be divided into two types: *pinnate* (or feather-shaped) leaves and *palmate* (or fan-shaped) leaves.

Fig. 22. *Borassus flabellifer.*

Fig. 23. *Eugeissona.*

In pinnate leaves, the stem runs right out to the end of the leaf and all divisions, or leaflets, run off this main stem at intervals.

In palmate leaves, the stem or stalk stops at the beginning of the leaf and all divisions, or segments, fan out from this common point in all directions.

In some very few palmate species, the petiole projects for a considerable distance into the leaf itself. Such leaves are considered palmate but are additionally described as being *costapalmate.*

It should be mentioned here that the leaves of certain species are not the same at all ages. A certain species may produce leaves forming less than a semicircle while immature; although later on, at maturity, it will produce leaves that are almost a complete circle of 360°.

Very young plants often produce, for as long as two years, leaves totally unrelated to their characteristic mature leaves. Many species produce simple, undivided leaves for many months or even years, although eventually they are to produce pinnate, or deeply cut palmate leaves.

Leaflets and segments vary from light green to dark green to blue green. They may be the same on both sides, or they may be lighter green beneath; or the under surface may have a glaucous or waxy appearance (usually white, but sometimes bluish). The under surface of some leaves may have hairs or spines, as may also the stem they cling to; and occasionally both leaf surfaces carry spines.

PINNATE LEAVES AND LEAFLETS

The largest of all pinnate leaves are those of *Raphia ruffia*, which are often 65 feet long and more than 12 feet wide.

The illustration of *Chrysalidocarpus*, Fig. 24, shows the most usual type of pinnate leaf. The leaflets are set at regular intervals on the stem. The leaflets near the center of the leaf are the longest and the widest; those at the base and at the end are generally smaller. Some species have the leaflets set alternately instead of in direct opposition. Some have leaflets set at closer, or wider intervals. Other species have very varied and irregular leaflets set at irregular intervals. Such species (like *Pinanga disticha*, Fig. 25) often have the two terminal leaflets united.

Fig. 24. *Chrysalidocarpus.*   Fig. 25. *Pinanga disticha.*

Fig. 26. *Mascarena lagenicaulis.*

Fig. 27. *Howea forsteriana.*

In some species, such as *Mascarena lagenicaulis*, Fig. 26, all the leaflets are set on the rachis (stem) at a sharply ascending angle, so that the general appearance of the leaf resembles a trough. Sometimes all the leaflets are attached to the stem on a horizontal plane, lending a flat or even drooping appearance to the leaf as in Fig. 27.

Some species have leaves with both flat and upright leaflets. The leaflets are attached to the rachis at various angles, forming several rows or ranks. In the sketch, Fig. 28, the upper drawing shows leaflets attached at about the same angle on both sides of the rachis, forming only two ranks. The lower drawing in Fig. 28 shows them attached at several angles, forming several ranks. The photograph, Fig. 29, illustrates a leaf with several ranks of leaflets.

Fig. 28.

Fig. 29. *Phoenix sylvestris.*

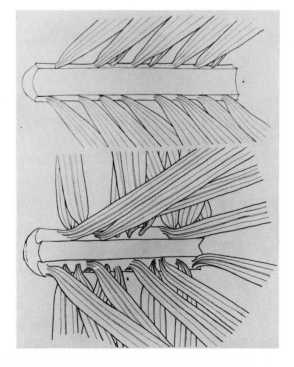

Two rather uncommon types of leaves are shown in Figs. 30 and 31. Figure 30 illustrates the leaf of *Caryota mitis* (fishtail palm). This leaf is *bipinnate*, i.e., instead of having the usual simple rachis, it has a many-branched rachis with leaflets attached to all the branches. Figure 31 shows one of the few palms with simple, undivided leaves. The leaves are pinnately veined and the sections are divided for a very short distance at the edges. This leaf of *Stevensonia* has a deep notch at its tip. Sometimes the winds tear these leaves into parts somewhat resembling leaflets.

Fig. 30. *Caryota mitis* (fishtail palm).   Fig. 31. *Stevensonia*.

Most pinnate leaves are attached to the stem with their edges turned downward, as in Fig. 32. Botanists refer to these leaflets as being "reduplicate in vernation" (arrangement within the bud). Figure 33 shows a leaf of *Phoenix rupicola*. *Phoenix* is one of the few pinnate genera in which the leaflets are folded into the rachis with their edges turned upward. Botanists refer to these as being "induplicate in vernation." The pinnate palm genera that have induplicate leaves are *Arenga, Caryota, Didymosperma, Phoenix,* and *Wallichia*. For an easy aid to memory, *in*duplicate leaves keep the moisture *in; re*duplicate leaves shed water.

Fig. 32. *Chamaedorea*.

Fig. 33. *Phoenix rupicola*.

Fig. 34. *Erythea brandegeei.*

Fig. 35. *Cryosophila.*

PALMATE LEAVES AND SEGMENTS

LEAF FORMATION

Many palmate leaves describe a semicircle or less, as in Fig. 34. Others describe a full circle of 360°, as in Fig. 35.

DIVISION OF SEGMENTS

The segments of some palmate leaves are divided for only a short distance from the outer edge, producing an almost solid and very attractive leaf, as in Fig. 36. In Fig. 37 the segments are divided almost all the way to the base.

In some few palmate species, a rib, which is really an extension of the petiole, projects well into the leaf, reaching almost to the outer edge, as in Fig. 38. In other species, it extends for a much shorter distance into the leaf. Such palm leaves have been described by Bailey as being

Fig. 37. *Rhapis excelsa.*

Fig. 38. *Sabal palmetto.*

Fig. 36. *Licuala grandis.*

Fig. 39. *Thrinax.*   Fig. 40. *Washingtonia.*

costapalmate. Figure 39 is included to illustrate another name coined by Bailey. Part of the leaf has been cut away to better reveal the *hastula*, a small protrusion which in some species grows out of the dead end of the petiole. In one exceptional species, *Copernicia rigida*, the hastula has been found to be 12–18 inches long. Figure 40 illustrates how some palmate leaves have long threads growing out of the segments at the points where they are joined.

FLOWERSTALK (SPADIX)

Palm flowers and fruits are borne on a fleshy spike (spadix) which is sometimes borne beneath the leaves (infrafoliar), as in Fig. 41, or in among the leaves (interfoliar), as in Fig. 42. In the latter case, the flowerstalks are usually short and the fruit is generally somewhat concealed among the leaves.

Fig. 42. *Latania.*

Fig. 41. *Mascarena.*

Fig. 43. *Pritchardia thurstonii.*　　　　Fig. 44. *Corypha umbraculifera.*

Figure 43, is an example of flowerstalks borne among the leaves but plainly visible because they are long enough to project well beyond the leaves. In rare cases the flowers and fruit appear above the leaves (suprafoliar), as in Fig. 44.

Most flowerstalks are branched, as in Fig. 45. The thick, single stalk is called the *peduncle.* The sheaths, from which it has emerged, are called *spathes.* The secondary branches are usually referred to as the *rachillae.* Figure 46 shows one of the few species in which the spadix in unbranched. The solitary spikes hanging downward are 6–7 feet long.

SPATHES

Flowerstalks are usually enveloped by one or more sheaths, or spathes. These sheaths may be very large or they may be very small, covering the flowerstalk only when it is very

Fig. 45. *Calyptronoma.*

Fig. 46. *Calyptrocalyx spicatus.*

young. They may be hardly noticeable, falling early from the tree; or they may, after they have opened out and freed the flowers, hang down like long streamers, adding greatly to the tropical appearance of the palm. The arrangements of the bracts, or sections of spathes, are extremely varied, and in this book they are not dealt with in detail.

Fig. 47. Inner spathe emerging from outer spathe (underneath). *Ptychosperma macarthuri.*

Fig. 48. Flowerstalk has emerged from spathe; others are still covered by spathes. *Mascarena verschaffeltii.*

FLOWERS, FRUITS, AND SEEDS

FLOWERS

Most palm flowers are small, greenish, and insignificant in appearance, although they may be very numerous and their large clusters impressive. Only certain species have flowers with any fragrance. This book avoids the descriptions of flower details as being too technical for any but the trained botanist to follow. The sexual characteristics, however, are always given and fall into the following general types:

1. *Hermaphrodite:* each flower having both male and female parts

2. *Monoecious:* male and female flowers separate but on the same plant, either on the same flowerstalk or on separate flowerstalks

3. *Dioecious:* male flowers on one plant, female flowers on another.

In dioecious palms, pollen must be transported from tree to tree by insects or the wind. This is made easy by special parts which release the pollen so freely at certain times that travelers speak of the date palms of Egypt being hidden at daybreak in a mist of pollen. Some few species are *polygamous*, which means that both hermaphrodite and unisexual flowers are borne on the same plant.

In some cases, like the talipot palm (*Corypha*), the tree flowers only once in a spray 25 feet high and estimated to contain 60 million blossoms. After the fruit has ripened, the tree dies.

In some cases, like *Caryota*, the tree will reach mature size before its first flowers spring from the nodes among the top leaves. Each successive flowering is from an axil of a lower leaf, and, after the fruits from the lowest stalks have ripened, the tree dies.

The term *monocarpic* is used for the condition found in both the *Corypha* and the *Caryota* just described, although one might easily expect them to be described with separate terms.

FRUITS AND SEEDS

Palm fruits, many of which are highly decorative, are more likely to attract attention than the flowers. The size and other characteristics vary greatly. The fruit of the *Euterpe* is the size of a small pea, while the fruit of the *Lodoicea*, weighing over 40 pounds, is the largest in the whole vegetable kingdom. A fruit usually holds one seed, but sometimes two or three. Seeds show corresponding variations in size, but always consist of a mass of endosperm (nutritional matter) in which is imbedded a tiny embryo. The vegetable ivory of commerce is the endosperm of *Phytelephas*. The soft white flesh of the coconut is the endosperm in a softer condition.

This endosperm is also known as the *albumen*. If a mature seed is cut across, the albumen is revealed. If this hard, white substance is solid and its surface uninterrupted, the seed is referred to as having an albumen which is "plain," or "equable," or "homogenous." If the albumen is found to be irregular, because irregular divisions or growths run into it, the seed is referred to as having *ruminate* albumen. The term *ruminate* means mottled, as if chewed. In ruminate albumen, the seed coat appears to be pushed into the seed. This usually, but not always, produces a wrinkled appearance on the outside of the seed. If seeds are available, this contrast in the albumen is often the quickest way to distinguish between certain genera.

Note: An asterisk (*) by the name of a genus in the pages following indicates that examples are to be found growing outdoors in one or both of the well-known botanical gardens in Florida: Fairchild Tropical Garden and the United States Plant Introduction Garden (unofficially known as Chapman Field), both located in Coconut Grove. A dagger (†) by the genus indicates that examples are grown outdoors in California at the Huntington Botanical Gardens, in San Marino.

I do not understand how anyone can be content until he has experienced the wonder of the tropics.

—DAVID FAIRCHILD in *The World Was My Garden*

Man *dwells* naturally within the tropics and lives on the fruit of the palm tree. He *exists* in other parts of the world and there makes shift to feed on corn and flesh.

—LINNAEUS

ACANTHOCOCOS

A pinnate-leafed, spiny genus, native to Paraguay, and not very widely known to cultivation. Toledo describes three species found in Brazil: *A. emensis*, *A. hassleri*, and *A. servicea*. (Not illustrated.)

ACANTHOPHOENIX
Greek, *acantha*, thorn, and *phoenix*, date palm

Two species of feather-leafed palms from the Mascarene Islands. Both have smooth, closely ringed trunks surmounted by a crownshaft. In these respects they somewhat resemble *Dictyosperma*, *Ptychosperma*, *Archontophoenix*, and *Veitchia* but are distinguished from them by having spines on leafbases, rachises, leaflet veins, and flowerstalks.

A. RUBRA
Latin, red

Common name: Barbel palm. **Origin:** Mascarene Islands. **Sex:** Monoecious. **Trunk:** 50–60 ft high, about 10 in. thick; spineless; topped by crownshaft. **Petiole:** Short; 4–6 in. long; smooth, spineless, except on base, which has straight black spines. **Leaf:** Pinnate; 6–12 ft long; long bristles on rachis (stem). **Leaflets:** Dark-green, silver beneath; bristles on veins. **Flowerstalk:** 2–3 ft long; from top of trunk, below crownshaft; straight, with black spines. Spathe, 1–2 ft long. **Flowers:** Many; reddish or purplish. **Fruit:** Globose; small, ⅜ in.

diameter; black, with ridge. **Seed:** Small. **Oddities:** Young plants have dark-green leaves with red veins.

A. CRINITA
Latin, hairy

Similar to *A. rubra*, but petiole covered with white, woolly hair, and leafbases have short, brown bristles instead of black spines.

The fruit is ovoid oblong; ½ in. long; black.

Oddities: Young plants have pale, yellow-green leaves.

Balfour says that *A. crinita* is quite common in Mauritius, while *A. rubra* is rare. He also states that leaflets of *A. rubra* are glaucous underneath, while the leaflets of *A. crinita* have silver-white backs.

Cultivation: Grown in the United States, but usually as hothouse specimens. U.S.P.I. Garden reports planting seeds of *A. rubra* which began germinating in 71 days. Bailey's *Cyclopedia* states that seeds frequently require 2–3 years to germinate.

ACANTHORRHIZA
(See *Cryosophila*)

ACOELORRAPHE
(See *Paurotis*)

From left to right:

Acanthophoenix rubra. Planted in Mauritius. Reprinted from *Gentes Herbarum*.

Acanthophoenix crinita. Planted in Mauritius. Reprinted from *Gentes Herbarum*.

Inflorescence in bloom of *Acanthophoenix rubra.* Reprinted from *Gentes Herbarum*.

Inflorescence of *A. crinita.* Mauritius. Reprinted from *Gentes Herbarum*.

ACROCOMIA*

Greek, *acro*, tip, end, and *komē*, hair, referring to the tuft of leaves on top

A very large genus, better known in Florida sixty years ago than it seems to be today. Acrocomias were listed for sale in the 1889–1890 plant catalogue of Reasoner's Nursery, Bradenton, Florida.

Perhaps the ubiquitous spines hurt sales, but the spines are just as unique, remarkable, and ornamental as they are untouchable.

There are generally two types:

1. The deciduous type, in which leafbases fall off tree as leaves die, leaving striking rings of black spines on the trunk (See *A. armentalis*)

2. The adherent type, in which leafstalks cling to trunk for years until they finally rot off, by which time spikes on trunk have largely worked or worn off, and the bottom part of trunk is fairly smooth. (See *A. mexicana*, etc.)

A. ARMENTALIS
(*A. crispa*)

Common name: Grugru palm, corojo or corozo. **Origin:** Cuba. **Sex:** Monoecious. **Trunk:** 45 ft high, 8–15 in. thick; spindle-shaped; alternate rings of spiny and smooth trunk (where leafbases fall off). **Petiole:** 3 in. long; armed with black spines. **Leaf:** Pinnate; 7–9 ft long; about 110 pairs of leaflets; rachis spiny. **Leaflets:** 18–24 in. long, ½–¾ in. wide; glossy green, blue-green beneath. **Flowerstalk:** 3–5 ft long; among leaves; reddish, hairy sheath. **Fruit:** Globose, 1 in. diameter; very smooth. **Seed:** Small.

A. MEXICANA

Common name: Grugru or corojo palm. **Origin:** southern Mexico. **Sex:** Monoecious. **Trunk:** 25 ft or less; cylindrical, not bulging; covered with old leafbases until maturity. Trunk is brown, woolly, and covered with spines 1–3 in. long. **Petiole:** Hairy, spines to 3 in. long. **Leaf:** Pinnate; to 12 ft; drooping; 110 pairs of leaflets. **Leaflets:** To 3 ft long, 1 in. wide; slightly woolly above, silvery beneath. **Flowerstalk:** 3–4 ft long; among leaves; brown, spiny sheath. **Flowers:** Small. **Fruit:** Globose; 1½ in. diameter; brownish mottled.

Acrocomia armentalis. Cuba. In this species the leafbases fall off leaving a naked trunk. Reprinted from *Gentes Herbarum.*

Acrocomia mexicana. In this species the leafbases cling to the trunk. Reprinted from *Gentes Herbarum.*

Other deciduous types: *A. aculeata* (leaves bright-green on both sides) from Cuba; *A. media* (leaves a trifle woolly), from Puerto Rico; *A. totai* (taller trunk) from Paraguay and Bolivia. Also, *A. chunta, A. fusiformis, A. karakurena, A. microcarpa, A. quisqueyana.*

Other adherent types: *A. sclerocarpa* (taller; seed has radiate markings) from Brazil; *A. vinifera* (trunk sometimes swollen at middle; fruit, black) of Nicaragua; *A. hospes* (origin unknown). Bailey mentions *A. sobernis* (largely without spikes) and *A. odorata* (no spines, and very fragrant flowers).

Cultivation: Seeds difficult to germinate. To encourage germination, seeds should be filed to weaken outer coat. Best procedure is to soak seeds for 2–3 weeks in water which is kept warm. Seeds treated thus should germinate in 4–6 months. Most acrocomias are reasonably hardy to cold. Huntington Gardens lost one *A. totai* in a freeze, but believe it would be happy in southern California. Does well in Florida. Plants are comparatively fast growers. Fairchild Tropical Garden lists as hardy for southern Florida the following species: *A. aculeata, A. armentalis, A. fusiformis,* and *A. mexicana;* as extra hardy, *A. sclerocarpa* and *A. totai.*

ACTINOKENTIA

A little-known monotypic genus native to New Caledonia. The only species is *A. divaricata*. (Not illustrated.)

ACTINOPHLOEUS
(See *Ptychosperma*)

ACTINORHYTIS CALAPPARIA*
Latin, *actis*, ray, and *rhytis*, fold

A tall, slender, monoecious, pinnate-leafed palm, native to Malaya, that somewhat resembles *Areca cathecu*, although it is not closely related. It is in cultivation at Atkins Botanical Gardens in Cuba, but is not known to be cultivated in the United States.

The stout, single trunk is 40 ft tall, the leaves 8–9 ft long, 4 ft wide. The fruit is red and the size of an egg, and it has medicinal uses.

Close-ups of trunks: (Left) The bulging trunk of *Acrocomia armentalis.* (Right) *Acrocomia mexicana.* Thickly covered with leafbases and spathes. Reprinted from *Gentes Herbarum.*

Actinorhytis calapparia. Photo by A. C. Langlois.

ADELONENGA

A genus described by Pichi-Sermolli as consisting of five species from New Guinea and New Ireland. Burret considers all *Adelonenga* species to be correctly *Hydriastele*. (Not illustrated.)

ADONIDIA
(See *Veitchia*)

AIPHANES*

A few species of low to medium-sized palms which always carry sharp, black spines on the trunk, leafstalks, and sometimes on the leaves themselves.

A. CARYOTAEFOLIA
(formerly *Martinezia caryotaefolia*)

The name *Caryotaefolia* means "leaves of *Caryota*," or leaves like the fishtail palm. The leaflets are short and rather wide with irregularly jagged ends. Their ruffled appearance produces a very graceful, tropic effect.
   Common name: coyure palm. **Origin:** Colombia, Venezuela, Ecuador. **Sex:** Monoecious. **Trunk:** To 30 ft; 4–6 in. thick; slender; attractive rings of long, black spines. **Petiole:** 4½-5 ft long; slender; covered with spines. **Leaf:** Pinnate; 3–6 ft long, with irregularly shaped and placed leaflets. **Leaflets:** 6–14 in. long; irregularly broad-ended; up to 6 in. wide;

Aiphanes caryotaefolia at U.S.P.I. Garden, Coconut Grove, Florida. Photo by H. F. Loomis.

Aiphanes acanthophylla in Puerto Rico. Reprinted from *Gentes Herbarum*.

ruffly; black spines on both sides. Glossy above, dull beneath. **Flowerstalk:** 2–2½ ft long; among leaves; spiny; at first covered with very spiny spathe. **Flowers:** Whitish. **Fruit:** Globose; ¾ in. diameter; red. **Seed:** Small, round, pitted. **Oddities:** Roots often appear above ground.

A. ACANTHOPHYLLA

A similar plant to *A. caryotaefolia*, but the leaflets are not as wide or uneven and are more closely and regularly placed. The whole leaf looks more like a solid flat mass and less ruffled.

Common name: coyure palm. **Origin:** Puerto Rico. **Sex:** Monoecious. **Trunk:** As *A. caryotaefolia*. **Petiole:** As *A. caryotaefolia*. **Leaf:** Pinnate; 3–6 ft long; leaflets more regularly placed than *A. caryotaefolia*. Whole leaf looks more entire; leaflets often clustered at apex. **Leaflets:** 1–2 in. wide; square, jagged-ended, but not ruffly; green above, lighter green beneath. **Flowerstalk:** As *A. caryotaefolia*. **Flowers:** Whitish. **Fruit:** Globose; red; dimpled, with thin flesh. **Seed:** Small, round, pitted. **Oddities:** Roots often appear above ground.

OTHER SPECIES

A. lindeniana (mountains of Colombia); *A. erosa* (West Indies); *A. granatensis* (Colombia). Many other species not described here.

Cultivation: Seeds germinate readily, usually in less than 2 months, sometimes in 1 month. Should have shade until 2–3 years old. May be grown outdoors in southern Florida. Fairchild Tropical Garden lists all its species as tender.

ANCISTROPHYLLUM

A spiny, climbing palm with pinnate leaves, native to West Africa. The specimen photographed is *Ancistrophyllum acutiflorum.*

Close-up of trunk of *Aiphanes acanthophylla.* Reprinted from *Gentes Herbarum.*

Ancistrophyllum acutiflorum. Photo courtesy of A. Dilmy, Bogor Gardens, Java.

ANTONGILIA

Not considered valid by Burret. A single species of this genus, *A. perrieri*, is described by Jumelle in *Flore de Madagascar* as a small palm, with trunk 6–12 ft high and 7½ in. through, with pinnate leaves 9–12 ft long. (Not illustrated.)

ARCHONTOPHOENIX*†
Greek, majestic palm

This genus bears some broad resemblance to *Veitchia*, *Ptychosperma*, and *Dictyosperma*. *A. alexandrae* has leaflets with the under surface prominently grayish, which will help to distinguish it from these genera; *A. cunninghamiana* does not have this distinguishing feature.

Archontophoenix alexandrae. The leaflets have silver backs. Photo courtesy of Huntington Botanical Gardens.

Archontophoenix cunninghamiana. The leaflets do not have silver backs. Photo courtesy of Huntington Botanical Gardens.

A. ALEXANDRAE
Dedicated to Princess Alexandra of Denmark, later Queen Dowager of Great Britain

Common name: King palm. **Origin:** Australia. **Sex:** Monoecious. **Trunk:** 60–70 ft high, 6 in. thick; slender; closely ringed; enlarged at base; glossy crownshaft. **Petiole:** 4 in. to 12 in. long. **Leaf:** Pinnate; 3–5 by 2½ ft. **Leaflets:** 1½ ft long, 1½–2 in. broad. Under surface prominently grayish-white; secondary ribs prominent, giving ridgy look; sword-shaped, pointed. **Flowerstalk:** Short; forms in crownshaft; appears at top of trunk; has short, fat peduncle, then branches for 18 in. Covered with two spathes, each 15–24 in. long, and satin-white inside. **Flowers:** White or cream. **Fruit:** ½ in. long; globose; red. **Seed:** See photograph. **Oddities:** First 4–6 leaves on young plants are usually simple.

A. CUNNINGHAMIANA
Named for Allan Cunningham, 1791–1839, British collector in Australia

Similar to *A. alexandrae*, except for these differences:

Trunk: Not swollen at base. (This is subject to some individual variations and not absolutely dependable.) **Leaflet:** Wider, 3–4 in. but still pointed; green on both sides, not white beneath. Secondary ribs not prominent. (These are dependable differences.) **Flowers:** Lavender (lilac), instead of white, as in *A. alexandrae*; slightly fragrant. **Seed:** More coarse; fibers cover seed.

A. ALEXANDRAE, var. BEATRICAE

Similar to *A. alexandrae*, but bottom of trunk is even more enlarged and the rings are so deep that they resemble steps. Leaves a little more erect.

Cultivation: Seeds of both species germinate easily and in less than 2 months. Plant is a comparatively fast grower. Smith's Nursery in Fort Lauderdale, Florida, considers both species fairly hardy and reports that they have many times withstood temperatures of 30° without damage. W. Hertrich, of Huntington Gardens, reports that leaves sunburn in very hot, dry sun. Huntington Gardens lost one large *A. alexandrae* during the frost of 1937 and reports that *A. alexandrae* is generally conceded to be more susceptible to frost.

Top row: seeds of *Archontophoenix alexandrae*.
Bottom: Seeds of *Archontophoenix cunninghamiana*.
Reprinted from *Gentes Herbarum*.

Archontophoenix alexandrae var. *beatricae*. Illustrating the deep rings on the trunk. Reprinted from *Gentes Herbarum*.

ARECA*

A variant of a Malayan name meaning "cluster of nuts"

Most *Areca* palms have multiple trunks, but the best-known one, *A. cathecu*, the betel nut palm, has a tall, thin, solitary stem.

A. CATHECU
(Sometimes spelled *catechu*) [1]

The orange-colored fruit of this species is the betel nut, the chewing of which is a widespread custom in various Asian and Polynesian areas. It is a mild stimulant (18 per cent tannin) and some natives are said to believe that it drives out ringworm. Bailey's *Cyclopedia* of 1914 states that the betel nut trade at that time amounted to $30,000,000 annually.

Common name: Betel palm. **Origin:** Malaya. **Sex:** Monoecious. **Trunk:** Usually 30 ft high, rarely to 100 ft, 2–5 in. thick; very straight; topped by crownshaft. **Petiole:** Short. **Leaf:** Pinnate; 4–6 ft long; arching; few lowest leaves often hanging; leaflets closely placed. **Leaflets:** To 18 in. long, 1¼ in. broad; soft; sometimes fastened together near tip; occasionally variegated; cut off at apex. **Flowerstalk:** 2 ft long; from lowest leafbases, and falls below crownshaft; branched. **Flowers:** White, fragrant. **Fruit:** 2 in. long; olive-shaped; soft, fibrous covering; orange or scarlet. **Seed:** ¾ in. diameter; reddish-yellow.

[1]Bailey, in *Hortus Second*, states that Linnaeus, the author of this name, spelled it *cathecu* in his *Species Plantarum*. However, both Beccari and Hooker spelled it *catechu*, and Moore has recently decided in favor of *A. catechu*.

Areca cathecu. At Bogor Botanic Gardens, Java. Photo courtesy of A. Dilmy, Bogor Gardens, Java.

Areca FTG 208. This species of *Areca* has not yet received any other name. It was photographed at the Retreat, the garden of Mr. and Mrs. A. C. Langlois in Nassau, Bahamas.

A. TRIANDRA

This graceful, clustered species bears little general resemblance to *A. cathecu*.
Common name: None. **Origin:** India, Malaya. **Sex:** Monoecious. **Trunk:** Multiple, each 5–10 ft high, 1–2 in. thick; strongly ringed; green. **Petiole:** 1 ft long. **Leaf:** Pinnate, 3–5 ft long; not arching, rather drooping. **Leaflets:** 1½–3 ft long, 1–1½ in. wide; fairly broad; curved downward, forming terminal clusters; bright green. **Flowerstalk:** 1 ft long; among leaves. **Flowers:** White, fragrant. **Fruit:** 1 in. long; olive size and shape; orange or scarlet; soft covering.

A. FTG NO. 208

One of the species illustrated does not have a species name, except for the rather irregular one above. The photograph was taken at the Langlois garden in Nassau. The leafsheaths are a magnificent orange and the leaflets are very broad.

OTHER SPECIES

There are many other species of *Areca* that are not cultivated widely and are little known in the United States. Ridley's *Flora de Malaya* mentions *A. latiloba, A. montana, A. pomila,* and *A. furcata. A. concinna* (Ceylon) is known to be cultivated in the United States.

Brown's *Useful Plants of the Philippines* describes *A. ipot* (Becc.) which somewhat resembles a dwarfed *A. cathecu*, never exceeding 12 ft in height. The fruits are densely crowded, compared to those of *A. cathecu*. Brown also mentions *A. mammilata,* very slender trunk (up to 1¼ in. thick, up to 9 ft high), and *A. whitfordii,* which is allied to *A. cathecu* but with thicker trunk (up to 9 in. through).

The name *Areca* has been much used in error. Many nurseries incorrectly speak of *Chrysalidocarpus lutescens* as the areca palm.

Areca cathecu. At Bogor Botanic Gardens, Java. The fruit clusters on the tree are the famous betel nuts. Photo by T. Satake.

Areca triandra. Young tree at Bogor Botanic Gardens. Photo by T. Satake.

There is a species, formerly known under the generic name *Mischophloeus*, which has been considered by Dr. C. X. Furtado to be a subdivision of the genus *Areca*. No species name has been given to it. In this book it is treated as *Mischophloeus* and is illustrated under that name.

Common errors:

Plants called *Areca normanbyi* probably are *Normanbya normanbyi.*

Plants called *Areca aliciae* probably are *Areca triandra.*

Plants called *Areca baueri* probably are *Rhopalostylis baueri.*

Plants called *Areca sapida* probably are *Rhopalostylis sapida.*

Plants called *Areca singaporensis* probably are *Ptychoraphis singaporensis.*

Plants called *Areca speciosa* probably are *Mascarena lagenicaulis.*

Plants called *Areca verschaffeltii* probably are *Mascarena verschaffeltii.*

Cultivation: *A. cathecu* has been known to fruit when only 6 years old and has a fruiting life of 30–35 years. In both species, *A. cathecu* and *A. triandra*, seeds must be fresh, as they lose their germinating capacity very quickly. *A. cathecu* is very subject to cold damage. De Leon reports that in one batch of seeds he planted, *A. concinna* took 43 days and *A. latiloba*, 27 days, for germination. U.S.P.I. Garden reports that one batch of seeds of *A. cathecu* took 79 days for germination. Fairchild Tropical Garden lists *A. cathecu* as tender.

ARECASTRUM*†

Known in many places and for many years as *Cocos plumosa*, this palm is an example of true confusion in nomenclature. In 1823 Adelbert von Chamisso discovered this palm, described it, and named it *Cocos romanzoffianum.*

In 1860 W. J. Hooker, unaware of the above, also "discovered" it and described it in a botanical magazine. He named it *Cocos plumosa*, under which name it was widely cultivated.

In 1916 Beccari broke up the *Cocos* family into seven genera and this particular palm was given the genus name *Arecastrum*. Following the rules of botanical nomenclature, he used the species name which had first been published (by A. von Chamisso). Hence, the palm became *Arecastrum romanzoffianum*, the now correct botanical name.

A. ROMANZOFFIANUM
Named for M. P. Romanzoff of Russia, 1754–1826

Common name: Queen palm. **Origin:** Central and southern Brazil. **Sex:** Monoecious. **Trunk:** 25 ft high, sometimes taller; 1–2 ft diameter; smooth; plainly ringed. **Petiole:** 3 ft long; set in mass of fibers. **Leaf:** Pinnate; 8–15 ft long; many narrow leaflets. **Leaflets:** Less than 1 in. broad; long; soft; drooping from middle out; green both sides. **Flowerstalk:** 3 ft long; from axils of lower leaves; branches hanging in fruit; at first covered by 2–3 ft spathe. **Flowers:** Cream-colored; small. **Fruit:** 1 in. long, 1¼ in. wide; broad ovoid; short-beaked; yellow, fleshy, fibrous exterior. **Seed:** Globose; ¾ in. diameter.

A. ROMANZOFFIANUM var. AUSTRALIS

As above, but more slender and graceful, with fruit less wide, more egg-shaped, 1 in. long, ⅝ in. wide. This variety is probably the one so widely sold and planted as *Cocos plumosa*.

A. ROMANZOFFIANUM VAR. BOTRYOPHORUM

As above, but more robust, with heavier trunk, bigger leaves, and larger fruit (1½ in. long, ⅘ in. wide). The delicate leaves tend to look straggly after exposure to strong winds.

Cultivation: All *Arecastrum* seeds germinate quickly (well under 2 months). It is a very variable palm whose vigor depends greatly upon soil conditions, a fast grower in wet soil, and hardy to cold and frost. Fairchild Tropical Garden lists *A. romanzoffianum* as hardy for southern Florida. Huntington Gardens reports *A. romanzoffianum* var. *botryophorum* to be more frost tolerant than other varieties.

A. romanzoffianum is grown everywhere in southern California and south and central Florida. Quite commonly used in recent years for street planting.

Arecastrum romanzoffianum. Photo courtesy of Huntington Botanical Gardens.

ARENGA*†
Origin of name unknown

This is a remarkable genus with several very individual characteristics. The trunks of all arengas are densely clothed with the black, fibrous remains of the leafbases. The trees do not flower until they reach maturity; then they flower from the top leaf axils, and then successively lower. After the last and lowest flowering, the tree dies. The leaflets are distinctive in that they are slightly notched several times along each side. *Arenga* is one of the few pinnate-leafed genera whose leaflets fold into the rachis with the inside of pleat facing upward.[1]

A. PINNATA
(*A. saccharifera*)

The solid, hairy, black mass of the trunk, broken at intervals by protruding tips of old leafbases and ascending strips of long spines, is surmounted by a dense crown of tall, erect, dark-green leaves. The leaflets have white satin backs which occasionally flash out of the otherwise somber scene.

Once maturity is reached (10–12 years), the huge fruit clusters begin to appear. The male flowers, in a dense cluster 4 ft long, are purple and have an unpleasant odor. The female flower clusters (on the same tree) are longer than the male and ripen very slowly into glossy,

[1]This characteristic is known botanically as leaflets induplicate in vernation, and is also found in the following genera: *Caryota, Didymosperma, Wallichia, Phoenix.*

Arenga pinnata in fruit at Fairchild Tropical Garden.

Arenga pinnata in fruit at U.S.P.I. Garden, Coconut Grove, Florida. Photo by H. F. Loomis.

brown, plum-sized fruits. Each new flower cluster is borne on a lower leaf axil; when the lowest is reached, and that fruit ripens (3–5 years later), the entire spectacle is ended and the tree dies. Since each flower takes about 2 years to become ripe fruit, there is almost always fruit on the tree during this period.

The coarse, black fibers (commercially known as gomuti fibers) are very resistant to dampness. They are used in filters, for calking ships, and for manufacturing ropes for use in salt water. Dr. Fairchild once asked Dr. C. F. Kettering about these fibers; Kettering said that they may consist of a cellulose of different chemical construction from that of ordinary fibers.

The sap yields arenga sugar.

The juice of the outer covering of the fruit is highly corrosive and may cause great pain and inflammation of the skin.

Common name: Sugar palm. **Origin:** Malaya. **Sex:** Monocarpic and monoecious. **Trunk:** 20–40 ft high. Old leafbases adhere, covering trunk with a mat of tough, black fibers and long spines. **Petiole:** 2–3 ft long; smooth; very stout; base covered with black fibers and very long, weak spines. **Leaf:** Pinnate; 20–28 ft long, up to 10 ft wide; very erect; 100 pairs of leaflets. **Leaflets:** Long, with jagged apex; faint, widely spaced notches on both sides; dark-green above, whitened beneath; induplicate in vernation. **Flowerstalk:** To 6–10 ft long; from axils of top leaves, then gradually downward. **Flowers:** Male flowers: 1 in. long; blackish-purple; unpleasant odor. Female flowers: solitary, large, 1 in. diameter. **Fruit:** Globose; 2 in. long; slow ripening; brown; appears only on lower half of spadix branches; outer skin is highly corrosive.

Trunk detail of *Arenga pinnata*.

Close-up of fruit of *Arenga pinnata*.

A. ENGLERI

A handsome dwarf, cluster palm, very different from *A. pinnata*, but retaining many characteristics of the genus. Grows up to 10 ft tall.

Common name: None. **Origin:** Formosa. **Sex:** Monoecious. **Trunk:** Multiple; very short, up to a few feet. **Leaf:** Pinnate; to 4 ft. Leaflets near base, narrow; end ones, broad. **Leaflets:** Varied, graceful shapes, whitish underneath; irregularly but attractively notched on both sides; induplicate in vernation. **Flowerstalk:** Short, 1 ft long. **Flowers:** Usually hidden among leaves. **Fruit:** Globose; 1 in. diameter; yellowish-red.

A. AMBONG

Appearance is much like that of *A. pinnata*, but trunk short and much thicker. Leaflets very unusual, up to 20 in. long, 4 in. wide, with deep, irregular indentations down to 2 in. Philippines.

A. WIGHTII

Trunks thick and forming clusters; otherwise resembles *A. pinnata*, except that the petioles (or naked parts of leafstalks) are unusually long, 6–8 ft. India.

OTHER SPECIES

Brown describes *A. tremula*, a trunkless species in the Philippines. Ridley describes *A. westerhouti*, a multiple-trunk species, growing in Malaya. Ridley considers *A. obtusifolia* a synonym for *A. westerhouti*. There are other species of *Arenga* that are not widely cultivated and are little known in the United States, including *A. mindorensis* which is growing in Bogor Garden, Java.

Cultivation: *A. pinnata* is not particularly hardy and, in the United States, can be cultivated outdoors only in southern Florida. The seeds germinate in less than 2 months. Plants grow fairly rapidly for palms.

A. engleri is much more hardy. Young plants are known to have survived the cold winter of 1957–1958 in Daytona Beach, Florida. In spite of three consecutive days of long frosts, these plants showed no damage, although nearby all plants of *A. pinnata* were wiped out. Huntington Gardens reports that *A. engleri* is hardy in San Marino, California. Seeds of *A. engleri* take up to 2 years to germinate.

Fairchild Tropical Garden lists as hardy in southern Florida *A. ambong, A. pinnata, A. undulatifolia, A. westerhoutii,* and *A. wightii;* as extra hardy, *A. engleri* and *A. tremula.*

Arenga engleri. Photo courtesy of Huntington Botanical Gardens.

ARIKURYROBA*

A. SCHIZOPHYLLA

A graceful palm that is easily recognized. The old leafbases that cover the trunk are so long and so upright that they look like a bundle of slats and lend the trunk a very individual appearance. Originally part of the genus *Cocos*. Very attractive as a young plant.

Common name: None. **Origin:** Brazil. **Sex:** Monoecious. **Trunk:** 2–8 ft high, 6–8 in. diameter; single; covered with old leafbases, which stand erect and are of a purplish-black color. **Petiole:** 2–3 ft long; dark purplish-black, especially on margins; strong spines on edges near base. **Leaf:** Pinnate; 4–8 ft long, 3 ft wide; gracefully arching. **Leaflets:** Long, 1 in. broad; notched at apex; dark-green both sides. **Flowerstalk:** 2–3 ft long, 8–10 in. wide; from axils of lower leaves. **Fruit:** Ellipsoid; 1 in. or more long; in grapelike clusters; bright orange-yellow. **Seed:** Small nutlet; fragile wall. **Oddity:** Juvenile leaves of young plants have large terminal lobes 4–6 in. wide.

Cultivation: Seeds germinate easily in less than 1 month. Plants seem to be very hardy to cold. Plants in southern Florida usually fruit in September or October, sometimes in August or December. They will tolerate full sun but prefer partial shade.

Arikuryroba schizophylla growing at Chapman Field. Photo by H. F. Loomis.

ASTEROGYNE

A. MARTIANA

A lovely little palm that grows in dense, wet lowlands along the Atlantic coast of British Honduras. The slender trunks are up to 4½ ft tall. The deep-green leaves are about 40 in. long. They are simple and are not divided into leaflets. The flowerstalks are about 2 ft long with several branches which are a dull, pale red. The flowers are white and fragrant. The bluish-black fruits are olive-shaped and smooth, and about ½ in. long. The general appearance is similar to some species of *Geonoma*. One other species is known in Colombia.

ASTROCARYUM*

Greek, *astron*, star, and *karyon*, nut from starlike markings on seed

A genus containing over 40 species, most of which have not been introduced into the United States. The few species mentioned are suitable only for planting in large areas and are included here because of their striking aspects and unusual seeds.

All former Hexopetions are considered by Moore to belong in the genus Astrocaryum. Burret disagrees and considers *Hexopetion* a separate genus.

A. ACULEATUM

Common name: Star-nut palm. **Origin:** British Guiana. **Sex:** Monoecious. **Trunk:** Multiple; to 24 ft tall, 6–8 in. thick; very spiny. **Petiole:** Very short; flat on one side, rounded on other; scattered black spines. **Leaf:** Pinnate; 8–12 ft long. **Leaflets:** 3 ft long, 1 in. broad; light-green above, whitish beneath. **Flowerstalk:** 2 ft long; spathe narrow; few spines; whitish and fuzzy. **Flowers:** Cream-colored; fragrant. **Fruit:** Rotund oblong; 1⅓ in. long; orange. (See illustration.) **Seed:** Peculiarly marked. (See illustration.)

Asterogyne martiana. Photo by A. C. Langlois.

Astrocaryum aculeatum at Bogor Botanic Gardens, Java. Photo by T. Satake.

A. STANDLEYANUM

Similar to *A. aculeatum*, but trunk single, to 40 ft tall, with very dark wood, almost black. It is also called black palm. Spathe much more spiny than *A. aculeatum;* flowers very fragrant. Native to Panama.

A. MEXICANUM
(Formerly *Hexopetion mexicanum*)

A species with a short, single trunk and bearing large clusters of striking orange-colored fruits.

Common name: None. **Origin:** Mexico and Central America. **Sex:** Monoecious. **Trunk:** To 6 ft high; 1–2 in. thick; covered with two-edged spines. **Petiole:** To 2 ft long; four-angled; upper surface spiny. **Leaf:** Pinnate; to 9 ft long. **Leaflets:** To 20 in. long; dark, shiny green above, white beneath. **Flowerstalk:** To 4 ft long; much branched. **Fruit:** Globular; 1½ in. diameter; in large clusters; covered with spines. Kernel is said to be edible, with a flavor similar to that of the coconut.

OTHER SPECIES

Bailey's *Cyclopedia* also describes *A. murumuru*, *A. ayri* (Brazil), *A. argentum* (Colombia), and *A. filulari* (origin unknown). There are many other species of *Astrocaryum* that are not widely cultivated and are little known in the United States.

Cultivation: *Astrocaryum* seeds are difficult to germinate because of their very hard shells. Germination can be hastened by soaking seeds in water which is kept warm, or hot, for 2–3 weeks. All three species at Fairchild Tropical Garden are listed as tender in southern Florida. U.S.P.I. Garden reports that seeds of *A. mexicanum* began to germinate in 38 days.

Fruits of *Astrocaryum standleyanum*, showing starlike marking on seed from which the genus gets its name. Reprinted from *Gentes Herbarum*.

ATTALEA*
Latin, *Attalus*, King of Pergamum

The distinguishing characteristics of the attaleas are the very long and very erect leaves. Set on strong, massive petioles, they reach almost straight up as much as 30 ft, spreading

Attalea crassispatha. Young tree not yet making trunk. Reprinted from *Gentes Herbarum.*

Drawing by Plumier, 1703, of the palm now known as *Attalea crassispatha.* An interesting example of the manner in which the various parts of a palm were presented in old botanical publications. Reprinted from *Gentes Herbarum.*

out their long leaflets into a gigantic feather before the tree begins to show any trunk. In warm countries these palms are often planted in double rows along streets or driveways. Their big, erect leaves form an impressive, high, cathedrallike arch of considerable majesty.

Attalea is very similar to the genera *Scheelea* and *Orbignya*.

The three genera collectively contain over 80 species, all of which are much alike in stature and fruits and differ mainly in their staminate flowers. Since their flowers may not be noticed by planters, the palms are often misnamed, causing much confusion. Only two species will be described and the descriptions are based on those by L. H. Bailey.

A. COHUNE
(Sometimes found as *Orbignya cohune*)

Common name: Cohune palm. (Also used for *Orbignya cohune*—See *Orbignya*.) **Origin:** Honduras. **Sex:** Monoecious. **Trunk:** 50–60 ft high, 1 ft thick; usually covered by old leafbases. **Petiole:** Very strong; flat above, rounded below; fibrous at base. **Leaf:** Pinnate; erect; 30–50 pairs of leaflets; up to 30 ft long. **Leaflets:** 18 (or less) in. long; stiff; dark-green. **Flowerstalk:** From lowest leaves; in woody spathe. **Flowers:** Small. **Fruit:** 3 in. long; egg-shaped; in big grapelike clusters. **Seed:** Yields valuable oil.

A. FUNIFERA

Common name: Piassaba palm. **Origin:** Brazil. **Sex:** Monoecious. **Trunk:** 18–30 ft high, 8–13 in. diameter; old leafbases persist, giving trunk a hairy appearance. **Petiole:** Very short; covered with long, hanging, hairy fibers (sold as piassaba fiber). **Leaf:** Pinnate; 18–30 ft long; erect. **Leaflets:** In clusters; stiff; dark-green both sides. **Flowerstalk:** From lowest leaves; in woody spathe. **Fruit:** 4 in. long; egg-shaped. **Seed:** Very hard; mottled brown.

Cultivation: Johnson reports that seeds germinate in less than 2 months. U.S.P.I. Garden reports planting *A. cohune* seeds which began germinating in 67 days. Plant is slow-growing.

Attalea macrocarpa growing in Bogor Botanic Gardens, Java. This specimen is just beginning to make some trunk. Photo by T. Satake.

Attalea sp. in Bogor Botanic Gardens, showing a substantial trunk. Photo by T. Satake.

BACTRIS*

Greek, *bactron*, staff, cane (young stems used for walking sticks)

This is a genus containing over 200 species and is very little cultivated in the United States. Most species, like the *Bactris minax* pictured here, form large impenetrable clusters covered with vicious spines.

In his *Palms of the Amazon* (1853), A. R. Wallace showed sketches of *B. elatior* and *B. macrocarpa*. These are delicate, graceful, small plants; but this type does not seem to have been much introduced into the United States, and is seldom encountered in botanical gardens anywhere. Bactrids are pinnate palms, native from Mexico to northern South America. They are monoecious. Their trunks, petioles, leafbases and spathes are usually very spiny. The fruit is more or less plumlike, often very attractive and considered edible.

Cultivation: Johnston reports that Bactris seeds lose germinating capacity very quickly. Fresh seeds germinate in less than 2 months. Young plants prefer shade. De Leon reports planting one batch of seeds of *B. ottostaffiana* (or *B. ottostaffeana*) which began germinating in 57 days.

Fairchild Tropical Garden lists *B. major* as hardy.

BACULARIA

Latin, *baculum*, staff, small walking stick

This is not actually a valid genus name under the rules of nomenclature. It is included with *Linospadix* by both Burret and Moore, but is described here because it was so widely

Close-up of trunk of *Bactris plumeriana*, showing typical pattern formed by spines. Reprinted from *Gentes Herbarum*.

Bactris minax in Bogor Botanic Gardens, Java. Many species of *Bactris* form these large clumps. Photo courtesy of A. Dilmy, Bogor Botanic Gardens, Java.

known in England under the *Bacularia* name. The descriptions are taken from Bailey who described two species as *Bacularia monostachya* and *Bacularia minor*.

A few small palms; so far, little cultivated in the United States, but included here because of their interesting, delicate, slender trunks and moderate size. *B. monostachya* is one of the smallest palms in cultivation and is very popular in England as an indoor plant.

B. MONOSTACHYA
(correctly *Linospadix monostachya*)

Common name: Walking-stick palm. **Origin:** Queensland. **Sex:** Monoecious. **Trunk:** 6–12 ft high; less than 1 in. thick; single; spineless. **Petiole:** Short. **Leaf:** Pinnate; 1½–4 ft long. **Leaflets:** Variable in width and length; longest is 12 in. **Flowerstalk:** Very long; beyond leaves. **Fruit:** Ovoid; ½ in. thick.

B. MINOR
(correctly *Linospadix minor*)

A delicate cluster palm; not widely known, but attractive.
Common name: None. **Origin:** Queensland. **Sex:** Monoecious. **Trunk:** Several 2–5 ft long; only ½ in. thick. **Petiole:** Short. **Leaf:** 3½ ft long, with only 12–14 leaflets. **Flowerstalk:** About 3 ft long, only 1/12 in. thick. **Seed:** ½ in. diameter.

Bactris militaris. A strange, simple-leafed species of this large and greatly varied genus. Reprinted from *Gentes Herbarum.*

Bacularia monostachya in Sidney Botanical Gardens, Australia. Photo by A. C. Langlois.

BALAKA
Fijian vernacular name

The true *Balaka* is one of the loveliest of small palms. Palms of *Ptychosperma* and *Drymophloeus*, to which it is related, are mistakenly called *Balaka*, but species of the real *Balaka* are described here because they are unusual and charming. They grow as underbrush in the deep forest. (Not illustrated.)

Slim *Balaka* trunks are used for spears by natives because of their strength and straightness.

B. SEEMANII

Common name: None. **Origin:** Fiji Islands. **Sex:** Monoecious. **Trunk:** To 12 ft high; ½ to ¾ in. thick; ringed, as if jointed. **Petiole:** Scaly. **Leaf:** Pinnate; only 8–10 leaves on tree; only 8–12 leaflets on a leaf. **Leaflets:** 4–6 in. long; wider at end than at base; jagged, square-ended. **Flowerstalk:** 1 ft long; below leaves.

B. PERBREVIS

Much like *B. seemanii*, but taller (to 16 ft). Leaflets are almost a triangle, with point at base, and very wide, square, jagged ends. Native to Fiji Islands.

OTHER SPECIES

There are seven or eight species in Fiji, Samoa, and Tahiti, which are not widely known elsewhere.

BARBOSA

A little-known genus of pinnate palms, native to eastern Brazil. The single trunks are up to 45 ft tall and 7–8 in. diameter. (Not illustrated.)

BARCELLA

A little-known Amazonian genus, with pinnate leaves. (Not illustrated.)

BASSELINIA

A genus of pinnate-leafed palms from New Caledonia. The ten species seem to be little known to cultivation. (Not illustrated.)

BECCARIOPHOENIX

A genus of one species, *B. madagascariensis* has a single trunk 18–30 ft tall and 8–12 pinnate leaves 11–15 ft long. Native to Madagascar. (Not illustrated.)

BEJAUDIA

A little-known genus of pinnate palms, native to Cochin China and Cambodia. (Not illustrated.)

BENTINCKIA*

Named for Lord Bentinck, Governor of Madras 1803–1805

Two species of pinnate-leafed Indian palms.

B. NICOBARICA

Common name: None. **Origin:** India. **Sex:** Monoecious. **Trunk:** 50–60 ft high; 7–10 in. thick; topped by long crownshaft. **Petiole:** Short; smooth. **Leaf:** Pinnate; 5–8 ft long. **Leaflets:** 1–2 ft long; tips 2-lobed; leathery. **Flowerstalk:** 1½–2 ft; many branchlets. **Fruit:** Size of cherry; scarlet. **Oddities:** Young plants have solid, simple leaves for first year, as do young coconut palms.

OTHER SPECIES

B. coddapanna of India is much more slender and is not much cultivated in the United States.

Bentinckia nicobarica in Bogor Botanic Gardens, Java. Photo by T. Satake.

Bentinckia nicobarica. Photo courtesy of A. Dilmy, Bogor Botanic Gardens, Java.

Cultivation: Seeds germinate in less than 2 months. Plants are fast growing. Chapman Field reports that one batch of *B. nicobarica* seeds began germinating in 75 days; De Leon reports that *B. coddapanna* seeds took 30 days to begin germination.

BENTINCKIOPSIS [1]

A pinnate-leafed genus, native to the Caroline Islands, and at one time considered to be part of the genus *Exorrhiza*. Not widely cultivated. (Not illustrated.)

BISMARCKIA*
Named in honor of Prince Bismarck

Known in some areas (including Madagascar) as *Medemia nobilis*. Both genera are valid; distinguished from each other by a small difference in the seed.

B. NOBILIS

A very heavy, dioecious fan palm, allied to *Latania* and *Hyphaene*, but faster growing. It is said sometimes to reach the incredible height of 200 ft.

Common name: None. **Origin:** Madagascar. **Sex:** Dioecious. **Trunk:** Up to 200 ft high, usually much less. **Petiole:** Very heavy and firm; blue-green, streaked with white. **Leaf:** Palmate; up to 10 ft across; rigid; broader than long. **Segments:** 2 in. wide; blunt apex; thread at each sinus; blue-green. **Flowerstalk:** Among leaves. **Fruit:** 1½ in. diameter; plumlike; brown. **Seed:** 1 in. diameter; wrinkled.

Cultivation: Johnston reports that seed germination occurs in less than 2 months and suggests that shell be removed from seed before planting in seedbed. In germination, taproot grows down about 12 in. before growing up. If placed in shallow seedbox, or container, root will become injured and twisted. De Leon reports planting one batch of seed of *B. nobilis* which began to germinate in 39 days.

[1]Burret considers *Bentinckiopsis* to be a valid genus. Moore and Fosberg unite it with *Clinostigma. Gentes Herbarum*, vol. 8, page 458 ff.

Bismarckia nobilis growing in Mrs. Jennings' garden in Florida.

Bismarckia nobilis at U.S.P.I. Garden at Coconut Grove, Florida. Photo by H. F. Loomis.

BORASSODENDRON

A little-known genus from Perak, Malaya. The leaves are palmate. (Not illustrated.)

BORASSUS*

A heavy, dioecious fan palm; not much in cultivation in the United States, but widely grown elsewhere.

It is believed that, next to the coconut, there are more numbers of *Borassus* palms in the world than of any other genus. They grow throughout tropical Asia and tropical Africa in huge stands which sometimes cover thousands of acres.

Quantities of strong, black lumber are obtained from the trunks of old trees. The wood is not really hard until the trees are about 100 years old. The older the tree, the harder the wood. Several authorities have claimed that the wood of the female tree is much superior to that of the male. Fairchild speaks of seeing rafters made of Borassus wood that were "black, with a beautiful yellow grain."

Large quantities of sugar are extracted from *Borassus* palms. One tree will yield 2–4 qt of sap per day for 5 months. One gallon of sap yields 1½ lb of jaggery sugar, which is 79 per cent saccharose.

A famous Indian poem, "Tala Vilasam," was written about the many uses of the various parts of the palmyra palm, *Borassus*.

The blue-green leaves are massive (10 ft wide) and stiff; and the saw-toothed petioles are heavy and very strong. The fruits are almost as big as coconuts (6–8 in. diam.) and the three seeds within are encased in a fiber so tough and matted that they are hard to remove.

A male tree cannot be distinguished from a female until flowers are borne, which usually occurs between the twelfth and fifteenth year.

Borassus flabellifer, the palmyra palm. This is a young specimen. Photo courtesy A. Dilmy, Bogor Botanic Gardens, Java.

Close-up showing powerful petioles (edged with black teeth) of *Borassus flabellifer*. Photo by T. Satake.

B. FLABELLIFER

Common name: Palmyra palm. **Origin:** India and Malaya. **Sex:** Dioecious. **Trunk:** To 90 ft high, to 6 ft thick; trunks of older plants are black and very hard, their upper part covered with dead leaves. **Petiole:** 3–4 ft long; strong, stiff; spiny teeth on margin. During early years, has black base and black edges. **Leaf:** Palmate; up to 10 ft across; rigid; 25–40 on one tree. Extension of petiole protrudes as a rib well into center of leaf, causing it to be costapalmate. **Segments:** Many; rigid; gray-green. **Flowerstalk:** Long and much branched; among leaves. **Flowers:** Small; male and female flowers on separate trees. **Fruit:** 6–8 in. diameter; very large; depressed globular; brown; smooth exterior, very fibrous interior. **Seed:** Encased in strong fiber; throws a shoot, or sinker, which grows downward 3 ft before producing growth at the top; this downshoot is considered a great delicacy by natives.

OTHER SPECIES

The African species, rarely seen here, is *B. aethiopium*. Other species are *B. deleg* (British Sudan), *B. heiniana* (New Guinea), *B. madagascariensis* (Madagascar), and *B. sambiranensis* (Madagascar). Ridley also describes *B. machadonis*, growing in Malaya.

Cultivation: Johnston reports that the seed is very hard and does not germinate readily. Germination is hastened by thinning the hard shell with a file or grindstone or by soaking seeds in hot water for long periods. Once germination begins, the seed throws a shoot directly downward 40–50 in., during a period of about 5 months. This shoot then turns upward and takes another 5 months to reach the surface and produce the first leaf. Consequently the seed *must* be planted in a very deep container or in its permanent position in the ground. Seeds may be started in small containers and closely watched. When first shoot is observed, it must then be more permanently planted.

Though in India the *Borassus* palm flourishes in greatest numbers in the hottest regions, it is found as far north as 30°, where it withstands cool winters and occasional frost.

Fairchild wrote that *Borassus* loves sandy beach conditions. He expected it to become almost as great a real-estate asset in southern Florida as the famous coconut, which thrives near the ocean. He may not have realized that the plants do not often survive transplanting.

Three ripe fruits of *Borassus flabellifer* and on the left several seeds germinating after the fibrous husk has been removed. These seeds have been dug up or the sinkers or roots would be growing straight down. These sinkers grow down 3 feet before growth begins out of the top. This downshoot is prized as a delicate vegetable in Ceylon. Photo from Fairchild's *Occasional Papers*.

A fruit cluster of *Borassus ethiopium* and above it a male flower cluster which was taken from another tree. Photo from Fairchild's *Occasional Papers*.

BRAHEA*†
Named for Tycho Brahe, Danish astronomer

All species of *Washingtonia* and some of *Erythea* were at one time part of the genus *Brahea*. Consequently, plants labeled *Brahea* may be suspect of belonging to *Erythea* or *Washingtonia*, its old name.

The genus *Brahea* is restricted to palms whose flowers are solitary, deeply imbedded in the stem, and immersed in heavy tomentum.

Brahea is often found growing on rocky hills and may be suited to, or even prefer, poor soils.

The only species known to have been cultivated in the United States is *B. dulcis*, though there are perhaps eight other species.

B. DULCIS
Latin, sweet

Common name: Rock palm. **Origin:** Mexico. **Sex:** Hermaphrodite. **Trunk:** 9–18 ft high, 7 in. thick; upper part covered with old leafbases, lower part ringed. **Petiole:** Slender; 24 in. long; fibrous at base; green, with pale margins, edged with small, downward-pointing teeth. **Leaf:** Palmate; 4–5 ft diameter; quite round; stiff; deeply cut beyond middle into 50 leaflets. **Segments:** Two pointed; few hanging filaments; underside has white powder that rubs off; blue-green. **Flowerstalk:** 5–7 ft long; many branched; extending beyond leaves; from lower leaves. **Flowers:** Immersed in fuzzy branches of flowerstalk. **Fruit:** ½ in. long; yellow; succulent.

Brahea dulcis in southern Mexico. Note the stiff leaf segments. Reprinted from *Gentes Herbarum*.

Common errors:

Brahea armata is correctly *Erythea armata*.
Brahea glauca is correctly *Erythea armata*.
Brahea edulis is correctly *Erythea edulis*.
Brahea filifera is correctly *Washingtonia filifera*.

Cultivation: Johnston reports seeds germinate in less than 2 months.

BRASSIOPHOENIX DRYMOPHLOEOIDES

A very unusual species of pinnate palm named by Burret from a specimen in Papua. The photograph was taken by L. J. Brass and is of the plant from which the type material of the genus was collected (Brass's No. 5665). It is believed that this palm has not been introduced into the United States. No plants or descriptions are available. Specimen is illustrated.

BRONGNIARTIKENTIA

A pinnate-leafed genus from New Caledonia. The sole species is *B. vaginata*. (Not illustrated.)

BURRETIOKENTIA

A monotypic genus native to New Caledonia whose one species is *Burretiokentia vieillardi*. Pichi-Sermolli published this name (in honor of Burret) for a genus formerly known as *Rhyncocarpa*. Pichi-Sermolli concluded that *Rhyncocarpa* was an illegitimate name because the same name had previously been validly published for a genus of the *Cucurbitaceae*. (Not illustrated.)

Brassiophoenix drymophloeoides. Top of tree cut off for photographing. Taken in Kubuna, Territory of Papua. Photo by L. J. Brass, courtesy of A. C. Langlois.

BUTIA*†

A genus, originally segregated from the once greatly varied genus *Cocos*, *Butia* species are very hardy, small to medium-sized palms, distinguished by their stiffish, recurved leafstalks that arch very sharply, their leaf tips sometimes touching the trunk. The gray-green leaflets stand well upward from the stem, forming a curved trough. Their large clusters of orange fruit may weigh up to 75 lbs.

Many species have been studied, but there is so much variation in plants within a species, that distinguishing characteristics are little more than tendencies. The confusion is increased, no doubt, by cross pollination.

B. CAPITATA

Common name: Yatay palm, jelly palm. **Origin:** South America. **Sex:** Monoecious. **Trunk:** 1–20 ft high, 18 in. thick; including a covering of old leafbases. **Petiole:** Slender; prominent teeth on margins. **Leaf:** Pinnate; several feet long; arching, sometimes recurving almost to ground or trunk. **Leaflets:** Standing upward from rachis before recurving; gray-green. **Flowerstalk:** Up to 4–5 ft; from lower leaves. **Fruit:** Oblong ovoid; about 1 in. long; yellow to red; pulpy; fibrous. **Oddities:** Bottom of trunk is round knob, from which roots grow.

Butia capitata growing in Huntington Botanical Gardens in California. Photo courtesy of Huntington Botanical Gardens.

OTHER SPECIES

B. bonnetii: Usually short, thick trunk; small in all parts, including fruit (Brazil). *B. capitata* var. *strictior:* The Pasadena specimen pictured seems to show great individuality; a handsome tree. *B. eriospatha:* Heavy trunk, 4–10 ft high; leafbases fall off. Fruit, $\frac{5}{8}$–$\frac{3}{4}$ in. diameter (southern Brazil). *B. yatay:* More often tall and treelike. Fruit, large, $1\frac{1}{2}$–2 in. long.

Cultivation: *Butia* is very hardy, perhaps the most hardy of all the pinnate palms. It grows all through Florida and even in North and South Carolina, as well as in most parts of California. Johnson reports outer shell of *Butia* seed should be removed before planting. Even with this treatment, germination is slow, taking up to 6 months. All *Butia* palms are relatively slow growing. U.S.P.I. Garden reports that one batch of *Butia* seeds began germinating in 142 days. Fairchild Tropical Garden lists all their specimens as extra hardy for southern Florida.

Butia yatay growing in Huntington Botanical Gardens in California. Photo courtesy of Huntington Botanical Gardens.

Butia eriospatha in Wright Garden, Riverside, California. Reprinted from *Gentes Herbarum.*

Butia capitata var. *strictior.* This tree in Pasadena, California, is the original tree on which this variety is founded. Reprinted from *Gentes Herbarum.*

CALAMUS*
Latin, reed

Bailey mentions the existence of over 300 species of this, the largest genus of the palm family. Since almost all are spiny climbers, intended for treetops they are little cultivated and an extensive study is hardly justified.

The *Calamus* species are polygamo-dioecious, pinnate, climbing palms, with very long, reedlike stems armed with hooked spines. They are native to tropical Asia and Africa, Malaya, and to the Philippines, New Guinea, and Australia.

They are known as the *rattan palms*, because their bamboolike stems are extensively used in the making of rattan furniture and other similar articles.

They are considered by some authorities not be be sufficiently hardy for southern Florida, and yet there are two good specimens of this genus (species unknown) at Fairchild Tropical Garden that have reached well into the treetops. The lower 4 ft of trunk of these two specimens is spineless and resembles bamboo; but from that point upward, the trunk is densely covered with sharp, black spines.

CALOSPATHE

A genus of pinnate-leafed climbing palms, from the Perak Mountains of Malaya. The only species is *C. schortechinii*, fully described by Ridley in his *Flora of the Malaya Peninsula*. (Not illustrated.)

Calamus sp. shown climbing through the trees at Bogor Botanic Gardens, Java. Photo courtesy A. Dilmy, Bogor Botanic Gardens, Java.

CALYPTROCALYX SPICATUS

A genus little-known in the United States, distinguished from other palms by its long, un-branched flowerstalk. Tall; slender, drooping, pinnate leaves.

   Common name: None. **Origin:** Moluccas, New Guinea. **Sex:** Monoecious. **Trunk:** To 40 ft high, usually less, 7–10 in. diameter, prominently ringed. **Petiole:** Short. **Leaf:** Pinnate; 8–12 ft long; oblong; many leaflets. **Leaflets:** Narrow. **Flowerstalk:** Among leaves; 6–7 ft long; unbranched. **Fruit:** Orange-colored.

CALYPTROGYNE

Greek, *Calyptra*, covering for head, and *gynē*, woman

A genus little-known in the United States. It was originally separated from the genus *Geonoma*, from which it is distinguished only by having little, if any, trunk and by some details of the flowers. It has since been confused with *Calyptronoma* and, along with that genus, bears the widely used common name of *manac palm*.

   Bailey found all the so-called *Calyptrogyne* plants he examined in Jamaica to be actually *Calyptronoma*. There are, however, valid species of *Calyptrogyne* in Mexico and Central America.

   Calyptrogynes are pinnate palms of small stature, with little or no trunk, very short petioles, and smallish, pinnate leaves. The leaflets are scythe-shaped, and the plant is particularly attractive when young. Not cultivated in the United States.

Calyptrocalyx spicatus. Note the two long *unbranched* flower-stalks, a distinguishing feature. Photo courtesy of A. Dilmy, Bogor Botanic Gardens, Java.

CALYPTRONOMA SWARTZII

A pinnate palm which is much like a coconut in general appearance. In Cuba it is known as the *manac palm;* in Jamaica, it is called *long thatch.* It often grows in morasses or even in several feet of water. It is little cultivated.

Common name: Manac palm or long thatch. **Origin:** Jamaica. **Sex:** Monoecious. **Trunk:** To 35 ft high; 8–10 in. diameter. **Petiole:** 8–10 ft long; concave above. **Leaf:** Pinnate; about 30 pairs of leaflets. **Leaflets:** Dark-green. **Flowerstalk:** From axils of lower leaves. **Fruit:** ¾ in. long, ½ in. wide. **Seed:** Small; brownish; albumen solid.

OTHER SPECIES

Bailey mentions *C. dulcis* (Cuba); *C. quisqueyana* (Haiti); *C. rivalis* (Puerto Rico).

CAMPECARPUS

A monotypic genus of pinnate-leafed palms whose only species is *C. fulcita.* Native to New Caledonia. (Not illustrated.)

CARPENTARIA

One species of Australian palm *Carpentaria acuminata* described by Pichi-Sermolli, but not recognized as valid by Burret and Potztal. (Not illustrated.)

CARPOXYLON

A genus of little-known, pinnate-leafed palm from New Caledonia. According to Burret, palms named *Kajewskia* are correctly *Carpoxylon.* (Not illustrated.)

At left:

Calyptrogyne microcarpa in Cuba. Courtesy of Herbario De La Salle.

Calyptronoma swartzii with its trunk deep in water in the Black River region of St. Elizabeth, Jamaica, West Indies. Reprinted from *Gentes Herbarum.*

CARYOTA*
Greek, *Karyou*, nut

The famous fishtail palms (*Caryota*) are among the most widely used of all the palms introduced into the United States. The two best-known species are *C. mitis*, with clustered, multiple trunks, and the single-trunked *C. urens*.

The unusual design of the leaflets is daintily attractive and universally admired.

Not particularly hardy, caryotas thrive outdoors in the United States only in southern Florida, but are popular indoor plants in other areas, being particularly suited to large areas, such as hotel lobbies and ballrooms.

Caryota has many characteristics uncommon to pinnate palms.

It is the only palm whose leaves are bipinnate. (See illustration.)

The leaflets are folded into their stems with the edges turned skyward, while most pinnate palms have the edges turned downward. [1]

It is monocarpic, that is, when the plants reach maturity, the first flowers appear from the upper leaf axils. Successive flowerings are from successively lower branches, and gradually downward (during 5–7 years) until the lowest branches are reached. When the lowest fruits ripen, that particular trunk dies. In the single-trunked *C. urens*, this means the end of the plant. In multiple-trunked *C. mitis*, only one trunk dies at a time and there are always new ones springing up.

The outer covering of the fruit contains stinging needlelike crystals which can be very painful to the skin. The flowerstalks of *C. mitis* are only 1–2 ft long, while those of *C. urens* are much longer, sometimes reaching 10–12 ft over all.

In its native land, *Caryota urens* is particularly useful. A valuable fiber is taken from its petioles and leafbases. The pith of the trunk is almost equal to the best sago of commerce, and great quantities of jaggery sugar (12 gal per day from one tree) are produced from the sap. Fairchild, having tasted jaggery sugar from many different palms, considered the flavor of that from *C. urens* to be the finest.

[1]Also true of *Arenga, Didymosperma, Wallichia, Phoenix.*

Caryota mitis growing in Palm Beach, Florida.

Caryota urens. An unusually large specimen growing at Fairchild Tropical Garden, Florida.

C. MITIS
Latin, mild, soft

Common name: Fishtail palm. **Origin:** India and Malaya. **Sex:** Monoecious. **Trunk:** Several, to 25–40 ft high. **Petiole:** 1–2 ft long. **Leaf:** Bipinnate (see illustration); 4–9 ft long. **Leaflets:** Short (6 in.), broad (5 in.); irregularly wedge-shaped. Veins thin and numerous; apex jagged and toothed, toothed and jagged portion occupying more than half the leaflet. Induplicate in vernation (edges of leaflet turned upward). **Flowerstalk:** First from axils— top leaves—then gradually downward; 1–2 ft long. **Fruit:** Globular; ½ in. diameter; red; outer covering contains numerous stinging needlelike crystals.

C. URENS
Latin, burning, stinging (from the fruit)

Common name: Fishtail palm. **Origin:** India and Malaya. **Sex:** Monoecious. **Trunk:** Single; 40–60 ft high, 1–1½ ft diameter. **Petiole:** 1–2 ft long, very stout, 3 in. across. **Leaf:** Bipinnate (see illustration); 20 ft long, to 15 ft broad. **Leaflets:** 6 in. long; 3–4 in. broad. Similar to *C. mitis*. Toothed and jagged portion occupying less than half the length of the leaflets; ribs fairly thick, not as numerous as *C. mitis*. All leaflets induplicate. **Flowerstalk:** 10–12 ft long. **Fruit and Seed:** Much like *C. mitis* in all respects.

C. RUMPHIANA

Single-trunk species, with leaflets up to 15 in. long, and fruit over 1 in. diameter. Flower-stalk up to 2 ft. Native to Australia and Malaya.

C. rumphiana var. *philippinensis* is much larger in every way than other *Caryota* species mentioned here.

C. CUMINGII

The specimen of *C. cumingii* at Fairchild Tropical Garden has a single trunk over 40 ft

The bipinnate leaf of *Caryota mitis*. Note the fishtail leaflets.

Caryota urens in Palm Beach, Florida. The fruits are its final ones and the tree is beginning to die.

tall and carries massive spathes and flowerstalks. The rings on the trunk are so deep they resemble steps. Native to the Philippines.

OTHER SPECIES

There are many other species that are not as widely cultivated and are not generally planted in the United States. Native to India, Malaya, Australia, and New Guinea.

Cultivation: In the United States, caryotas are hardy outdoors only in southern Florida. Johnston reports that most *Caryota* seeds germinate in 3–4 months. De Leon planted seeds of the rather rare variety, *C. cumingii*, and reports that it took 317 days for the first signs of germination to appear.

CATOBLASTUS

A South American genus of cluster-forming, pinnate-leafed, stilt palms, allied to *Ireartea*, and not known to be cultivated in the United States.

C. andinus is illustrated.

C. praemorsus grows in a cluster of 12–15 trunks to a height of 50 ft. The trunks are covered with a very hard, black bark and are favored for fence posts. The egg-shaped, wrinkled fruit is about 1½ in. long, and of a lustrous, blue-black color. Native to Colombia and Venezuela.

CATOSTIGMA

A genus of pinnate-leafed palm, native to Colombia, and little-known to cultivation. (Not illustrated.)

Catoblastus andinus. Courtesy of M. B. Foster.

CERATOLOBUS

A genus of five or six species of climbing unisexual palms, native to Malaya.

Ridley describes *C. kingianus*, with climbing trunk 25–50 ft long, 1¼ in. thick; petioles 6–8 in. long; leaves, pinnate, 3–4 ft long; with few leaflets, 6–9 in. long, 3–4 in. wide; toothed on edges, and white underneath. Fruit, spherical, ¾ in. diameter, covered with brown scales. Native to Malaya.

Ridley also describes *C. laevigatus*, in Malaya, whose trunk is only 9 ft long.

CEROXYLON

Latin, *cera*, wax, and Greek, *xylon*, wood

Before the California redwoods were discovered, these wax palms of the Andes were said to be the tallest trees known, growing to a height of 200 ft.

These palms, whose straight, tall trunks are covered with a layer of wax, producing the appearance of marble columns, are found growing at remarkable altitudes. The general altitude limit of the palm family is approximately 4000 ft and yet these amazing plants grow at an altitude more than 6000 ft above that. At Quindio Pass in Colombia, *C. andicola* grows at 10,000 ft and one shorter-trunked species grows at an altitude of 13,450 ft (between Colombia and Chile).

Many efforts have been made to grow *Ceroxylon* in various parts of the United States, but so far with little success. The U.S.P.I. Garden at Coral Gables, Florida, has made repeated efforts and H. F. Loomis is confident that they simply will not grow in Florida. Bailey's *Hortus Second* (1930) reports plants having been introduced into southern California with "indifferent

Ceratolobus laevigatus in Bogor Botanic Gardens, Java. Photo courtesy A. Dilmy, Bogor Botanic Gardens, Java.

Catostigma sp. taken in Central Andes region of Colombia. Photo courtesy of A. Dugand.

success." Efforts in colder areas may one day be successful. Their tall, waxy trunks would add an astonishing touch to some of the hillsides of Oregon or Washington.

The palms are the official symbol of the Colombian nation and may be seen on Colombian postage stamps.

C. ANDICOLA
Native of the Andes

Common name: Wax palm. **Origin:** In the mountains of South America: Colombia and Venezuela. **Sex:** Monoecious. **Trunk:** Up to 200 ft in height, 1–2 ft thick; very straight; sometimes a trifle swollen at the middle, or above; covered with layer of wax. **Petiole:** Stiff, strong. **Leaf:** Pinnate; 20 ft long; only 6–10 in number, all at top of tree, making heavy crown. **Leaflets:** Linear; very stiff; split at end. Dark-green above, whitish powder underneath; almost hairy. **Flowerstalk:** Among leaves. **Flowers:** Large, for palms. **Fruit:** 1 in. diameter, or less; berry-shaped. **Seed:** Round; bony; large as a hazelnut.

OTHER SPECIES

Much confusion exists as to the various species of *Ceroxylon*. Humboldt, who discovered them, thought them all to be one species. Dahlgren's *Index of Palms* (1936) lists 16 species. Their inaccessibility hinders further study and makes final conclusions difficult.

Cultivation: Johnston reports that fresh seeds are very difficult to obtain, as they quickly lose their viability. Bailey once stated that *C. andicola* thrives in a warm moist house and that the seeds germinate well under similar conditions.

Ceroxylon andicola near Talueye, Colombia. The famous wax palm of the Andes. These trunks, the tallest among palms, are covered with a layer of wax. The nearest tree shows a small area where this wax has been removed. Photo courtesy of New Crops Research Branch, U.S. Department of Agriculture.

CHAMAEDOREA*†

A group of shade-loving, small, graceful, and delicate palms. The slender, green trunks, which may be single or clustered, are often attractively ringed or jointed.

Usually the few pinnate leaves form small crowns, leaving the trunk clearly visible. The flower clusters are formed among the leaves, or below them, and are generally small and delicate. If sheltered from the sun and from strong winds, the foliage is very rich in color and texture, making the plants attractive for porch and patio use.

Chamaedorea is a large and imperfectly known genus with over 100 species having been described as growing in Mexico and Central and South America alone. True breeding requires a male and female plant of the same species and the positive identification of most cultivated species is puzzling and hazardous.

Plants are available for study under certain species names, but it is not certain that these names were properly applied in the first place.

Harold E. Moore, Jr., of the Bailey Hortorium, is engaged in a full study of this genus and of its history. When his study is completed, it will establish whether *Eleutheropetalum* is a separate genus or really part of *Chamaedorea;* and it is possible that *Collinia elegans* may become only a subdivision of *Chamaedorea.* Prior to completion of that study, detailed description of any species would be speculative.

Listed below are a few species most frequently encountered and some general description of them as they are known today. For simplification, some species are divided according to types and a limited description offered.

Multiple trunk: *C. erumpens:* Trunks to 10 ft high; up to 40 in a clump. Leaf, pinnate, 18–20 in. long, with about 20 leaflets, all about the same width, but becoming shorter near end of leaf. Terminal pair twice as wide, and only 5–6 in. long (Mexico); *C. seifritzii:* Multiple trunks; gray-green, narrow leaflets, spaced about an inch apart (Mexico); *C. stolonifera:*

Chamaedorea erumpens var. *fairchildii* at Fairchild Tropical Garden. Has only 10–12 leaflets per leaf with a very wide terminal pair. Photo by H. T. Loomis.

Chamaedorea seifritzii in Florida. Photo by H. F. Loomis.

Trunks to 3 ft high; dense cluster of growth near base, forming many new trunks, which are very slender (Mexico).

Climbing trunk or trunks: *C. desmoncoides:* Multiple, slender trunks; begins to climb after becoming few feet high. Leaves 2–3 ft long, with drooping, narrow leaflets a foot long (Mexico); *C. elatior:* Single, climbing trunk; covered with leafbases. Leaves 6–8 ft long; leaflets 2 ft long, 1 in. wide (Mexico).

Single trunk; simple, undivided leaves: *C. geonomaeformis:* Trunk 4 ft in height; leafbases adhere; leaves simple, oblong, deep green, 8–12 in. long, 6 in. wide; deeply indented at apex (Guatemala); *C. ernesti-augustii:* Trunk ringed; brace roots at base; leaf, simple, oblong, 18 in. long, 9 in. wide; deeply indented at apex (Mexico).

Single trunk, pinnate leaves: *C. arenbergiana:* Trunk 5–6 ft in height; leaves pinnate, recurved. Leaflets only 16–30 in. long; apex hanging; fruit in dense clusters (Central America); *C. corallina:* Trunk to 4 ft; leaves 2 ft long; leaflets 8–12 in. long, 3 in. broad in middle, with short point; terminal pair confluent (Venezuela); *C. fragrans:* Trunk 4–6 ft in height; less than 1 in. thick; only about 5–6 leaves on tree, each 1 ft long; 2-lobed below the middle. Flowers fragrant (Peru); *C. glaucifolia:* Tall trunk, 20 ft in height; single; leaves pinnate, 4–6 ft long; leaflets glaucous (powdery), gray-green on both sides, very numerous, very narrow and long-pointed (Guatemala); *C. graminifolia:* True specimens not believed to be in the United States, though plants are offered under this name. Those offered usually form multiple trunks, whereas the true species has a solitary trunk (Guatemala); *C. pacaya:* Trunk to 10 ft in height; leaves 2–3 ft long; leaflets, only about 7 altogether, the terminal pair much broader than others and dull green. Many plants not fitting this description are incorrectly offered under this name (Costa Rica); *C. sartori:* Trunk 8–14 ft tall, ringed, covered with leafbases; leaves, 3 ft long; leaflets broad, rather soft, 12 in. long, 2½ in. wide, abruptly long-pointed (Mexico); *C. tepejilote:* Trunk to 10 ft in height, strongly and closely ringed, with swollen joints, like bamboo; many aerial roots; leaves, pinnate, ascending, to 4 ft long; leaflets, dark-green, 18 in. long, 1½–2 in. broad. Flowerstalks pointing directly upward while in spathe.

Trunks very short or absent: *C. martiana:* With leaflets only 6–8 in. long (Mexico); *C. radicalis:* Cluster palm; leaves to 3 ft long; leaflets 14 by ¾ in., arching stiffly toward tip (Mexico).

Common errors: *C. pringlei* = *C. radicalis. C. elegans* = *Collinia elegans. C. ernesti-augustinii* and *C. sartori* are considered by some authorities to be *Eleutheropetalum* instead of *Chamaedorea.*

OTHER SPECIES

Principes vol. 2, fascicle 2, describes *C. falcifera* from Guatemala with slender trunks and orange-colored, sickle-shaped fruit. Terminal pair of leaflets 6–7 in. long and 2¼ in. wide. The remaining three pairs of leaflets each are smaller in all directions, the basal pair being 3 in. long, 1 in. wide.

Cultivation: Johnston reports that fresh seeds of most species germinate in less than 2 months. Most species prefer deep shade even when mature. U.S.P.I. Garden reports that one batch of seeds of *C. erumpens* began germination in 222 days. De Leon reports, with the use of bottom heat in seedbed, the following results: *C. glaucifolia*, 89 days; *C. scheeliana*, 44 days; *C. corallina*, 95 days.

Chamaedorea geonomaeformis at Fairchild Tropical Garden. Photo by H. F. Loomis.

Chamaedorea graminifolia in California. Photo courtesy of Huntington Botanical Gardens.

CHAMAEROPS*†
Greek, *chamai*, ground, and *rhops*, shrub or bush

C. HUMILIS

The European fan palm is the only palm native to Europe. It is among the hardiest of palms and very widely planted both here and abroad.

It is an oddity in nomenclature because, as one species of one genus, it grows in much more variable forms than one would ordinarily expect.

Under the same specific name, it may have one trunk, or many; it may be 4 ft tall, or 20 ft tall; it may have green leaves, or glaucous-blue leaves. Certain forms have at times been given other names, but only as varieties of the species *C. humilis* and not as separate species.

Chamaerops humilis is usually a low, bushy palm, forming a clump of several trunks. Its deeply cut leaves are palmate. The leafstalks are long and firm. The leaflets are stiff, almost bristly. These stiff leaflets are the most recognizable characteristic and are readily noticed in the illustrations.

Common name: European fan palm. **Origin:** Mediterranean area. **Sex:** Dioecious, or occasionally polygamous. **Trunk:** To 20 ft high (usually 3–5 ft); often covered with old leaf-bases. **Petiole:** Long, slender; strongly spined. **Leaf:** Palmate segments, deeply cut, almost to stalk; 2–3 ft across; very stiff. **Segments:** Sword-shaped; split at ends; green, gray-green, or powdery blue; firm, not drooping. **Flowerstalk:** Among leaves; short. **Flowers:** Yellow; hidden among leaves. **Fruit:** Globose or ovoid; 3-sided near base; ½ to 1½ in. long; brown or yellow.

Where grown in United States: California, Gulf Coast, Atlantic Coast (south of North Carolina). For some reason, much more widely planted in California than elsewhere.

Chamaerops humilis, bushy type. Photo courtesy of Huntington Botanical Gardens.

Chamaerops humilis, single-trunk type. Note large *Phoenix canariensis* in background. Photo courtesy of Huntington Botanical Gardens.

Cultivation: Johnston reports that seeds germinate in 3–4 months, sometimes less. Plants are quite hardy to cold but grow slowly.

CHAMBEYRONIA

Comprised of two recognized species of tall, monoecious, unarmed, pinnate palms, both often cultivated erroneously as *Kentia* or *Kentiopsis*. There are true *Kentia* species and one true *Kentiopsis* species, but these are rare, probably never cultivated in the United States.

C. MACROCARPA

Common name: None. **Origin:** Australia and New Caledonia. **Sex:** Monoecious. **Trunk:** To 60 ft tall, and more; slender. **Petiole:** Yellow, when young; later, brown. **Leaf:** Pinnate; 4 ft long. **Leaflets:** 3–4 in. wide, obtuse end; strong rib on margin as well as on midrib; reddish underneath when young; later both sides are green. **Flowerstalk:** Below leaves; branched. **Flowers:** Numerous. **Fruit:** Ovoid elliptic; 1–½ in. long.

C. HOOKERI

Much like *C. macrocarpa* but leaflets paler underneath, and fruit is about 2 in. long.

CHELYOCARPUS

A little-known genus of palmate palms from Central America. (Not illustrated.)

Chamaerops humilis type with short petioles. Photo courtesy of Huntington Botanical Gardens.

Chambeyronia (formerly *Kentiopsis*) *macrocarpa* growing in Rio Botanical Gardens in 1938. Photo by A. C. Langlois.

CHRYSALIDOCARPUS*†

Named by Wendland, because the fruit without its endocarp has the appearance of a chrysalis

A group of dioecious, pinnate palms, native to Madagascar.

C. LUTESCENS

Latin, *luteus*, yellow
(Once known in the United States as *Areca lutescens*)

This species, widely cultivated in U.S. nurseries, is sold for outdoor planting in southern Florida and very widely elsewhere in the United States in pots or tubs for indoor use.

It grows in dense clusters, throwing off many extra trunks as suckers. The leaves are arched and the leaflets, firm, the feathery foliage usually running to the ground and obscuring the trunk.

Unfortunately, nurserymen often still refer to this *Chrysalidocarpus* plant as the areca palm. Although this name has been erroneous for many years, let us not confuse the genus *Chrysalidocarpus* with the genus *Areca*. Both are valid.

Common name: None. **Origin:** Madagascar. **Sex:** Dioecious. **Trunk:** Up to 25–30 ft high, 4–6 in. diameter; several to many; surmounted by crownshaft. **Petiole:** 2 ft long; deep furrowed; expanded at base; yellow. **Leaf:** Pinnate; 6–8 ft long, 3 ft wide; arching; 40–60 pairs of leaflets. **Leaflets:** ½ in. broad, but firm, with ends not drooping. **Flowerstalk:** Among leaves; much branched. **Fruit:** ¾ in. long; obloid; violet-black.

C. LUCUBENSIS

Unlike *C. lutescens*, this species has a single, stout trunk.

Common name: None. **Origin:** Forest of Lucuba, on island of Nossi-be off northwest

Chrysalidocarpus lutescens growing in garden at Palm Beach, Florida.

coast of Madagascar. **Sex:** Monoecious. **Trunk:** To 30 ft high, 10 in. broad; single, enlarged at base; ringed; with short crownshaft. **Petiole:** Short—generally attached at 3 different angles forming 3 distinct vertical rows or ranks. **Leaf:** Pinnate; leaflets in clusters. Set into rachis in several ranks, or rows, each row being at a different angle, producing a somewhat rounded, or bottle-brush effect. **Leaflets:** Wider than *C. lutescens;* glossy on top; ¾ in. wide, 1½ ft long. **Flowerstalk:** Among leaves; about 2 ft long; much branched. **Fruit:** Oblong ovoid; ¾ in. long; exterior thin and hard.

C. MADAGASCARIENSIS
(Once known as *Dypsis madagascariensis*)

Similar to *C. lutescens*, but the trunks are heavier and the foliage is more dense, leaves more numerous, and each leaf has many more leaflets (90 pairs). The leaflets are weaker and much more inclined to droop. Fruit, ½ in. long.

OTHER SPECIES

Flore de Madagascar lists about 21 species in Madagascar.

Cultivation: Johnston reports that seeds of *C. lucubensis* germinate in well under 2 months. Seedlings prefer shade; adult plants can be grown in full sun, but will do best in 50 per cent shade. Grows rather rapidly for a palm.

U.S.P.I. Garden reports one planting of *C. lutescens*, in which seeds began sprouting at the end of 31 days. De Leon reports that, even with bottom heat, *C. lucubensis* seeds waited 150 days before producing growth. A batch of *C. madagascariensis* seeds took 145 days. This, no doubt, partly explains the absence of the last two species in many nurseries where *C. lutescens* is readily available.

Chrysalidocarpus lucubensis, the single-trunk variety, growing in Puerto Rico. Reprinted from *Gentes Herbarum*.

Chrysalidocarpus madagascariensis growing in Mrs. Jennings' garden in Florida.

CHUNIOPHOENIX

A genus of palmate palms, native to Indochina and little-known to cultivation. (Not illustrated.)

CLINOSPERMA

Greek, *klinein*, to incline, and *sperma*, seed

A genus of palmate palms to 40 ft tall. Not widely cultivated, particularly in the United States. Native to New Caledonia. (Not illustrated.)

CLINOSTIGMA [1]

Greek, *klinein*, to incline, and stigma

Short, pinnate palms with crownshaft, native to Australia and the Pacific islands. Somewhat resembling *Howea*. Not very widely cultivated in the United States.

Plants known as *C. mooreanum* are considered by Burret to be *Lepidorrhachis mooreanum*.

Cultivation: De Leon reports that seeds of *C. ponapensis* began germination in 48 days.

CLINOSTIGMOPSIS

Two species of palms described by Pichi-Sermolli. These two species are considered by Burret and Potztal to be correctly *Exorrhiza*. Native to Fiji and New Hebrides. (Not illustrated.)

[1]In *Gentes Herbarum*, vol. 8, pages 458–466, Moore and Forsberg give their reasons for uniting all *Exorrhiza* species with *Clinostigma*. Burret lists *Exorrhiza* and *Clinostigma* as separate, valid species. In this book *Exorrhiza* species are described under *Exorrhiza* which please see.

Clinostigma mooreanum, Sidney Botanical Gardens. Photo by A. C. Langlois.

COCCOTHRINAX*

Greek, *cocco*, grain, seed, and *thrinax*, three–pronged fork

A fully recognized genus of about 30 species, native to southern Florida and the West Indies, and particularly widespread in Cuba. They are small to medium palms and include several species that have unique, highly decorative, individual characteristics. *C. crinita* has a short trunk completely covered with long, brown hair. *C. argentea* and *C. argentata* have leaflets with flashing white backs. *C. miraguama* has very gracefully formed, small, pointed leaves, that retain their immature grace well into maturity.

Originally separated from the *Thrinax* genus by Sargent in 1899; the differences are easily recognized and are listed.

Coccothrinax fruit is black, or very dark, when ripe; that of *Thrinax* is white.

Coccothrinax flowerstalks are shorter than the leafstalks; in *Thrinax*, they are longer.

Coccothrinax leafbases adhere almost indefinitely; thus, the trunk is almost always completely surrounded by the solid wrapping of woven fiber, from which these leafbases emerge. *Thrinax* leafbases fall off after some years, leaving the bare trunk exposed. Even while still attached, the fibers of *Thrinax* leafbases are more scanty, less interwoven, and do not so completely envelop the trunk.

Coccothrinax seed shows a wrinkled exterior; *Thrinax* seed is smooth.

C. CRINITA

Latin, hairy; with long hair.

Recognizable by its trunk, which is completely buried in long, brown hair, forming a bearded mass about 6 in. or more in diameter. The hair is already apparent when the trunk is only 6 in. tall. Each leaf is a perfect circle of narrow leaflets, deeply cut and widely separated.

Coccothrinax miraguama at Fairchild Tropical Garden. A strikingly beautiful palm.

Coccothrinax crinita at the U.S.P.I. Garden at Coconut Grove, Florida. The heavily bearded trunk is unique.

Common name: None. **Origin:** Cuba. **Sex:** Hermaphrodite. Both sexes in one flower. **Trunk:** To 30 ft tall, usually less. **Petiole:** Up to 2 ft long, slender. **Leaf:** Palmate; deeply divided. **Segments:** ¾–1½ in. broad, short; split at end. When young, segments have short points and definite shoulders. Glossy green above, gray-green beneath. **Flowerstalk:** Among leaves; shorter than petiole. **Fruit:** To ¾ in. diameter, on short, thick branches. **Seed:** Wrinkled.

C. MIRAGUAMA

A delicately graceful plant with slender petioles and small, deeply cut leaves, which have the appearance of small pinwheels.

Common name: None. **Origin:** Cuba. **Sex:** Hermaphrodite. **Trunk:** To 20 ft tall, usually less; attractively covered with woven fiber, from which tips of dead leafbases protrude. **Petiole:** Up to 3 ft long; slender. **Leaf:** Palmate; comparatively small for a palm leaf (about 2 ft diameter in mature tree); deeply cut. **Segments:** 1½ in. wide, 12–15 in. long; very dark-green above, light gray-green beneath. **Flowerstalk:** Among leaves; shorter than petiole. **Fruit:** Black when ripe. **Seed:** Wrinkled.

Brother Hermano Leon's *Flora de Cuba* describes four varieties of *C. miraguama:* var. *arenicola,* var. *cupularis,* var. *macroglossa,* var. *roseocarpa.*

C. ARGENTATA
Latin, silvery

A small palm, whose trunk may eventually grow to 20 ft high, but which often begins fruiting when trunk is only 2 ft high. The leaflets have very white backs that flash in the sun when turned up by the wind.

Close-up of the hairy trunk of *Coccothrinax crinita.*

Coccothrinax leaves. One leaf near top is showing its silver back.

Common name: Silver palm. **Origin:** Southern Florida and the Bahamas. **Sex:** Hermaphrodite. **Trunk:** To 20 ft high, wrapped in layers of fiber with a woven appearance. **Petiole:** Slender. **Leaf:** Palmate; leaflets deeply divided. **Segment:** Less than 1 in. broad; glossy green above, very silvery white beneath. **Flowerstalk:** Among leaves. **Fruit:** $\frac{3}{8}$–$\frac{5}{8}$ in. diameter; dark brown at maturity. **Seed:** Wrinkled.

C. ALTA

Trunk to 20–30 ft high, with large leaves and broad, drooping segments; silvery underneath, up to 1½ in. broad. Fruit, ⅓ in. diameter; blackish-brown (Puerto Rico).

The author has been told that *C. alta* leaflets have the whitest underside of all. There are not enough mature plants available to confirm this.

C. FRAGRANS

Much resembles the true *C. argentea*, but has yellow, fragrant flowers (Cuba).

C. ARGENTEA
Latin, *argentum*, silver

Quite similar to *C. argentata*, but trunk grows to 30 ft high. Leaflets are dull green above, silvery beneath, but not as white as *C. argentata* (Hispaniola).

True *C. argentea* specimens are very rare in the United States.

Bailey, in *Gentes Herbarum*, vol. 4, p. 249, shows pictures of *C. argentea* with firm, protruding leaflets; whereas, the photograph on page 222 shows *C. argentata*, with very drooping leaflets. The difference was hardly as definite, as these photographs suggest, on examination of plants in the United States under those names.

Coccothrinax argentata on Big Pine Key, southern Florida. Reprinted from *Gentes Herbarum.*

OTHER SPECIES

There are many other species of *Coccothrinax* not described here, including *C. martii*.
C. dussiana was formerly known as *C. barbadensis*.

Brother Leon's *Flora de Cuba* describes the following additional species, all of which he dis-covered and named in Cuba: *C. acunana, C. alexandri, C. bermudezii, C. clarensis, C. garciana, C. gundlachii, C. hiorami, C. litoralis, C. muricata, C. pauciramosa, C. pseudorigida, C. salvatoris, C. saxicola, C. victorini, C. yuruguana*, and many others.

Common errors:

C. anamola is really *Zombia antillarum*.
C. garberi is really *C. argentata*.
C. jucunda is really *C. argentata*.
C. barbadensis is a confused name.
C. radiata is a confused name.

Cultivation: Johnston reports that all fresh *Coccothrinax* seeds germinate in less than 2 months but that the plants grow very slowly. U.S.P.I. Garden records show that *C. crinita* seeds began sprouting 37 days after planting; those of *C. miraguama* began in 104 days; and seeds of *C. fragrans* did not germinate until the 237th day. On the other hand, another batch of *C. fragrans* germinated in 45 days.

Coccothrinax dussiana showing one leaf turned up, exposing its silver back. Photo at U.S.P.I. Garden, Coconut Grove, Florida, by H. F. Loomis.

COCOS* ¹

Portuguese, monkey (from the nut, which suggests a monkey's face)

The coconut is the most important of all the cultivated palms. It is a typically tropical plant and thrives best where the mean average temperature is above 72°, where there are no great seasonal differences in temperature, and where there is an annual rainfall of well over 40 inches. In such climates, it is cultivated in large groves as a commercial crop. The juice, or *toddy*, that can be drawn from its flowerstalks contains 16 per cent sucrose and is used in the production of sugar, or more frequently, alcohol. The production of strong liquor in this way is a business of some importance in parts of the Philippines. The outer husk of the fruit is used to produce *coir*, a fiber used for making cordage.

[1]In 1916 Beccari broke up the old genus *cocos* into six genera: *Butia, Rhyticocos, Arecastrum, Arikuryroba,* and *Cocos*. The only species left in the genus *Cocos* was *C. nucifera*, the coconut.

A fine specimen of the coconut tree (*Cocos nucifera*) growing on Trinidad, West Indies. Reprinted from *Gentes Herbarum*.

The principal commercial product of the coconut is copra, which is the dried meat, or hard endosperm, of the fruit, and which is used in great quantity in the production of various oils. Copra is, according to the 1957 *World Almanac*, the leading export of the Philippines.

In subtropical, southern Florida, the coconut is planted for ornament. To visitors and residents it is the symbol of the tropics. Motorists, who know little about palms, know that they are reaching Florida's subtropical area when coconuts begin to dot the roadside.

Since coconuts are usually more numerous near the seacoast, many believe that they require the salt air. It is true that the coconut can endure the intense and drying light of the seashore, can resist strong winds and salt spray, and can even endure salt water about its roots for short periods of time. There may be, as many believe, something about a seaside location that it prefers. Bailey, however, believed that, with an ample supply of water in the soil, dryness of atmosphere is favorable to the best production. He also believed that, near the shore, the ground water from higher country comes near enough to the surface to be reached by the roots of the coconut. Thus, in dry months at the seashore the dry atmosphere and ample soil moisture often combine to form the ideal conditions for the coconut. While not as numerous there, coconuts are nevertheless found in substantial numbers at points far inland.

Blatter says that there are some countries, including Panama, where the coconut refuses to grow inland "with as much pertinacity as it does in the conservatories of Europe, where after having attained the age of 8 or 10 years, it begins to sicken and soon dies."

The coconut is so widely cultivated throughout tropical and subtropical areas that its native origin is obscure. Various opinions have been offered. The fruit is buoyant and the

A new coconut tree growing out of a coconut which is actually the seed.

A coconut tree leans out over the ocean in characteristic fashion.

skin strongly waterproof. It has been stated that a coconut can float across the widest ocean without losing its power to germinate. However, some authorities contend that a floating coconut becomes waterlogged and rotted on the inside within four to five weeks.

Martius considered it reasonable to suppose that the original home of the coconut was on the Pacific islands near the coast of Panama. Cocos Island,[1] 200 miles west of Panama, was found densely covered with coconut trees by its first discoverers, with no signs of human habitation. It is not difficult to imagine the westerly spread of the nuts from there, by the regular currents to the islands of the Pacific, thence to the islands of the Indian Archipelago. Indubitably, this spreading about the earth was much assisted by man.

VARIETIES

There is a large number of varieties of the coconut. In some localities in the Philippines, there are strains that carry very large nuts, so large that only half as many are required to produce a ton of copra (3,000 nuts, instead of the usual 6,000).

One interesting variety is the *dwarf malayan* coconut, which is much shorter than the usual tree and whose fruits, though like a coconut in size and structure, are of a golden-yellow color. It was brought into the United States from the Federated Malay States by an expedition sponsored by W. J. Matheson. Plants were established on the Biscayne Plantation of Mr. Matheson and specimens were established in Fairchild Tropical Garden.

[1]There is also a group of Cocos Islands in the Indian Ocean.

A special variety of coconut known as the Dwarf Malayan variety. It never grows as tall as ordinary coconuts and its fruits are a golden yellow. It is sometimes called the Golden Coconut.

A close-up showing the golden-yellow fruit of the Dwarf Malayan variety.

Another Philippine variety, described by Fairchild and known as *makapuno*, has a fruit whose interior is filled with soft, sweet tissue, which is used in the Philippines as a table delicacy. Fruits of this variety sell locally for four times the price of ordinary coconuts. *Makapuno* is a Tagalog word meaning "filled."

Brown's *Useful Plants of the Philippines* states that these abnormal makapuno fruits are not a separate variety but are produced on the same trees as normal nuts, that they will not germinate, and that only a small percentage of the coconut trees in any area will produce the makapuno nuts.

Twenty-four nuts of variety *nina* were sent at Fairchild's instigation to Matheson's plantation on Key Biscayne in 1939. A few were planted at the Montgomery Estate. Four were sent to Chapman Field and several were planted at Fairchild Tropical Garden.

Although there are splendid fruiting specimens in southern Florida, the coconut is not usually as productive outside its native, tropical zone.

Fairchild tells of having tasted the husk of the *nawasi* coconut in Ceylon. The husk of this variety is soft and edible.

C. NUCIFERA
Latin, nut-bearing

Common name: Coconut palm. **Origin:** Questionable, probably islands off the Pacific coast of Panama. **Sex:** Monoecious. **Trunk:** 40–80 ft in height; more or less crooked, and leaning or inclined. Prominently, irregularly ringed, and covered with vertical cracks or chinks. Often enlarged at base, where it may be 2 ft thick, although the upper portion of the trunk is seldom more than 1 ft thick, usually less. **Petiole:** 3–5 ft long, stout, channeled above. Base of petiole wrapped with broad swathes of coarse, very strong, woven fiber. **Leaf:** Pinnate; 6–15 ft long. Leaflets set across from each other and at very even, regular intervals. **Leaflets:** 2–3 ft long; sword-shaped; leathery; yellowish-green. **Flowerstalk:** From lower leaves; 4–6 ft long; at first covered by spathe 2–3 ft long. This spathe splits lengthwise revealing the spadix and all its branches, intricately and beautifully folded into the limited space. Fruit requires 9–10 months to mature. **Flower:** Insignificant. **Fruit:** The coconut; covered with a tough, fibrous husk; 8–12 in. long, obovoid; albumen lining the endocarp; the cavity large, filled with a sweet and sometimes milky fluid known as *coconut milk*. **Seed:** The coconut. The entire fruit including the husk is planted for germination.

Cultivation: A coconut may bear some fruit when four or five years old, but more often it begins fruiting in its seventh year. No important yield can be expected until the tenth year. In the most favorable climates, a very good tree yields as many as 75 nuts a year.

Coconuts are easily transplanted and easily grown, but they do not like cold. A severe cold wave in 1958 in Palm Beach killed many full-grown coconuts and damaged or destroyed thousands of leaves and fruit. 100 miles further north, where the cold wave was a little more severe, most of the coconut trees were destroyed, even though they had previously prospered for years. In most areas, coconuts actually seemed to have fared worse than royal palms. All the varieties seem to require approximately the same conditions.

U.S.P.I. Garden records one batch of coconuts that began sprouting 119 days after planting. The usual germination period is 4–5 months.

COELOCOCCUS AMICARUM
(See *Metroxylon amicarum* (correct name))

COLEOSPADIX

A few species, including *C. oninensis* and *C. litigiosus* from New Guinea, which resemble *Drymophloeus*. Bailey seemed to feel *Coleospadix* would eventually be joined with the genus *Drymophloeus*. Beccari and Burret recognize five valid species of *Coleospadix*.

Not widely cultivated. Some few plants were cultivated under this name in the United States, but Bailey believed them to have been incorrectly identified and to have been referable to *Ptychosperma*. (Not illustrated.)

COLLINIA ELEGANS [1]*†
(Formerly *Chamaedorea elegans*)

A graceful, dainty palm, sold for many years and in great quantities as a potted plant for indoor use, usually under the incorrect name of *Neanthe bella*.

When grown in containers, the slender, ringed trunks are seldom over 1½ in. thick, and 4 ft tall (although specimens have reached to 6–8 ft). They often put out aerial roots from above the base. There are usually 6–8 pinnate leaves, each leaf carrying about 14 smoothly textured leaflets, green on both sides. The tiny flowerstalks have many small branches carrying attractive, but small, reddish-orange fruits. The pale yellow male and female flowers are on separate plants. Native to Mexico.

Planted outdoors, *C. elegans* prospers and its stature increases, but it would still be classified as a small palm. Many nurseries in the United States devote large areas to growing *C. elegans* plants which are shipped in volume to florists and large chain stores.

[1]H. E. Moore, Jr. has recently stated that in his opinion *Collinia elegans* should be united with *Chamaedorea* and that its correct name is *Chamaedorea elegans*.

Coleospadix oninensis growing on Trinidad, West Indies. Photo by T. Satake.

Collinia elegans widely, but improperly, known as *Neanthe bella*. Probably the most popular potted palm. Grown by the thousands for chain-store sale.

COLPOTHRINAX

Bailey considered this genus name to be correct, although Burret agrees with Beccari that the correct name is *Pritchardia wrightii*. Beccari united *Colpothrinax* with *Pritchardia* in 1907, but Bailey, in *Gentes Herbarum* 4:10–360 (1940), disagreed and considered *Colpothrinax* a valid genus distinct from *Pritchardia*. Burret agrees with Beccari.

A one-species genus of palmate palm distinguished by its trunk, which is singularly swollen at, or about, the middle, into a strange, hollow bulb.

Indigenous to sandy areas in Cuba and the Isle of Pines, where it grows in groves, or colonies, it is for some reason not usually successfully grown in the United States. Plants have been tried in Fairchild Tropical Garden, but to date, without success.

C. WRIGHTII

Common name: Barrel palm. **Origin:** Cuba, Isle of Pines. **Sex:** Monoecious. **Trunk:** 15–20 ft tall. For first few years, covered with old leafbases and closely woven fibers, eventually becoming smooth and slender. From fruiting age onward, develops a large tumor (at, or about, the middle) which becomes 2 or 3 times as big around as the trunk. **Petiole:** Smooth, but bearing long fibers and stiff, woven fabric on its base. **Leaf:** Palmate; blue-green; 50 segments in compact head of perhaps 10 leaves. Segments divided to about ⅓ their depth. **Segments:** Strong and firm; blue-green. **Flowerstalk:** 3–4 ft long; below leaves; at first enclosed in spathe. **Fruit:** Globular or oblong globular; ⅓ in. diameter; brown or black. **Seed:** Prominently striped; free in shell, but filling it.

Cultivation: Johnston reports that fresh seeds germinate in 2 months or less. A slow-growing palm. U.S.P.I. Garden records show that one batch of seeds of *C. wrightii* began germinating after 55 days.

Colpothrinax wrightii. The peculiar Cuban belly palm growing on the plains of Pinar del Rio in western Cuba. The two palms on the right have been cropped for thatch. Between these two trees is a short specimen of the same species which has no tumor. The tumor does not develop until a certain age. Reprinted from *Gentes Herbarum*.

A specimen of *Colpothrinax wrightii* in which the shell of the bulge has fallen away from decay following injury. Reprinted from *Gentes Herbarum*.

COPERNICIA*†
From Copernicus

A genus of spectacularly beautiful fan palms, the species of which are surprisingly uncommon in cultivation in the United States. The species show considerable variety, but have the following points in common.

The palmate leaves are very firm and erect. The two outside segments of each leaf are armed with small, saw teeth on their outer edges. The petioles are armed with strong, well-spaced teeth. The spadices are long and much branched, always reaching out to the end of the leaves, and usually projecting well beyond them. The fruits are brown, globose ovoid in shape, and from 5/8–1 in. long.

At present the most widely known copernicias are two South American species: *C. australis*, and the famous carnauba wax palm of Brazil, *C. cerifera*.

In 1939, Brother Leon, of Havana, Cuba, who had written a paper on the spectacular copernicias of Cuba, sent a complete collection of their seeds to his friend David Fairchild. The seeds were planted at Fairchild Tropical Garden and the plants have now reached an age that reveals the strikingly erect appearance of their remarkable leaves.

The impressive showing of these plants is bound to be remembered by many visitors. Many are producing fruit; and seeds are being distributed among members of the Garden. It is logical to predict that within the next decade these Cuban palms will enjoy a great popularity in the United States.

COPERNICIA: SOUTH AMERICAN SPECIES*†

C. CERIFERA
Latin, wax-bearing

This famous wax palm is grown in great commercial groves in Brazil. The coating of its leaves furnishes a product known in commerce as *carnauba wax*, an important ingredient in floor and furniture polishes, carbon paper, candles, lipsticks, and phonograph records. In 1956 the United States alone imported $11,350,000 worth of carnauba wax.

A scene at the Johnson Experimental Plantation in Ceara, in northeast Brazil. Here selection and hybridization studies are being conducted in the genus *Copernicia* with particular emphasis on *C. cerifera*. Photo courtesy of S. C. Johnson & Son, Inc.

Copernicia cerifera. An 18-year-old specimen at U.S.P.I. Garden, Coconut Grove, Florida. This tree at this stage is equivalent to a tree ready for harvesting for the wax which covers its leaves. Photo courtesy of S. C. Johnson & Son, Inc., the makers of Johnson's Wax.

One tribe of Indians of northern Brazil, the Carnaubeira, was so completely dependent on the products of this palm that it received its name.

The wood of the trunk is among the hardest known.

Common name: Carnauba wax palm. **Origin:** Brazil. **Sex:** Hermaphrodite. **Trunk:** To 30–40 ft tall; swollen near base; lower part of trunk covered with leafbases in a very recognizable pattern. **Petiole:** 2 ft or more long; armed with large teeth about 1 in. apart; stiff, strong; flat above, rounded below; yellow-green. **Leaf:** Palmate; 4–5 ft in diameter; nearly orbicular; divided beyond the middle into about 60 segments; light green, with a waxy covering. **Segments:** 30 in. long, 1¼ in. wide at widest point; narrow; with very long, narrow points; outer edge of the outside segments only are armed with tiny teeth; light green, covered with a waxy substance. **Flowerstalk:** 5–6 ft long; thrice branched; from lower leaves. **Flowers:** In clusters. **Fruit:** Globose ovoid; 1 in. long.

C. AUSTRALIS

The appearance of the trunk of *C. australis* is somewhat unique. It is covered with leafbases in a spiral, geometric pattern. These leafbases are a dark, glossy brown and give the trunk a general color effect much like that of a polished piece of furniture.

Common name: None. **Origin:** Paraguay, Argentina. **Sex:** Hermaphrodite. **Trunk:** To 70 ft in height, enlarged at base. Lower part covered with old leafbases in an attractive,

Copernicia australis growing at Fairchild Tropical Garden.

Close-up of trunk of *Copernicia australis* at Fairchild Tropical Garden. The leafbases are a glossy chestnut brown.

Copernicia fallaense, a tree about 20 years old at Fairchild Tropical Garden. The palm in the background is of the same species and age.

spiral pattern. The leafbases are usually dark-brown and glossy. **Petiole:** 2½–3 ft long, 1½ in. wide; very firm; armed with dark-brown teeth about ½ in. long, set about 1½ in. apart; base of petiole dark-brown; flatly channeled above, rounded beneath. **Leaf:** Palmate; 2½–3 ft in diameter; orbicular; deeply divided into about 48 narrow segments with few hanging threads. **Segments:** 27 in. long, 1 in. wide; long pointed; split at apex; dull light green on both sides. Outside edge of two outer segments armed with small teeth. **Flowerstalk:** From among leaves; branches covered with a white, woolly substance. **Fruit:** ¾ in. long; olive-shaped; brown.

COPERNICIA: CUBAN SPECIES*

Space does not permit a detailed description of all the Cuban species. Brother Leon's *Flora de Cuba* very briefly describes over 25 species and some additional varieties.

The Fairchild Tropical Garden collection includes 14 Cuban species. These are all about 18 years old and perhaps at their most attractive age. The photographs in *Flora de Cuba* show these same species 20–40 years old, and with tall trunks. The striking leaf characteristics are recognizable, but they are not quite as surprising when seen at the distant top of the tall trunks.

The following descriptions of the plants at Fairchild Tropical Garden are as they were in 1958 and give some idea of the changes to be expected with great age. Peculiarly, in Brother Leon's *Flora de Cuba*, all species are described and photographed as single-trunk species. At Fairchild Tropical Garden, *C. glabrescens* and a few unidentified species are beginning to sucker.

C. FALLAENSE
(Description of an 18-year-old specimen at Fairchild Tropical Garden in 1958; described out of alphabetical order as the best species for comparison)

This species seems to have the biggest and most upright leaves of all the species. The leaves are also more bluish-green than the others. The trunk is at present 3½ ft tall, and it is covered with massive leafbases still standing very erect. The petioles are very light green and very glaucous, 1 ft wide at the base and 6 in. wide at the leaf. They are edged with teeth about ⅜ in. long and are flatly channeled above and rounded below. The leaves stand absolutely erect and are about 7 ft in diameter. They are divided only about one quarter of the distance to the base, into very strong, blue-green segments about 1½ in. wide. These segments are very deeply pleated and are fastened together in a manner unique in palm leaves. Their edges overlap and form a joint seam which is as much as ¾ in. deep. This deep seam runs along each segment joining from the base of the leaf to the point where the segments separate. It is on the upper surface of the leaf. The outside segments are armed with saw teeth.

This tree was not in flower, but the spadices are known to be several feet long, projecting out to the edge of the leaves and sometimes beyond. According to *Flora de Cuba*, this species will eventually have a trunk 30–50 ft high and 18–30 in. in diameter, which will be free of adhering leafbases.

C. BAILEYANA
(Description of an 18-year-old specimen at Fairchild Tropical Garden in 1958)

Much like *C. fallaense*, but the trunk is already free of leafbases. The leaves are not quite as large and are bright green, instead of blue green. The teeth on the petiole seem a trifle smaller. The trunk, now about 6 ft tall, should eventually reach 20–35 ft and a maximum diameter of 24 in.

C. BURRETIANA
Somewhat similar to *C. fallaense*, but with generally smaller proportions.

C. COWELLII
This is one of the many species described in *Flora de Cuba* but not represented in Fairchild Tropical Garden. It is the only missing species requiring particular mention. It is much like *C. rigida* and *C. torreana*, but the segments are much wider and the petticoat formed by the dead leaves has a much coarser look. The plant is distinctive and attractive at all ages.

C. CURBELOI

Much like *C. baileyana*. The specimens examined had either a short trunk or had not yet formed any. This may indicate slower growth habits. The mature trunk, like that of *C. baileyana*, should eventually reach 20–35 ft, with a somewhat smaller diameter (12–18 in.)

Copernicia baileyana, 8 years old. Photo by Lola Smith.

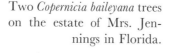

Two *Copernicia baileyana* trees on the estate of Mrs. Jennings in Florida.

C. GIGAS

Plants examined had not yet developed any trunk. The leaves and petioles promise to be very similar to those of *C. fallaensis*. The unique seam, by which the segments are held together, is not as deep as in *C. fallaensis* or *C. baileyana*.

C. GLABRESCENS

Similar to *C. gigas*, but with smaller leaves (2–3 ft diameter.) Trunk covered with erect and comparatively narrow leafbases. Petioles, yellowish-green. Plants are beginning to sucker.

C. HOLGUINENSIS

Very like *C. glabrescens*, but petioles are noticeably glaucous white.

C. HOSPITA

Similar to *C. rigida*, described below.

C. PAUCIFLORA

Young plants at Fairchild Tropical Garden much resemble *C. torreana*, described below.

Copernicia cowellii in Cuba. Courtesy of Herbario De La Salle.

A *Copernicia gigas* at the Fairchild Tropical Garden, about 20 years old.

A *Copernicia gigas* in Gamboa, Oriente Province, Cuba. Age undetermined. Courtesy of Herbario De La Salle.

C. TORREANA
(Description of an 18-year-old specimen at Fairchild Tropical Garden in 1958)

The Cuban petticoat palm is well named. It carries a solid mass of dead- leaf "petticoats" reaching compactly to the ground.

The petticoats form a solid, circular tower, consisting of a thick, circular mass of dead leaves about 8 ft in diameter, closely hugging the ground and extending upward like a pillar. It is surmounted by the twisted, spiral mass of living leaves. The living leaves are very large (5–6 ft wide) and are so numerous and so closely packed together on such short petioles that their side edges are always hidden from view. No full leaf is ever visible and its measurements can be taken only by tearing the tree apart. The hidden trunk is about 8 in. in diameter. The fruit stalk is up to 8 ft long and projects well beyond the leaves. The leaflets are a glossy green.

Photographs in *Flora de Cuba* show plants 30 ft tall, growing in the wilds, which show about 10 ft of bare trunk, with petticoats covering only the upper half. Whether the lower petticoats were burned off, worn off, or removed is not stated. The specimens at Fairchild Tropical Garden have such a solid, strong mass of this shag that it is difficult to imagine it ever disappearing in a natural way.

C. RIGIDA
Latin, stiff, unbending, rigid
(Description of an 18-year-old specimen at Fairchild Tropical Garden in 1958)

A striking but forbidding plant, not easy to examine. The specimens are still only 7–8 ft high and look like closely and erectly tied packages of very strong, pointed leaves. These wedge-shaped leaves have almost no petioles and, like *C. torreana*, are so closely packed that no full leaf is visible.

Copernicia torreana, 20 years old, at Fairchild Tropical Garden. Note projecting flowerstalks.

Older specimen of *Copernicia torreana* showing a substantial amount of trunk. Courtesy of Herbario De La Salle.

The lower leaves adhere to the trunk for long periods after they die and form a mass of shag, which is not quite as thick and even as that of *C. torreana*. One unique feature of this plant is the unusually long hastula, or ligule, which juts out from the petiole 8–10 in. or more beyond the leaf. This is not a rib going into the leaf, but a projection outside it.

Flora de Cuba shows illustrations of old plants with about 20 ft of bare trunk and with a very tight, round crown of leaves. The shag of dead leaves underneath has become rounded, so that the combination of crown and shaft makes an almost perfectly round ball. If these plants could be offered to gardens, as illustrated, they could command a handsome price.

C. YAREY
(18-year-old specimen at Fairchild Tropical Garden)

Not described.

Cultivation (Cuban Species): Johnston reports that all fresh *Copernicia* seeds germinate in less than 2 months. The plants grow slowly. *C. baileyana* seems to grow more rapidly than most others.

U.S.P.I. Garden reports the following number of days before germination began in seed batches of the species indicated: *C. hospita* (37); *C. burretiana* (37); *C. cowellii* (37); *C. vespertilionum* (14)—a hybrid; *C. torreana* (22); *C. gigas* (73). De Leon reports that one batch of seed of *C. glabrescens* began germinating in 18 days.

CORNERA

A genus name published in 1955 in Gardens Bulletin, Singapore. It was published as a segregate from *Calamus*, but is not included in Burret and Potztal's list of valid genera.

Copernicia rigida at Fairchild Tropical Garden, about 20 years old. Photo by H. F. Loomis.

COROZO*

Vernacular name

A genus containing only one species, which is known as the American oil palm. This is not to be confused with the African oil palm, *Elaeis guineensis*, though there are certain similarities. The creeping trunk of *Corozo* (which may not be present) causes an entirely different general appearance from the straight trunk of *Elaeis*. But some marked similarities in the fruit of the two genera have, at times, caused certain botanists to unite the two.

Both *Elaeis* and *Corozo* have very short, female flower clusters that nestle in close to the trunk and, when in fruit, somewhat resemble a bird's nest. In *Corozo* they lie in the remains of the fibrous spathe; in *Elaeis* they sit up, porcupine fashion, not surrounded by fiber.

Corozo leaflets are all on one horizontal plane, producing a flat leaf; *Elaeis* leaflets are attached to the rachis at various angles and the leaf is not flat.

The greatest similarity is in the male flowers, which are on very short, furry fingers, sitting in close to the trunk on a short peduncle. These fingers adhere for long periods and are usually present on a fruiting tree at all seasons. Dead or alive, they maintain their unique and easily recognizable appearance. The presence of these short, finger-size fringes of male flowers is typical of both *Corozo* and *Elaeis*.

C. OLEIFERA
Latin, oil-bearing

In *C. oleifera* the trunk creeps along the ground for several feet, producing new roots before turning upright.

The exterior flesh of the fruits yields an oil which early colonizers were said to have used for making candles.

It has been occasionally cultivated under the erroneous name of *Elaeis melanococca*.

Common name: American oil palm. **Origin:** Central America, Panama, Colombia, and Amazon regions. **Sex:** Monoecious. **Trunk:** Creeps along the ground and eventually turns upright, attaining a height up to 5 ft. Leafbases cling to trunk. **Petiole:** 5 ft long; spiny. **Leaf:** Pinnate; 12 ft or longer; 60 or more leaflets on one horizontal plane, producing a flat leaf. **Leaflets:** Up to 3–4 ft long, 2 in. broad. **Flowerstalk:** In crown of tree; short; held in close to trunk; remains within spathe. **Fruit:** Oblong ovoid; 1–1¼ in. long, broad at base; tapering at apex; oily; fleshy exterior; deep-orange color at maturity. **Seed:** Black.

Common errors:
Elaeis Melanococca is correctly *Corozo oleifera*.
Alfonsia oleifera is *Corozo oleifera*.

Cultivation: Less hardy to cold than the African oil palm. Johnston reports that seeds germinate in 3–4 months.

Fruit head of *Corozo oleifera*. The fuzzy strips in the foreground are the male flowers. Reprinted from *Gentes Herbarum*.

rozo oleifera. Characteristic lean-g or creeping trunk of the Ameri-n oil palm. Reprinted from *entes Herbarum*.

CORYPHA*

Greek, *Koryphè* summit, or top, whence the flowers grow

The talipot palm is one of the wonders of the palm family. It grows very slowly into a great size, the trunk going up as straight as a flagpole to a height of 40–80 ft.

When young, a healthy specimen produces very large, palmate leaves, 12 ft wide and 10 ft long. The amazingly long and very strong petioles jutting out 12 ft in all directions are a truly spectacular sight.

No flowers are borne until maturity (20–80 years), at which time the tree begins producing somewhat smaller leaves and develops a gigantic flowerstalk at its very top. This flowerstalk finally expands into a much-branched pyramid which towers 20 ft above the tree and covers an area well over 200 sq ft. It is said to contain over 60 million tiny blossoms.

As the tree begins to flower, the leaves begin to wither and fall, leaving the creamy white blossoms more fully exposed. Each flower takes over a year to ripen into fruit and, during this period, the plant gradually dies. The trunk remains tall and straight but has only dead leaves and a broken flowerstalk hanging from its top.

The 12-ft-wide leaf, much used by the natives, when dried is still strong and limber and unusually light in weight. It will cover fifteen men and keep them dry or shaded, but it folds up into a very small and lightweight package which is easily carried. Ancient records have been written on the leaves of these plants and they have resisted the ravages of time for many generations.

Fairchild tells us that fibers drawn from the unopened leaves of *Corypha* are used to make the finest quality hats in the Philippines (Calasaio hats and Pototan hats, both named after the towns that originated them).

The true talipot palm is *C. umbraculifera*. It is generally considered to grow the tallest and to have the thickest trunk and the biggest leaves. The petiole is wider than other species but has tiny teeth.

C. elata grows almost as tall, but the trunk is more slender. The leaves are not quite as big; the petioles are as long, but are more slender and have very large teeth. It can be distinguished from the other two species by the spiral pattern formed on the trunk by the scars of the old leafbases. On other species, the leafbases surround the trunk and their scars are rings. *C. elata* leafbases go only part way around the trunk. Their smaller scars form a spiral pattern.

C. talliera is the shortest, growing only to 30 ft or less. It has the stoutest trunk and its petioles are more brownish than those of the other species.

C. ELATA

Latin, tall

Common name: None. **Origin:** Bengal and Burma, according to Bailey. Beccari considers this species native to the Philippines, Indochina, and several Pacific islands. **Sex:** Hermaphrodite. **Trunk:** 60–70 ft high, 1½ ft diameter; more slender than *C. umbraculifera;* sometimes covered with leafbases. When bases have fallen, scars leave prominent markings, forming definite but faint spiral pattern from top to bottom of trunk. **Petiole:** 8–12 ft long; with black margins and widely spaced strong teeth. Not as thick or heavy as that of *C.*

umbraculifera. **Leaf:** Palmate; 8–10 ft diameter, sometimes less; segments divided halfway to center. End of leafstalk is extended into the leaf, forming a rib which extends 12–20 in. or more into the leaf itself, thereby making the leaf costapalmate. **Segments:** Firm; blunt apex; dented in center. Bright green both sides. **Flowerstalk:** At very top, above leaves; 20 ft high; much branched. Tree produces only one. **Flowers:** Up to 60 million on one plant; tiny; creamy white; unpleasant odor. **Fruit:** 1 in. diameter; olive-colored; one-seeded; monocarpic (fruits once and dies).

C. TALLIERA

Already briefly described, this is the most spectacular when in flower, because the flowerstalk is as tall as the rest of the tree. It is also the most rare and is fast becoming more so. In the nineteenth century, cultivated plants were fairly common in Calcutta, India, but in his *Trees of Calcutta*, Benthall reported that in 1943 the only specimen in the Calcutta area was the one in the Royal Botanic Garden.

Corypha elata at Fairchild Tropical Garden. Note the very long and sturdy petioles.

C. UMBRACULIFERA
Latin, umbrella-bearing

Common name: Talipot palm. **Origin:** Ceylon and Malabar Coast. **Sex:** Hermaphrodite. **Trunk:** 40–80 ft (usually 40 ft), 2 ft thick; often covered with old leafbases; ringed after leafbases fall off. **Petiole:** To 12 ft long, 2 in. broad, 4 in. thick; deeply channeled, with short teeth, often in pairs. **Leaf:** Palmate; up to 10 ft long, 12–16 ft broad; 80–100 leaflets. An extra rib, an extension of the leafstalk, protrudes 10–20 in. or more into the palmate leaf, thus making it costapalmate. **Segments:** About 3½ in. wide; stiff; with blunt apex dented in center; bright green both sides. **Flowerstalk:** At very top, above leaves; 20 ft high; much branched. Tree produces only one. **Flowers:** Up to 60 million on one tree; tiny; creamy white; unpleasant odor. **Fruit:** Subglobose; 1½ in. diameter; olive-colored; one-seeded; monocarpic (fruits once and then dies).

Cultivation: All species of *Corypha* grow extremely slowly, at least in the first 10 years.

Johnson reports that seeds of *C. elata* lose their germinating power very quickly. Fresh seeds germinate in less than 3 months. Seeds of *C. umbraculifera* retain their viability for longer periods but are very slow germinating. The U.S.P.I. Garden records show that two batches of *C. umbraculifera* seeds were planted; one began germinating in 52 days, the other did not begin for 108 days.

Terminal flower crown of *Corypha umbraculifera*, the talipot palm of India, growing in Jamaica, West Indies. This tree has reached maturity, has flowered once, and is about to die. Reprinted from *Gentes Herbarum*.

Corypha umbraculifera at Mrs. Jennings' garden in Florida.

CRYOSOPHILA*
(Now includes all former *Acanthorrhiza*)

About four species of pinnate palms, distinguished by their large and very round leaves and by the unusual rootspines growing out of the trunk. These rootspines are really small aerial roots (sometimes branched). Some of the lower ones become true roots, but the upper ones do not grow long enough to reach the ground. Some plants have only a few rootspines while others are thickly covered. The leaf is distinctive, the leaflets being fastened to the hastula in a full 360° circle, irregularly but very deeply cut.

The species most cultivated in the United States is *C. warscewiczii*. *C. nana* (*C. aculeata*) is sometimes found in U.S. nurseries, but the two species are so much alike that identity is always questionable.

Cryosophila (formerly *Acanthorrhiza*) *warscewiczii* growing in Panama. Reprinted from *Gentes Herbarum*.

C. WARSCEWICZII
(Formerly *Acanthorrhiza warscewiczii*)

Common name: Rootspine palm. **Origin:** Southern Mexico and Panama Canal Zone. **Sex:** Hermaphrodite. **Trunk:** To 40 ft, generally much less; slender; covered with short, though sometimes branched, spinelike aerial roots, the lowest of which pass into roots at the enlarged base. Upper part of trunk often loses some or all of its rootspines. **Petiole:** Slender, 4–6 ft long, less than 1 in. thick; flat. Long threads at base. **Leaf:** Palmate (forms complete circle); to 6 ft across; 60 segments, divided about halfway, but groups of 2, 3, or 4 segments then parted nearly to base. Hastula short and blunt but protruding. **Segments:** 2–3 ft long, 1–3 in. broad; strong midrib; green above, light-gray beneath. **Flowerstalk:** From among leaves; 2 ft long; downward curved; covered with velvety paperlike sheaths. **Flowers:** Creamy white; peculiar odor. **Fruit:** Pear-shaped; 1 in. long; ⅝ in. broad.

OTHER SPECIES

C. nana: Similar to *C. warscewiczii.* Accurate information on differences not available.
Acanthorrhiza aculeata = C. nana.
Cryosophila chuco = Tessmanniodoxa chuco.

CUATRACASEA

A Brazilian genus of pinnate-leafed palms, much like *Ireartella* from which it differs only in flower detail. (Not illustrated.)

Close-up of trunk of *Cryosophila warscewiczii* covered with the famous rootspines. Photo taken in Bogor Botanic Gardens, Java, by T. Satake.

Pear-shaped fruit of *Cryosophila warscewiczii*, about natural size. Reprinted from *Gentes Herbarum*.

CYPHOKENTIA [1]
Greek, *kyphos*, hump (from hump on fruit)

A little-known genus native to New Caledonia. The two species have pinnate leaves. Not to be confused with *Siphokentia* to which it is not in any way related. (Not illustrated.)

CYPHOPHOENIX

A genus of pinnate-leafed palm from New Caledonia, little-known to cultivation. (Not illustrated.)

CYPHOSPERMA

A monotypic genus of pinnate-leafed palms, native to New Caledonia. (Not illustrated.)

CYRTOSTACHYS
Greek, a curved spike (referring to the inflorescence)

A group of beautiful cluster palms, little-known in the United States, highly prized for their beautiful scarlet leafbases and scarlet petioles. They are unaccountably known as sealing-

---

[1]Some species of *Cyphokentia* were united with *Clinostigma* by Moore and Fosberg. *Gentes Herbarum*, vol. 8, page 465. Burret retains *Cyphokentia* as a separate genus.

Cyrtostachys lakka (sealing-wax palm). Photo by J. F. Reck in Singapore; photo courtesy of New Crops Research Branch, U.S. Department of Agriculture.

Cyrtostachys lakka in Bogor Botanic Gardens, Java. Photo courtesy A. Dilmy, Bogor Botanic Gardens, Java.

wax palms, perhaps because their glossy, scarlet leafstalks suggest the look of shiny sealing wax in its most common color.

The U.S. Plant Introduction Garden, Coconut Grove, Florida, has made several attempts to grow this plant and is convinced that it will not thrive in Florida.

C. LAKKA

Common name: Sealing-wax palm. **Origin:** Malaya and Pacific islands. **Sex:** Monoecious. **Trunk:** Clustered, to 15 ft tall; slender; smooth; surmounted by crownshaft tinged with red. **Petiole:** Very short, 6 in. long; bright scarlet. Leafbases, which form crownshaft, are 2 ft long and scarlet-tinged. **Leaf:** Pinnate; arching; 50 leaflets. **Leaflets:** 18 in. long; slender; strong midrib and veins; glaucous beneath. **Flowerstalk:** Below leaves; 1–2 ft long; branched; green, turning red. **Fruit:** ⅖ in. long; oblong ovoid; black with scarlet base. **Seed:** Ovoid; ⅓ in. long.

OTHER SPECIES

C. renda: Similar to *C. lakka,* but taller, and seed is round. *C. renda* var. *duvivieranum* has very bright-red markings.

Cultivation: Evidently a very tender plant and not easy to raise successfully. Johnston reports that the small seeds germinate quickly. Ridley says that in Malaya this plant grows in water in wet woods by tidal rivers. This may give an indication of some of its requirements.

The sealing-wax palm, *Cyrtostachys renda,* in the Botanical Garden at Kingstown, St. Vincent. Photo courtesy of New Crops Research Branch, U.S. Department of Agriculture.

Cyrtostachys renda in Aedan, Sumatra. Photo courtesy of New Crops Research Branch, U.S. Department of Agriculture.

DAEMONOROPS*
Greek, *daimón*, spirit, and *rhops*, shrub

A many-specied genus of very spiny, climbing, pinnate-leafed palms, native to tropical Asia, India, and Malaya, where their slender, flexible stems are used as rattan.

Somewhat similar to the genus *Calamus*, these climbers are equipped with various and numerous spines and thorns, and the ends of the leaves have long, whiplike projections to aid in climbing.

Cultivation: This may be one of the more cold-tolerant climbers. Johnston reports that one unidentified species of *Daemonorops* came through the deep freeze of 1958 without loss in his open-air nursery at Vero Beach, Florida. The plants were still quite young.

DASYSTACHYS DECKERIANA

A small, simple-leafed, pinnate-nerved palm, native to Guatemala, and certainly not widely known or cultivated. No detailed descriptions are available. The photograph was supplied by A. C. Langlois and was taken in Costa Rica.

Dasystachys deckeriana in Costa Rica. Photo by A. C. Langlois.

Daemonorops longipes climbing through the trees of the Bogor Botanic Gardens. Photo courtesy A. Dilmy, Bogor Botanic Gardens, Java.

DECKENIA NOBILIS

One species of pinnate palm, native to the Seychelle Islands, allied to *Dictyosperma*, but growing to a greater size. The trunk, which may grow to 120 ft, is erect and slender (10–14 in. diameter). The leafbases are spiny in young plants but eventually become almost smooth. The petiole is 1 ft long, pale green, and smooth. The pinnate leaves are 9–14 ft long. Leaflets are hairy underneath. The flowerstalk comes from below the leaves and is at first enclosed in a very spiny, short spathe. It later develops to an over-all length of 4–5 ft, with long, drooping branches. Fruit is oblong ovoid; ½ in. long; dark mauve.

Cultivation: This seems to be a tender palm. One large group of seedlings, grown from seed in Vero Beach Nursery at Vero Beach, Florida, all died at a very early age.

Balfour reports that it is becoming scarce in its native habitat in the Seychelles.

DESMONCUS*

Greek, *desmos*, bond, and *onkos*, barb, hook (in reference to the leaflets which are modified into hooks)

A large group of more than 40 species of very spiny, climbing palms, native to the American tropics. Allied to *Bactris*, they have very bristly, spiny, short spathes that can be seen here and there as the plant climbs through the treetops. It is rarely cultivated in the United States, except in botanical gardens, although young plants of some species are unusually attractive.

Cultivation: Like most climbing palms, these are tropical plants and may require warm temperatures. However, the author has several young plants growing in his garden that came unscathed through the unusually cold winter of 1957–1958 at Palm Beach, Florida.

DICTYOCARYUM

A genus of pinnate-leafed palms from tropical America. (Not illustrated.)

Deckenia nobilis in Bogor Botanic Gardens, Java. Photo by T. Satake.

Desmoncus macroacanthus, a sketch reprinted from Wallace's *Palm Trees of the Amazon*. The plant sketched here was over 50 feet high. Note the spiny projections at end of each leaf to assist climbing.

DICTYOSPERMA*

Greek, *dictyon*, net, and *sperma*, seed

A genus which bears a broad resemblance to *Ptychosperma, Veitchia,* and *Archontophoenix,* because each has a crownshaft and a slender to medium trunk, with pinnate leaves.

Dictyosperma can be distinguished by its dark-gray trunk, with its many vertical cracks or slits, and by the fact that new leaves always have their tips tied together by a green binding surrounding the leaf. This occurs in other palms, but in *Dictyosperma,* the binding is prominent and persists for a longer period before breaking up and releasing the leaflets.

These palms flower at an early age, and the spathe that first surrounds the flowerstalk is unmistakable. It is about 12–14 in. long, 4–5 in. broad, and very flat, resembling a protruding canoe paddle.

It is difficult to recognize or to identify separately each of the three varieties, particularly since they are so seldom reliably named when purchased or observed.

Full tree of *Dictyosperma album* at Fairchild Tropical Garden. Photo by H. F. Loomis.

D. ALBUM

Common name: Princess palm, hurricane palm. **Origin:** Mascarene Islands, Mauritius. **Sex:** Monoecious. **Trunk:** Blackish-gray; to 30 ft tall, dilated at base; with many vertical cracks; topped by crownshaft 8–9 in. thick. **Petiole:** Short, 6–12 in.; grooved on face; whitish appearance. **Leaf:** Pinnate; 8–12 ft long; arching; new leaves edged with binding. **Leaflets:** 2½–3 ft long, 2–3 in. broad; long, pointed, drooping; whitish-green veins. **Flowerstalk:** Below crownshaft; at first covered with an odd, paddle-shaped spathe 1 ft long, 5 in. wide, and very flat. **Flowers:** Large, for palms; reddish-yellow. **Fruit:** Egg-shaped, pointed; ½ in. long; set at right angles to the branches; purplish. **Seed:** Wrinkled.

VARIETIES

Though generally conceded to be varieties of *D. album*, many still consider the following to be separate species:

D. album var. *rubrum* very like *D. album*, but young plants have very dark-green leaves with dark-red veins. Flowers are whitish-yellow.

D. album var. *aureum* differs from *D. album* by having shorter, slimmer trunk. Flowers are smaller and are whitish-yellow. Leaflets have shorter points and less distinct veins. Leaves in young plants have orange veins. Fruit ¾ in. long.

D. album var. *furfaraceum* is rarely cultivated. It is like var. *rubrum*, but petiole and base covered with white, woolly hair.

Cultivation: Plants require plenty of water. Their greatest enemy is dry, hot air. Seeds are easy to germinate and plants are fairly hardy to cold.

U.S.P.I. Garden reports planting *D. album* var. *aureum* seeds that began germinating in 75 days.

Head of princess palm in flower. *Dictyosperma album.*

Head of *Dictyosperma album* var. *rubrum.*

DIDYMOSPERMA
Greek, double-seeded

A genus allied to *Wallichia, Caryota,* and *Arenga.*

A group of low, bushy, but very ornamental East Indian, pinnate palms with multiple slender trunks. Not very widely cultivated, particularly in the United States.

The leaflets, irregularly toothed on the edge, are of odd and eccentric shapes, somewhat resembling those of the fishtail palms. *Didymosperma* is one of the few pinnate-leafed genera whose leaflets are induplicate.

Bailey briefly describes *D. porphyrocarpon* and *D. nanum.*

Blatter describes *D. nana* and *D. gracilis.*

Ridley describes *D. hookeriana* and *D. hastata.*

Cultivation: De Leon reports planting seeds of *D. caudata* which began germinating in 65 days.

DIPLOTHEMIUM*
Greek, double-sheathed

All plants of *D. caudescens* (the *Diplothemium* usually found in the United States) have been found to be *Polyandrococcos caudescens,* which see.

D. MARITIMUM

Diplothemium is a valid genus of several species, including the salt-loving *D. maritimum,* which forms large colonies on seashore dunes in Brazil, its native land.

D. maritimum is a trunkless palm, the waxy leaves arising directly from the ground to a

Didymosperma districhum, a handsome bushy specimen in the Botanical Garden at Roseau, Dominica, West Indies. Photo courtesy of New Crops Research Branch, U.S. Department of Agriculture.

height of 7–8 ft. The leaves are pinnate. The leaflets are 2 ft long, 1 in. wide, very dark green on the upper side and hairy white underneath. The flowerstalk is shorter than the leaves. The fruit is green and edible.

OTHER SPECIES

D. campestre of Brazil is similar to *D. maritimum* but smaller and the fruit is yellow.

Cultivation: De Leon raised seeds of *D. maritimum* and found that first germination began in 73 days. Johnston reports that fresh seeds are rare, as they seem to lose their oil content very quickly.

A few young plants of *D. maritimum* and *D. campestre* have recently been raised in the United States from Brazilian seeds. The young plants are handsome and, if sufficiently hardy, these two species may prove to be a valuable addition to Florida seaside planting.

DOLICOKENTIA
(Spelled *Dolichokentia* by Burret and Potztal)

A little-known genus of pinnate-leafed palms, native to New Caledonia. The sole species is *D. robusta*. (Not illustrated.)

DRYMOPHLOEUS*

In *Gentes Herbarum*, vol. 8, p. 298 (1953), H. E. Moore, Jr. united *Coleospadix beguinii* with *Drymophloeus*, and it is believed that all species of *Coleospadix* are to be united with *Drymophloeus* in the near future.

About 12 species of charming, small, pinnate palms from Australia and the Pacific islands. The seeds of several species were brought to the United States by David Fairchild in 1940. Plants from two of these species have now reached maturity and have fruited. Seeds and young plants have been distributed to a few growers in southern Florida.

Both *D. olivaeformis* and *D. beguinii* are splendid additions to United States gardens. They are shade-loving, delicate, small to medium-sized plants, with slender trunks and very graceful, broad, and ruffled leaflets.

A close-up of the odd leaves of *Didymosperma districhum*. Photo by T. Satake.

Diplothemium maritimum in Botanical Garden, Rio de Janeiro, Brazil. Photo by A. C. Langlois.

D. BEGUINII

Common name: None. **Origin:** Dutch East Indies. **Sex:** Monoecious. **Trunk:** 9–15 ft high, 1½ in. thick; wood hard, dark; topped by crownshaft. **Petiole:** 10 in. long. **Leaf:** Pinnate; 4½ ft long; 11–13 pairs of leaflets. **Leaflets:** Unusual (see illustration); wedge-shaped and ruffled; dark-green, glossy; terminal leaflets are large, but not joined at tip. **Flowerstalk:** Below crownshaft. **Fruit:** ½–⅜ in. long; ovate oblong; red. Takes 6 months for flower to mature into fruit. **Seed:** Ovoid, wrinkled; ½ in. by ¼ in. **Oddities:** Sometimes flowers when trunk is only few feet high. Seedlings have solid, entire leaf, which has wedge-shaped piece missing at end.

D. OLIVAEFORMIS

Very similar to *D. beguinii*, but grows taller. Terminal leaflets are joined at apex into one fanlike leaflet. Seed is smooth instead of wrinkled. The wood of the trunk is soft and light,

Two sketches illustrating the differences between *Drymophloeus beguinii* and *Drymophloeus olivaeformis*. Reprinted from *Gentes Herbarum*.

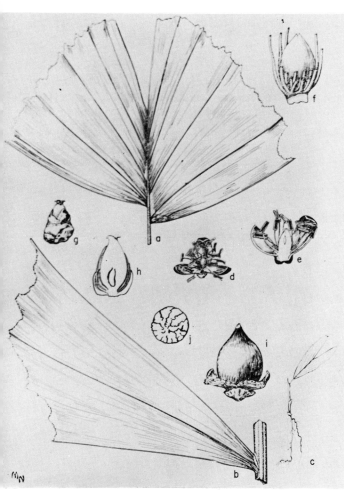

114. Drymophlœus Beguinii (*Fairchild Tropical Garden Expedition 402, Langlois*). a, apical pinnæ ×⅓; b, median pinnæ ×⅓; c, seedling leaf ×⅓; d, staminate flower ×2; e, staminate flower longitudinal section ×3; f, pistillode ×8; g, pistillate flower ×2; h, pistillate flower longitudinal section ×3; i, fruit ×2; j, seed cross-secton ×2.

111. Drymophlœus olivæformis (*Fairchild Tropical Garden Expedition 331, Langlois*). a, apical pinnæ ×¼; b, median pinnæ ×¼; c, seedling leaf ×⅓; d, staminate flower ×2; e, staminate flower longitudinal section ×2; f, pistillode ×3; g, anthers ×5; h, pistillate flower ×2; i, pistil ×2; j, pistil longitudinal section ×2; k, fruit ×1⅓; l, fruit with exocarp removed ×1⅓; m, seed ×2; n, seed cross-section ×2.

not hard and dark, and there are differences in details of the flowers and their branches. Seedling of *D. olivaeformis* has completely solid leaf, with no section missing.

OTHER SPECIES

D. appendiculatis of the Moluccas and New Guinea and several other species are not widely cultivated and are believed not to have been introduced into the United States.

Cultivation: U.S.P.I. Garden reports that seeds of *D. beguinii* began germinating at the end of 26 days. Most young *Drymophloeus* plants so far seem fairly hardy in southern or central Florida, but they definitely prefer shade.

DYPSIS

A many-specied genus of pinnate palms, native to Madagascar. They are mostly small, cluster palms, with jointed bamboolike stems. In several species the small leaves are simple and undivided, and in others the leaves are divided into a very few leaflets of unusual shapes, which might be said (very broadly) to resemble some of the unusual leaflets found in various species of *Pinanga*.

It is doubtful that there are any true species cultivated in the United States. Due to a mix-up centuries ago, most of the plants cultivated in the United States under the name of *Dypsis* are properly *Chrysalidocarpus*.

True *Dypsis* species should be introduced into the United States. Humbert's *Flore de Madagascar* describes 21 species, almost all of which are small and unique and should be delightful for indoor use in pots or tubs. Many species may prove hardy for outdoor use, since other palms from Madagascar grow outdoors in Florida.

Cultivation: Seeds are said to be very easy to germinate and usually do so in well under 2 months.

Drymophloeus beguinii. At Jennings' Garden in Florida. Photo by H. F. Loomis.

Drymophloeus beguinii, a young plant in Florida.

ELAEIS GUINEENSIS*

Greek, *elaia*, olive tree, and *guineensis*, of Guinea (Africa)

The famous oil palm of tropical Africa is the best-known species of the genus *Elaeis*, and the only one known to be cultivated in the United States.

Its valuable fruits grow in short, wide clusters huddled in close among the leaves. Its male flowers are short, furry fingers of unique and recognizable appearance, set close to the trunk on short peduncles. These fingers adhere for long periods and, dead or alive, are usually present to identify any tree that has flowered. The female cluster is illustrated.

The palm oil of commerce is extracted from the pulp of this fruit by a fermentation process.[1] Palm-kernel oil, a separate product, is extracted from the seed kernels by crushing or by a solvent process.

In 1955 Nigeria alone exported over 182,000 tons of palm oil and 433,000 tons of palm kernels.

The plant grows slowly at first, being 6–8 years old before the pinnate leaves begin to show their normal dimensions. The new leaves grow very erect on strong, straight petioles, eventually arching with age.

For differences from American oil palm, see *Corozo*.

Common name. African oil palm. **Origin:** West and Central Africa. **Sex:** Monoecious. Male and female flowers in separate clusters on the same tree. **Trunk:** To 60 ft tall, normally much less; 12 in. diameter; leafbases adhere. **Petiole:** 4–7 ft long, 5–8 in. broad; saw-toothed; broadened at base; fibrous; very green. **Leaf:** Pinnate; 10–15 ft long; 100–150 pairs of leaflets. **Leaflets:** 2–4 ft long, 1½–2 in. wide; central nerve very strong, particularly at base,

---

[1]The development of the oil palm is said to have played a part in minimizing the African slave trade. Tribal chiefs sometimes found that it paid as well to keep their subjects laboring at the oil palms as it did to sell them into foreign captivity.

David Livingstone, Scottish missionary and explorer in Africa, is said to have carried oil-palm seeds with him for distribution among various tribes.

A good-sized specimen of the African oil palm, *Elaeis guineensis*, at Fairchild Tropical Garden.

Young tree of the African oil palm, *Elaeis guineensis*, in Bogor Botanic Gardens, Java. Photo by T. Satake.

where it is almost like strong wire; green both sides. **Flowerstalk:** From lower leaf axils; 4–12 in. long, 4–12 in. wide; male flowers are on short, furry, fingerlike branches 4–6 in. long. **Fruit:** Large cluster of 200–300, sits in close to trunk on short, very heavy peduncle; individual fruits: ovoid oblong; 1½ in. long; black when ripe, red at base. See illustration.

The oldest oil palm in Indonesia and the mother of all cultivated oil palms in that area. Moved from Africa in 1868, it is now well over 100 years old. It is so much taller than young and middle-aged palms that planters often fail to recognize the species. Photo courtesy A. Dilmy, Bogor Botanic Gardens, Java.

Fruit head of *Elaeis guineensis*. This may be compared with fruit head of American oil palm, *Corozo oleifera*, illustrated on p. 67. Reprinted from *Gentes Herbarum*.

Cultivation: *E. guineensis* flourishes sufficiently to warrant commercial culture in areas within 16° north or south of the equator.

The United Fruit Company in 1955 had 17,000 acres planted to oil palm in Central America. In these areas the company reports that its best germinating results are obtained by placing the seeds (with the long axis horizontal) about ¼ inch deep in sand frames and covering them with sawdust. The frame is kept fully exposed to the sun but is kept moist. The sawdust helps to retain the moisture. In warm climates, 50 per cent of the seeds will germinate within 8 weeks.

Elaeis can be grown outdoors as an ornamental tree in many subtropical areas, including southern Florida.

The U.S.P.I. Garden in Florida reports planting three batches of oil-palm seeds. The first batch began germinating in 146 days, the second batch in 137 days, but the third batch, with the same general treatment, began germinating in 64 days.

Johnston believes that best results can be obtained by grinding down the hard shell of the seeds or by soaking them for 2 weeks in hot water (or both) before planting.

ELEIODOXA

A genus of pinnate-leafed palms, native to India, Siam, and Malaya. (Not illustrated.)

ELEUTHEROPETALUM [1]*

A pinnate genus, closely allied to *Chamaedorea* and resembling it in all ways, except in the details of the flowers. The sexes are borne on separate plants and almost all species are small and graceful.

Native to Mexico, few true eleutheropetalums are cultivated in the United States. (Not illustrated.)

ENGLEROPHOENIX
(See *Maximiliana*)

EREMOSPATHA
Greek, solitary spathe

A few species of spiny, climbing palms, with pinnate leaves, broad leaflets, and long, slender, strongly ringed trunks.

Native to tropical Africa. Not widely cultivated, particularly in the United States. (Not illustrated.)

---

[1]Moore recently asserted that he cannot maintain *Eleutheropetalum* as a separate genus and that all *Eleutheropetalum* species are correctly *Chamaedorea* species.

ERYTHEA*†
One of the Hesperides, daughter of Evening, or of the West

The genus *Erythea* was separated from *Brahea* in 1800 by Watson. Honoring its West Coast origin, he named it after Erythea who, in Greek mythology, dwelt on an island on the western edge of the world and guarded the golden apples.

The erytheas are widely cultivated in gardens and even for street plantings throughout southern California, but nurserymen in southern Florida generally report that the "Daughter of the West" does not seem to want to grow in the southeastern soil. Some good plants are found in Florida, but they do not seem quite happy and do not usually become as fine specimens as are found in California.

The several species of *Erythea* are single-trunked fan palms, varying in height but generally having strong leaves and leaflets that are stiff, pointed, and not drooping.

E. EDULIS
Latin, edible.

Common name: Guadalupe palm. **Origin:** Guadalupe Island, Lower California. **Sex:** Hermaphrodite. **Trunk:** To 30 ft in height; stout; 18 in. thick at base. **Petiole:** Slender, to

Erythea edulis in fruit in San Marino, California. Photo courtesy of Huntington Botanical Gardens.

5 ft long; hairy near base; a few short teeth, or sometimes none. **Leaf:** Palmate; 3 ft diameter; 70–80 segments; cut halfway to base. **Segments:** 1 in. broad; deeply cleft at apex; few threads in sinuses; green both sides, paler underneath. **Flowerstalk:** Very long, 4–5 ft. **Fruit:** In heavy, long, hanging cluster; globose; 1 in. diameter; black, with sweet pulp. **Seed:** ¾ in. diameter.

E. ARMATA
Latin, armed (as with thorns)

Common name: Big blue hesper palm. **Origin:** Lower California. **Sex:** Hermaphrodite. **Trunk:** To 40 ft, stocky, bulged at bottom; covered with dead leaves, as is *Washingtonia*. **Petiole:** 3 ft long, with strong, curved, white teeth; 2 in. broad near base; 1 in. broad near leaf. **Leaf:** Palmate; 3–5 ft across; deeply cut into about 50 segments; very stiff; blue-gray, waxy. A rib extends several inches into the leaf, like an extension of the leafstalk, or hastula, making it costapalmate. **Segments:** Blue-green, waxy. **Flowerstalk:** Among leaves; very long, up to 15–18 ft; arching; projecting beyond leaves. **Flowers:** Profuse; gray-white. **Fruit:** ½–¾ in. long; ovoid; shiny, paperlike, brown, marked with spots and stripes. **Seed:** Oblong; globular.

Well-conditioned tree of *Erythea armata* planted in southern California. Note long flowerstalks projecting beyond leaves. Reprinted from *Gentes Herbarum*.

E. BRANDEGEEI

Common name: San José hesper palm. **Origin:** San José, Lower California. **Sex:** Hermaphrodite. **Trunk:** Up to 100 ft or more; slender; fast-growing; dead leaves adhering but eventually fall off, if not cut off. **Petiole:** 3 ft long; heavily armed with recurving spines; yellow margins. **Leaf:** Palmate; 3–5 ft. diameter; upper ones ascending, lower ones drooping. **Segments:** Very long, pointed, deeply split at apex; many veins; not as stiff as other *Erytheas;* waxy whitish-green underneath. **Flowerstalk:** Among leaves; little shorter than ends of leaves. **Flowers:** Profuse and tiny. **Fruit:** ½ in. diameter; slow-ripening; papery, puffy exterior; shining, smooth brown, with flecks of lighter color.

E. brandegeei var. *spirales* has the leafbases falling into an attractive spiral arrangement on the trunk. One splendid specimen is planted on the grounds of J. H. Wright of Riverside, California.

Erythea brandegeei in Huntington Botanical Garden. Photo courtesy of Huntington Botanical Gardens.

E. ELEGANS
Latin, elegant

A dwarf species, with smaller, but very firm, leaves. Specimen at Huntington Gardens is only 4 ft tall over all, with less than 2 ft of trunk, and has been flowering and fruiting for several years. A very decorative, small plant.

Common name: Franceschi palm. **Origin:** Sonora, Mexico. **Sex:** Hermaphrodite. **Trunk:** Few feet high, stout; leafbases adhere. **Petiole:** 2 ft long; sharply armed. **Leaf:** Palmate; 18–22 in. across; divided halfway; about 15 on tree. **Segments:** Powdery glaucous on both sides, particularly so on underside; long, pointed; few short threads. **Flowerstalk:** About length of leaves, or longer; erect at first, then gracefully bending with weight of fruit. **Fruit:** Globose; ¾ in. diameter; yellowish. **Seed:** Loose in shell.

OTHER SPECIES

E. aculeata is like *E. edulis*, except that the petiole is very slender and bears many teeth. Not known to be cultivated in the United States.

E. roezlii, similar to *E. armata*, but flowerstalks not projecting quite as far. Not known in cultivation in the United States.

Cultivation: De Leon reports one batch of seeds of *E. brandegeei* began germinating in 44 days. Johnston reports that all *Erythea* seeds are easy to germinate and require no special treatment. They should germinate well within 2 months.

Erythea elegans, a dwarf species. This California specimen is only 4 feet tall over all, with less than 2 feet of trunk, but has been flowering and fruiting for several years. Photo courtesy of Huntington Botanical Gardens.

EUGEISSONA

A genus of pinnate palms, with little or no trunk and with huge, erect leaves and soft, drooping leaflets.

Native to Indonesia and the Malay Peninsula, and not believed to be widely cultivated elsewhere, particularly in the United States.

In his *Flora of the Malay Peninsula*, Ridley describes *E. tristis*. The following information is drawn from that description.

E. TRISTIS

Petioles: 7–10 ft long.[1] **Leaves:** 15–20 ft long, very erect. **Leaflets:** 1 ft long, ½ in. wide, soft and drooping. **Flowerstalk:** 4–6 ft long. **Flowers:** Terminal on branches, 2 in. long and almost woody. **Fruit:** 2–3 in. long, 1½ in. through, ovoid, and beaked; brown. **Seed:** 1 in. through.

Ridley also describes *E. brachystachys*.

Cultivation: In Malaya, Ridley says that these species grow on "dry hills in forests." De Leon reports germinating seeds in 4 months.

EUPRITCHARDIA*
(See *Pritchardia*)

EUTERPE
Mythological name

A large group of perhaps 40 species of monoecious pinnate palms, native to tropical America. Although widespread from Cuba to Trinidad, and to Central and South America, *Euterpe* is not widely cultivated in the United States. *Euterpe* is often confused with *Prestoea*.[2]

---

[1]Ridley does not describe the petioles as spiny, but this photograph, sent in by Mr. Dilmy of Bogor Gardens shows prominent spines on these members.

[2]Bailey considers *Prestoea* a separate genus because it carries no crownshaft. Burret considers *Prestoea* as part of *Euterpe*.

Eugeissona tristis in Bogor Botanic Gardens, Java. Photo by T. Satake.

Huge fruit cluster of *Eugeissona tristis*. Photo by T. Satake.

Although there is nothing quite like the columnar trunk and wide-spreading crown of the royal palm (*Roystonea*), euterpes have been taken for medium-sized royals, because of the slightly swollen, though more slender, trunk and the prominent crownshaft. In most species the leaflets are drooping and give a plumed effect to the crown.

E. oleracea of Brazil is known as the assai palm. Assai, a thick, plum-colored liquid prepared from the fruits, is a very popular refreshment in Brazil, Paraguay, and nearby regions. The trunk of *E. oleracea* grows to 80 ft, although only 4–6 in. thick. The flowerstalk is about 3 ft long and bears a purple fruit 1 in. long.

E. panamensis of Panama grows to 60 ft, with a very smooth, slender trunk. The fruit is white and about ½ in. long.

E. globosa of Cuba grows to 40 ft with trunk 7–9 in. thick. It bears black, globular fruit, about ½ in. diameter.

Cultivation: U.S.P.I. Garden reports planting one batch of seed of *E. longibracteata* which began germinating in 24 days.

EXORRHIZA [1]
Greek, *exō*, out, and *rhiza*, root

A group of about 6 pinnate-leafed palms supported by spectacular, spiny, aerial roots. The only species known in the United States is *E. wendlandiana*, from the Fiji Islands. Its single trunk grows to about 35 ft. The leaves surmount a glossy crownshaft and are about 10–12 ft long and have leaflets 4 ft long, 1–2 in. wide. The flowerstalk appears below the crownshaft, at first enclosed in a thick, leathery, boat-shaped spathe, but later branches out 2–3 ft beyond it. The handsome fruits are about 1 in. long, and red.

All stilt palms are rare in the United States. There are no specimens at Chapman Field, Fairchild Tropical Garden, or Huntington Gardens.

Cultivation: Little is known in the United States about the cultivation of *Exorrhiza*. Many growers believe that stilt palms will not grow in subtropical areas such as Florida and that they require the actual tropics.

[1]Burret considers *Exorrhiza* a valid genus. In *Gentes Herbarum*, vol. 8, pages 458–466, Moore and Fosberg give their reasons for uniting *Exorrhiza* with *Clinostigma*. In their opinion all species previously known as *Exorrhiza* should now be known as *Clinostigma*.

Euterpe globosa in Oriente Province, Cuba. Courtesy of Herbario De La Salle.

Eugeissona tristis, close-up of spiny petioles. Photo courtesy A. Dilmy, Bogor Botanic Gardens, Java.

GAUSSIA*
Probably from a personal name

Two species of slender, pinnate-leafed palms of Cuba and Puerto Rico, where they grow on rocky cliffs with their woody roots exposed. These visible, creeping roots are characteristic and still occur when the plant is in good soil.

It has not been concluded whether *Gaussia*, usually a rather scrawny-looking plant, manages in spite of the poor, rocky soil or whether there is something about such conditions that it prefers.

G. PRINCEPS
Latin, chief, the most distinguished

Gaussia is described as having a slender trunk, enlarged basally. The specimen of *G. princeps* at Fairchild Tropical Garden is about 8 in. thick throughout the bottom 4 ft of trunk. During the next 4 ft it gradually diminishes until it is 4 in. thick and, from that point upward, it maintains this smaller diameter. Several photographs of *Gaussia* palms in Cuba show the trunks to be enlarged above the base and generally cigar shaped.

Common name: Llume palm. **Origin:** Cuba. **Sex:** Monoecious. **Trunk:** 8 in. at base and throughout the next 4 ft, then graduates to 4 in., a diameter which is then maintained to the top. Trunk grows to a height of 15–20 ft. **Petiole:** 15 in. long; firm; dark-green. **Leaf:** Pinnate; 5 ft long, 3 ft wide; crowded with close-together leaflets. **Leaflets:** 15 in. long; linear; pointed. **Flowerstalk:** Below leaves; long, slender, to 4–5 ft. **Flowers:** Very small. **Fruit:** Ellipsoidal; small; purple to red.

G. ATTENUATA
Latin, tapering (referring to narrowing of trunk)

This species is found on limestone hills and has visible roots. Its trunk reaches a height of 60–100 ft and never exceeds a thickness of 6 in. It has large clusters of red-orange fruits, each about the size of a cherry. Native to Puerto Rico.

Cultivation: U.S.P.I. Garden reports show that one batch of seeds of *G. attenuata* began germinating in 43 days.

Johnston reports that *Gaussia* seeds are easy to germinate without any special care. Plants seem fairly hardy to cold.

GEONOMA*
Greek, *geonomōs*, colonist (explanation obscure)

A very large group of well over 200 species, little cultivated in the United States and native to tropical America, where plants grow as underbrush in deep woods.

Most species of *Geonoma* are usually of low height and have slender, ringed trunks. The pinnate leaves, in proportion, are large and are divided only at wide intervals, and sometimes

Gaussia attenuata. Tall specimen at U.S.P.I. Garden at Coconut Grove, Florida. Photo by H. F. Loomis.

Gaussia princeps at Fairchild Tropical Garden. Note that trunk retains most of its thickness for about 4 feet and then begins to taper. Photo by H. F. Loomis.

not at all. Species are found growing as high as 4,000 ft above sea level, which suggests at least some hardiness to cold.

Exotic in appearance and small enough for most gardens, it is surprising that so few geonomas are encountered in Florida gardens or patios, where they could be given the protection from the sun and wind, to which they have been accustomed. Chapman Field has one unidentified species of *Geonoma* from Colombia.

G. DECURRENS

Common name: None. **Origin:** Costa Rica. **Sex:** Monoecious. **Trunk:** 6 ft in height, 1½ in. diameter; ringed. **Petiole:** 1½ ft long; slender; dilated at base. **Leaf:** Pinnate; only 8–10 leaves on plant, each 4–5 ft long, 12 in. broad; deeply notched at apex, but otherwise entire, except that some leaves are occasionally divided irregularly into varied, broad leaflets. Sometimes this occurs on only one side of the leaf. **Leaflets:** Sometimes none, as mentioned under **leaf. Flowerstalk:** 12–15 in. long; single, slender spike. **Fruit:** Elliptic, pointed either end; ⅓ in. long; at right angles to stem; greenish-yellow.

G. PROCUMBENS
Latin, leaning or bending forward

Common name: None. **Origin:** Panama. **Sex:** On separate flowerstalks, sometimes on separate plants. **Trunk:** Short, inclined; sometimes none. Tallest ever seen was 6 ft high, 3 in. diameter. **Petiole:** To 3 ft; no spines. **Leaf:** Pinnate; 3–4 ft in addition to petiole; 24 pairs of leaflets, widely spaced. **Leaflets:** 18 in. long, 1½ in. wide; terminal pair 4 in. wide. **Flowerstalk:** From trunk; a single, slender, vertical spike, to 7 ft long, with a cattail-like

Geonoma decurrens, one of the few palms with simple, undivided leaves, pinnately nerved. (Note stilt roots of palm in background.) Photo by H. F. Loomis.

Geonoma procumbens. In this plant, only the male flowers appeared. Note single spike arising from the ground. Reprinted from *Gentes Herbarum.*

thickening the last 18 in. **Fruit:** Ovoid; tapering on both ends; ⅓ in. long, greenish. **Seed:** About ¼ in.; smooth.

G. BINERVIA

Common name: None. **Origin:** Panama, Guatemala, Nicaragua, Costa Rica. **Sex:** Monoecious. **Trunk:** To 15 ft tall, 1½ in. thick; ringed every 2–3 in. **Petiole:** 1–2 ft long. **Leaf:** Irregularly pinnate; 5–6 ft long; forms umbrellalike, flat crown; 25 pairs of leaflets. **Leaflets:** Irregular, long, pointed; varying in width ¾–3 in., with a terminal pair 5 in. wide. **Flowerstalk:** 6–7 in. long; upstanding; branched. **Fruit:** Globular, oblong; ⅙ in.; dark-green or black. **Seed:** Smooth.

OTHER SPECIES

The many species of *Geonoma* cover such a great variety that division into types is impractical. Wallace, in his *Palms of the Amazon*, describes and illustrates three small and very unique geonomas, that would be a valuable addition to any garden. These are *G. multiflora*, *G. paniculigera*, and *G. rectifolia*.

Bailey describes *G. acaulis*, *G. elegans*, *G. pohliana*, *G. riedeliana*, *G. schottiana*, *G. seemannii*, *G. spixiana*.

Hortus Second describes two very small varieties: *G. elegans* (Brazil), *G. gracilis* (Costa Rica).

Cultivation: U.S.P.I. Garden records show one seed batch of *G. longipetiolata* which began germination in 74 days. De Leon reports seeds of the same species which did not begin germination until the 119th day.

Geonoma sp. at Chapman Field in Florida.

Geonoma pumila growing in Colombia. Courtesy M. B. Foster.

GIGLIOLIA

A little-known genus of pinnate-leafed palms whose two species are native to Borneo and little known to cultivation. (Not illustrated.)

GLAZIOVA*
(See *Syagrus*)

GONIOCLADUS

A monotypic genus of pinnate-leafed palms, native to the Fiji Islands. The one species is *G. petiolatus*. (Not illustrated.)

GONIOSPERMA

A pinnate-leafed genus whose two species are native to the Fiji Islands. (Not illustrated.)

GRONOPHYLLUM

A pinnate-leafed palm genus from Indonesia which is little cultivated outside its native land. No detailed description is available. *G. oxypetalum* is illustrated, growing in Bogor Gardens, Java.

GUILIELMA*

A few tropical American species of very spiny feather palms, one of which, *G. gasipaes*, is the famous peach palm of Central and South America.

G. GASIPAES

Closely allied to *Bactris*, *G. gasipaes* has long, black spines on its trunk, petiole, and on the veins on both sides of the leaves.

The reddish-yellow fruit is of a triangular, oval shape and hangs in large, very attractive

Gronophyllum oxypetalum (Burret). A photograph sent to the author from Bogor Botanic Gardens, Java. It was impossible to check the correctness of this species which the author has never seen. Photo by T. Satake.

clusters from beneath the leaves. The fruit is not eaten raw like a peach but is boiled or roasted and has a slightly oily flavor. The fruits are also ground into a flour and, as such, form an important part of the diet in some of the native villages.

Common name: Peach palm. **Origin:** Central and South America. **Sex:** Monoecious. **Trunk:** Sometimes single, usually several, or many; to 60 ft tall; closely covered with long, black spines. **Petiole:** Short; very spiny. **Leaf:** Pinnate; 8–12 ft; many leaflets; rachis covered with spines. **Leaflets:** Spines on veins; dark-green above; light-green beneath. **Flowerstalk:** Beneath leaves; covered by short, wide, woody spathe. **Fruit:** 1–2 in. long; triangular ovoid; yellow-red. It hangs in large, heavy clusters and is of superior quality. **Oddities:** According to L. H. Bailey, a seedless form is known.

G. speciosa is correctly *G. gasipaes*.

G. utilis is correctly *G. gasipaes*.

Cultivation: No information available. It grows in southern Florida and, being of tropical origin, probably will not grow much farther north. De Leon reports that plants of *G. gasipaes* grow quickly and that seeds germinate in about 3 months.

GULUBIA

A little-known genus of 10 species of pinnate-leafed palms, native to New Guinea, the Moluccas, and the Solomon Islands. The species illustrated is *G. costata*.

Guilielma gasipaes in fruit at Mrs. Jennings' garden, Florida.

Gulubia costata, a species rare or unknown in the United States, growing in Sturt Island, Territory of Papua. Photo by L. J. Brass, courtesy of A. C. Langlois.

GULUBIOPSIS [1]

A monotypic genus whose only species, *G. palauensis*, is native to Palau Island. (Not illustrated.)

HAITIELLA

A little-known genus of palmate palms. (Not illustrated.)

HEDYSCEPE CANTERBURYANA†

One species of unarmed, monoecious, pinnate palm, with a dense crown of arched, recurving leaves.

Very similar to *Howea*, from which it differs only in some details of the flowers. Native to Lord Howe Island in the South Pacific. Grows more slowly than *Howea*. Seldom planted in the United States, except perhaps mistakenly as *Howea*.

Cultivation: Johnston reports that seeds come from Lord Howe Island but seem to be obtainable only about every fourth year.

HEMITHRINAX
Greek, *hemi*, half, and *thrinax*, three-pronged fork

A genus of Cuban fan palms, similar to *Thrinax*, differing in flower details. The fruit is white when ripe, as in *Thrinax*. Not described here, as it is rare in cultivation outside Cuba and description would be so generally similar to *Thrinax*.

H. compacta is briefly described by Hawkes in his papers. Brother Leon, in his *Flora de Cuba*, describes *H. compacta, H. ekmaniana, H. rivularis,* and *H. savannarum.*

---

[1]Burret considers *Gulubiopsis* a valid separate genus. In *Gentes Herbarum*, vol. 8, page 453, Moore and Fosberg give their reasons for uniting *Gulubiopsis* with *Gulubia*.

Hedyscepe canterburyana. Photo courtesy of New Crops Research Branch, U.S. Department of Agriculture.

HETEROSPATHE*

Greek, *hetero*, other, different, and *spathē*, spathe

Several species native to the Philippines and South Sea Islands, one of which, *H. elata*, is sometimes planted in southern Florida. It is distinguished by its long, pointed, slender, gracefully tapering leaflets and by the fact that new leaves when they first open are an odd shade of pinkish brown, a natural characteristic that is often mistaken for an ailment.

H. ELATA

Common name: Sagisi palm. **Origin:** Philippines and South Sea Islands. **Sex:** Monoecious. **Trunk:** To 45 ft tall, 7 in. thick; slender; enlarged at base; smooth; ringed. **Petiole:** 27 in. long. **Leaf:** Pinnate; 10 ft long; 65 pairs of leaflets, which are very evenly spaced and curve very gracefully. Leafbase fibrous. **Leaflets:** 2–3 ft long, 1½ in., or less, wide; narrowed at base and also to a long point at end. New leaflets are pinkish-brown when they first open. **Flowerstalk:** Among leaves; up to 3 ft long; branched. **Fruit:** ¼ in. diameter; pealike; rugose; white, when ripe.

Cultivation: Johnston reports that the small seeds are easy to germinate well within 2 months. The palm is quite tender to cold.

HEXOPETION MEXICANUM* [1]

(See *Astrocaryum mexicanum*)

[1]Burret includes *Hexopetion* in his list of valid genera. Moore considers that *Hexopetion* species properly belong in *Astrocaryum*. In this book *Hexopetion mexicanum* is described under *Astrocaryum*.

Heterospathe elata, the sagisi palm, growing at Fairchild Tropical Garden. Photo by H. F. Loomis.

HOWEA [1]*†

Named for Lord Howe, as was the island where the two species grow

The two species of *Howea* are among the most popular palms in the United States. Though often found in gardens in southern California and southern Florida, they are grown in even greater quantities in pots or tubs for indoor use.

Their nomenclature has been, and still is, somewhat confused. Perhaps this history will help to clarify:

1870: C. Moore and Von Mueller described both species and temporarily called them *Kentia belmoreana* and *K. forsteriana*, realizing that further study might displace them from the genus *Kentia*.

1875: Wendland and Drude, convinced on closer study that these two palms were not true *Kentias*, proposed the name *Grisebachia*.

1877: Beccari, finding that the name *Grisebachia* had been used as far back as 1838 for plants of another family, proposed the names *Howea belmoreana* and *H. forsteriana*. These are now the accepted names.

While the two species are somewhat alike, there are the following differences:

H. Belmoreana: Petioles very short. Petioles and leaves strongly ascending and arching. Leaflets are somewhat upright on stem and very closely placed, with midrib prominent only on upper surfaces. Flowerstalk is simple spike, 2 ft or more long and unbranched.

H. forsteriana: Petioles long and not strongly arching. Lower leaves almost horizontal. Leaflets are not upright on stem but flat and horizontal and attached 1 in. or more apart. Midrib prominent on both surfaces. Flowerstalk is 3 ft long and branched. There are other differences in fruit and flowers not detailed here.

---

[1]This spelling used by Bailey, Burret and some other authorities. Beccari preferred *Howeia* although he has used both. Moore considers *Howeia* to be Beccari's original spelling and hence the correct spelling.

Flowering tree of *Howea belmoreana*. Note the short arching petioles, the upright ascending leaflets, and the flowerstalks which are single spikes. Reprinted from *Gentes Herbarum*.

Howea forsteriana. Note the longer, more drooping petioles and the flat drooping leaflets. Photo courtesy of Huntington Botanical Gardens.

H. BELMOREANA
Named in honor of DeBelmore, Governor of New South Wales

Common name: Sentry palm. **Origin:** Lord Howe Island. **Sex:** Monoecious. **Trunk:** Single; to 24 ft or more; expanded at base; ringed. **Petiole:** Short, 10–18 in.; arching. **Leaf:** Pinnate; 16 ft long; decidedly arching. Leaflets standing somewhat upright on rachis and very closely placed. **Leaflets:** 1 in. wide, 1½–2 ft long; curving upward, thus forming a trough. Green both sides; not spotted or scaly underneath. **Flowerstalk:** From lower leaves; 2–5 ft or longer; a single, downward curving spike without branches. **Fruit:** To 1¼ in. long, suddenly narrowed to beak at apex; not closely packed in cluster; lemon-shaped. **Seed:** ¾ in. long.

H. FORSTERIANA
Named for William Forster, Senator, New South Wales

It may prove easy to remember that the species beginning with the letter "f" is the flat palm with flat, and not upward arching leaflets.

This species is much more common in cultivation than *H. belmoreana*. It is so different from *H. belmoreana* that O.F. Cook in 1926 tried to give it the new genus name of *Denea*, but this has been rejected by most botanists.

Common name: Sentry palm. **Origin:** Lord Howe Island. **Sex:** Monoecious. **Trunk:** To 40 ft or more in height; single; not enlarged at base. **Petiole:** Long, to 5 ft; ascending and not arching except with weight. **Leaf:** Pinnate; to 9 ft long; not arching. Leaflets emerge from rachis on horizontal plane and give leaf its flat appearance. Leaflets spaced about 1 in. apart on rachis. **Leaflets:** Fastened to rachis on horizontal plane; green both sides; spotted and scaly underneath. **Flowerstalk:** From lower leaves; to 3½ ft; branched; hanging. **Fruit:** Up to 2 in.; closely packed on spadix; slightly longer and less fat than *H. belmoreana;* narrowed gradually to apex, not beaked. **Seed:** ¾ in. long.

Cultivation: Johnston reports *Howea* seeds germinate easily without any special attention within 2 months.

Ripe fruits of howeas compared: left, *H. belmoreana;* right, *H. forsteriana.* Reprinted from *Gentes Herbarum.*

Howea belmoreana, a specimen growing under lath. The petioles are longer than normal because they are reaching for the sun. The leaflets are upright. Photo courtesy of Huntington Botanical Gardens.

HYDRIASTELE

Greek, *hydro*, water, and *stele*, column

Most plants known to planters in the Western Hemisphere as *Hydriastele wendlandiana* have been found to be *Ptychosperma elegans*.

There are three or four true species of *Hydriastele*, which apparently are not widely planted outside their native land. They are very tall, slender, monoecious, unarmed, pinnate-leafed palms of Australia and New Guinea. They generally are found in wet places in the humid forest. They have somewhat the general appearance of *Ptychosperma*. They are not described here because botanical information available seems confused. Three photographs are shown. One is of the true *H. wendlandiana;* the other two were sent to the author by usually reliable sources, as *H. rostrata*.

HYOPHORBE

This formerly large genus now consists of only two species. Those former *Hyophorbe* species, with swollen and constricted trunks, whose seed was attached inside the shell, have all been transferred to the genus *Mascarena*.

Hydriastele rostrata. Photo courtesy A. Dilmy, Bogor Botanic Gardens, Java.

The only two remaining hyophorbes—*H. indica*, and *H. vaughnii*—have straight trunks and their seed is free and loose inside the shell. They are not very ornamental, are not known to be widely cultivated, and are not described here. Native to Mascarene Islands.

Hyophorbe amaricaulis is correctly *Mascarena lagenicaulis*.

H. verschaffeltii is correctly *Mascarena verschaffeltii*.

Cultivation: U.S.P.I. Garden reports seeds of *H. indica* began germinating in 75 days.

HYOSPATHE

Greek, hog spathe, i.e., hog palm: vernacular

A few species of South American palms, not widely cultivated in the United States, although descriptions make them seem suitable for small garden and patio use. The slender reedlike stems are usually less than 10 ft high. The leaves in some species remain entire and undivided.

H. CONCINNA

Common name: None. **Origin:** Panama. **Sex:** Monoecious. **Trunk:** Single; to 9 ft in height; less than ½ in. thick. **Petiole:** 4 in. long; convex below, flat above. **Leaf:** 12–15 in. long; simple, undivided, except for deep indentation dividing the two points to about ⅓ their length; pinnately nerved. **Leaflets:** None. **Flowerstalk:** Beneath leaves; 8-branched. **Flowers:** Pink. **Fruit:** Obovoid; small; purple.

OTHER SPECIES

H. elegans of the Amazon, described by Bailey, has several jointed trunks 6 ft high and 1 in. thick; pinnate leaves, 3–4 ft long, almost entire at first, but becoming irregularly divided.

H. pallida of Colombia has pinnate leaves divided into many leaflets, which are greatly varied in length and width.

Hydriastele rostrata in Bogor Botanic Gardens. Photo by T. Satake.

Hydriastele wendlandiana. Reprinted from Blatter's *Palms of British India and Ceylon*.

HYPHAENE*

Greek, *hyphaenein*, to weave (referring to the fibers of the fruit)

There is mention of the doum palm in Egyptian writings as far back as 1800 B.C. Often found at oases, *H. thebaica* seems to survive the intense light and great heat of African deserts, as long as its deep roots can find some water.

Hyphaene is the only palm genus in which the trunks fork naturally into several branches (though injury may cause any palm trunk to form an unnatural branch).

The costapalmate leaves are gray-green and very firm and stiff. The petioles are armed with black teeth. The thick, strong branches of the flowerstalk grow from among the lower leaves; and the fruits are large, 1½–3 in. long, pear-shaped, or obovoid, with a woody exterior and a fleshy interior. Male and female flowers are on separate trees.

While there are understood to be well over 30 species, only a few have been imported into the United States and it is not known whether these were correctly named. Of a dozen plants now reaching maturity at Fairchild Tropical Garden, only two have species names, the balance being "unidentified species" at the time this was written.

When Egyptian seeds of *H. thebaica* are planted in the warm, luxurious climate of Ceylon, they develop trunks twice as thick with shorter, more numerous branches and larger, more numerous leaves, than they do in their native land.

H. THEBAICA

H. thebaica is also known as the gingerbread palm because of its fruits, which are said to have the taste and somewhat the consistency of gingerbread.

Doum palm of Africa, *Hyphaene thebaica*, growing in British Guiana. Photo by T. Satake.

Common name: Doum palm, gingerbread palm. **Origin:** Egypt and the west coast of India. **Sex:** Dioecious. **Trunk:** 12–18 in. thick, 10–30 ft high. Forked, or branched. **Petiole:** 3 ft long. Strong, with strong, black teeth. Channeled above, rounded below (Blatter says triangular below); conspicuously whitened at and near the base. **Leaf:** Costapalmate (with extra rib extending from base of petiole into center of leaf; in this case, almost to the outer edge.); 20–30 on each branch; 2–2½ ft long, and a little more in width. Cut more than halfway into 20 or more segments. **Segments:** Stiff, strong, decidedly gray-green, glaucous. **Flowerstalk:** Among leaves; 4 ft long; thick and strong; much branched. At first, erect; later, hanging. **Flowers:** Yellow. **Fruit:** To 3 in. long; pear-shaped; very deep orange; woody exterior, fleshy interior. **Oddities:** Since the roots of all hyphaenes must go down as much as 18–36 in. before the leaves begin to appear, they can be germinated only in the ground or in exceptionally deep pots.

OTHER SPECIES

Bailey mentions *H. ventricosa* as a species with "bulging trunks." Blatter describes *H. indica* of India. *Hortus Second* mentions and briefly describes, *H. crinita* (South Africa), *H. natalensis* (Natal), and *H. schatan* (Madagascar). There are over thirty species including some that are imperfectly known.

Cultivation: The plants introduced so far seem to thrive in protected places in southern Florida.

Hyphaene seeds are large. The outer covering can be removed, leaving a bare seed and hastening germination. Taproot goes down at least 18 in. before returning to first leaf, so that pot culture is not practical, except in very large pots. Seeds usually take 5–6 months to germinate.

Hyphaene sp. in fruit at Mrs. Jennings' garden in Florida.

IGUANURA

A genus of several species with short, multiple trunks and leaves that are either simple or irregularly pinnate.

They are native to the Malay Peninsula and not widely cultivated elsewhere.

Ridley's *Flora of the Malay Peninsula* describes 10 species, including the species illustrated.

I. wallichiana has several trunks which are only 2–4 ft tall at maturity. The leaves are small with pinnate veins and are only 30 in. long and 9 in. wide.

The fruits of *iguanura* have an interesting characteristic. When they ripen, they are at first white, then red, then black, and all three colors can often be seen simultaneously on one flowerstalk.

INODES

(Genus separated from *Sabal* by Cook; not now accepted. See *Sabal*)

IRIARTEA

Named for Bernard Iriarte

A genus of South American, pinnate-leafed palms of very striking and unusual appearance.

The trunks of all species are supported on a pyramid of aerial roots and are surmounted by a glossy, dark crownshaft. To add to the exotic appearance, the leaflets are somewhat tri-angular, irregularly notched, and often twisted or curled.

I. exorrhiza, as described by Wallace, is a curious and beautiful tree, reaching to 50–60 ft in height. The gracefully curved leaves, unlike most other palm leaves, have triangular, deeply notched leaflets which stand out from the midrib at various angles. The crownshaft is a deep green. The small flowerstalks appear below the crownshaft and bear small, oval, red fruits. The stilt roots spring from the stem, each new one coming from a higher point than

A young specimen of *Iguanura wallichiana* in Bogor Botanic Gardens, Java. Photo courtesy A. Dilmy, Bogor Botanic Gardens, Java.

A splendid specimen of *Iriartea exorrhiza* showing a mass of stilt roots. Photo by M. B. Foster in Botanical Garden, Rio de Janeiro, Brazil.

the last. As the new ones emerge, older, lower ones die. It is not uncommon to see a tall tree supported by only 3 or 4 roots so tall that a person may walk between them without stooping, or he may stand erect, with a tree 70 ft high, growing from a level above his head. Young plants are good reproductions of their parents, except that they seldom have more than three legs, which gives them a strange and somewhat ludicrous appearance. Native to Amazon region of South America.

I. ventricosa, according to Wallace, has a trunk a little thicker than *I. exorrhiza*. It grows up to 100 ft tall and, at about its middle, is swollen for a length of about 10 ft with a tumor twice its own diameter. These tumors are of greatly varying sizes and are absent in some specimens, because they have not yet developed. The aerial roots are 6–8 ft high and are more slender than the roots of *I. exorrhiza*. The leaflets are wider and of very eccentric shape. The crownshaft is of a deep, bluish-green color. The fruit is globular and about 1 in. in diameter. Found on hillsides and on banks of brooks and springs. Native to Brazil.

I. setigera is a smaller palm. The trunk is only 15–20 ft high and "varying from the thickness of a finger to the thickness of a wrist." It is very strongly ringed, and the aerial roots appear only a few inches above ground. The leaflets have broad and very jagged ends and are set well apart on the midrib. The fruit is oval and orange in color. The trunks, with the pith removed, and the bore highly polished, are used by the natives for blow guns. Native to Brazil, upper Amazon area. This may be more correctly *Iriartella setigera*.

The foregoing descriptions, much of which is borrowed from Wallace's *Palms of the Amazon*, draws a picture of a much-to-be-desired palm and brings up the question of whether it can be grown outdoors in subtropical areas, such as Florida. It should, and will, be tried, but the evidence for success is not too encouraging. Its native lands are near the equator, suggesting a lack of hardiness to cold. It must also be mentioned that for some unknown reason palms with stilt roots have not generally thrived in Florida. As to indoor cultivation, Wallace, in 1853, stated that there were then young *Iriartea* plants in the great glass palm house at Kew Gardens in London.

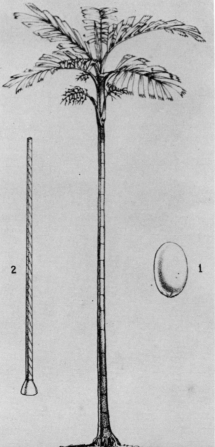

Sketch of roots of an *Iriartea* reprinted from Wallace's *Palm Trees of the Amazon*.

Sketch of *Iriartea setigera*. At the left is one of the native blow-guns that were once made from the trunks of this palm. The fruit is sketched at the right. Sketch reproduced from Wallace's *Palm Trees of the Amazon*.

IRIARTELLA
(Closely allied to, if not synonymous with, *Iriartea*, which see)

JESSENIA

A genus of pinnate-leafed palms, with very long, erect leaves, and drooping leaflets. Native from Trinidad to the Amazon.

J. OLIGOCARPA
Latin, few-fruited

Common name: None. **Origin:** Trinidad. **Sex:** Monoecious. **Trunk:** 40–50 ft in height, 15 in. thick. **Petiole:** 3–4 ft long; grooved. **Leaf:** Pinnate; 16 ft long, 9 ft wide; many leaflets. **Leaflets:** 5 ft long, 1–3 in. wide; very shiny on upper surface, powdery white underneath. **Flowerstalk:** From lower leaves; long; branched. **Fruit:** 1¼ in. long; black; oblong, with short apex.

Four other species, native to South America, are not described here.

JUANIA AUSTRALIS

This pinnate-leafed genus, native to and named for the Island of Juan Fernandez (Robin-

Jessenia oligocarpa in dense forest group in Trinidad, West Indies. Photo by A. C. Langlois.

A stocky specimen of *Jubaea spectabilis* in California. Photo courtesy of Huntington Botanical Gardens in San Marino, California.

son Crusoe's island), is practically lost to cultivation. It is reported to be quite hardy, but seeds are difficult to obtain and the palm is reported to be almost extinct on its own island.

JUBAEA*†
Named after Juba, King of Numidia

Jubaea has only one species, *J. spectabilis*, the wine palm of Chile, the palm which, in South America, grows farther south of the equator than any other palm. It seems to be equally hardy in the northern hemisphere, where it thrives in California.

Jubaea trunks are probably the thickest of all palm trunks.

A full-sized trunk yields about 90 gallons of sugar sap, which is boiled down by the Chileans and called *miel de palma*, or palm honey. This is extensively served as a delicacy in shops and hotels on the west coast of South America.

J. SPECTABILIS
Latin, remarkable, worth seeing (also known as *Jubaea chilensis*)

Common name: Chilean wine palm. **Origin:** Chile. **Sex:** Monoecious. **Trunk:** To 80 ft or more; 4–6 ft diameter; studded with scars of old leafbases. **Petiole:** Short; margined with stiff, hairy filaments, not really spines. **Leaf:** Pinnate; 6–12 ft long; many leaflets. **Leaflets:** 2 ft long, 1 in. broad; split at apex. **Flowerstalk:** From lower leaf axils; long spathes persist and hang. **Fruit:** 1½ in. long; globose ovoid; yellow. **Oddities:** Seedlings produce several simple leaves before developing pinnate ones.

Cultivation: Very hardy to cold. Franceschi says, "It can endure drought and many degrees of cold and, liberally treated, it makes a large tree in a few years." It thrives in the cool climate of the French Riviera and is one of the most popular palms in southern California, where it grows into a huge tree, with an unusually heavy trunk.

J. spectabilis does not seem to thrive in Florida. Two specimens at Fairchild Tropical Garden are alive and growing but do not take on the noble proportions or exhibit the same vigor as do the plants in California. Many younger plants have failed in private gardens in southern Florida.

U.S.P.I. Garden reports planting seeds of *J. spectabilis* which began germinating in 113 days. Johnston reports that seeds lose viability quickly and fresh seeds must be shipped by air. Seedling plants do not do well in Florida.

Close-up of trunk of a very large specimen of *Jubaea* in California. This trunk looks to have a diameter of 6 feet or more. Photo courtesy of David Barry.

Fruiting cluster of *Jubaea spectabilis*. Photo courtesy of Huntington Botanical Gardens, San Marino, California.

JUBAEOPSIS CAFFRA

A one-species genus, similar to *Jubaea*.

A native of South Africa, not usually cultivated elsewhere. Three specimens were planted at Huntington Gardens, but died during the freeze of 1949.

KAJEWSKIA

Pichi-Sermolli describes a monotypic genus, *Kajewskia aneityensis*. Burret and Potztal consider the correct generic name for this palm to be *Carpoxylon*. Native to Aneityum Island (New Hebrides.)

KALBREYERA

A genus of pinnate-leafed palms, native to Colombia and little planted elsewhere. (Not illustrated.)

KENTIA
Named for William Kent, horticulturist

As currently understood, there are only two true species of the genus *Kentia* and neither one is known to be cultivated in the United States. They are *K. procera*, native to New Guinea, and *K. ramsayi*, native to northern Australia. (Not illustrated.)

Some 50 species names have been claimed as *Kentia*, but most of them upon closer study have been transferred to other genera. Consequently, for years, many palms have been erroneously grown and sold as kentias.

K. baueri is correctly *Rhopalostylis baueri*.

K. belmoreana is correctly *Howea belmoreana*.

K. canterburyana is correctly *Hedyscepe canterburyana*.

K. forsteriana is correctly *Howea forsteriana*.

K. joannis is correctly *Veitchia joannis*.

K. lindenii is correctly *Chambeyronia lindenii*.

K. macarthuri is correctly *Ptychosperma macarthuri*.

K. macrocarpa is correctly *Chambeyronia macrocarpa*.

K. sapida is correctly *Rhopalostylis sapida*.

KENTIOPSIS
Like *Kentia*

According to *Hortus Second*, the only true *Kentiopsis* is *K. olivaeformis*, a lofty tree of New Caledonia, not cultivated in the United States. Pinnate-leafed and not described here.

K. macrocarpa correctly is *Chambeyronia macrocarpa*.

Close-up of leaves of *Korthalsia*. Photo by A. C. Langlois.

Korthalsia sp. climbing up a tree in Bogor Botanic Gardens, Java. Photo by T. Satake.

KORTHALSIA

Named for Peter Korthals, German botanist

A genus of interesting climbing palms, easily recognized by the striking appearance of the variously shaped leaflets which are short and broad, varying in shape from triangular to cuneate, to rhomboidal. The wide ends are toothed and jagged. Native to Burma, Malaya, and Indonesia.

The korthalsias are pinnate-leafed palms, the ends of the leaves being prolonged into a whiplike part bearing sharp claws for climbing. The stems are very slender, usually less than ½ in. in diameter, and spiny. The leaves are usually small, from 1–2 ft long. The leaflets, varying in length from 2–8 in. or more, are usually almost as wide as they are long, whitish on the underside.

Beccari states, "A peculiar character of *korthalsias* is the great development of the appendage at the mouth of the leaf sheaths (the ochrea), which at times is transformed into a swollen and entirely closed ant-harboring organ."

Bailey mentions *K. robusta*.

Hawkes describes *K. laciniosa* and *K. echinometra*.

Ridley describes 11 species in his *Flora of the Malay Peninsula*.

Blatter describes *K. laciniosa*.

The korthalsias are not known to be cultivated in the United States. They are said to be plants that will grow only in shade.

LACCOSPADIX

Pichi-Sermolli describes two species of pinnate leafed palms from Australia and New Guinea under the above name. Burret and Potztal consider these species to belong to the genus *Calyptrocalyx*.

LATANIA*
Vernacular term

Three splendid palm species from the Mascarene Islands that are widely planted and fruitful throughout southern Florida and the American tropics.

The large clusters of plum-sized brown fruits are attractive and the big, round, 8–ft leaves are almost as stiff as metal.

One characteristic immediately identifies juvenile *Latania* palms. During the first 5 or 10 years, the petioles are purplish-red; each deeply divided segment is prominently edged and centered with purplish-red or yellow-orange veins. The color of all these parts changes gradually to green as the plant matures.

Probably the most characteristic feature of old plants is the very heavy, white, woolly substance that covers the petioles and parts of the leaves.

L. COMMERSONII
(*L. borbonica*) [1]

Common name: None. **Origin:** Mascarene Islands. **Sex:** Dioecious. **Trunk:** To 35 ft in height, 8–10 in. thick; swollen only at base. **Petiole:** 4–6 ft long, 4–8 in. wide; heavily tinged with red until old. Thickly covered with white tomentum, which increases with age. Toothed until old. **Leaf:** 6½–8 ft diameter; thick texture. Costapalmate, i.e., a rib extends from the petiole 18 or more in. into the leaf. **Segments:** About 3 in. wide; ridged underneath; edged with very tiny saw teeth; veins and margins prominently tinged with red; dark gray-green, paler beneath. **Flowerstalk:** From among the leaves; 3–6 ft long. **Flowers:** Male and female on separate trees. **Fruit:** Globose, 1½–1¾ in. diameter; drupe; smooth with surface slightly roughened; brown and glossy. Very slow ripening. **Seed:** See photographs. Albumen homogeneous. Mesocarp, thick and spongy. 1⅙–1½ in. long.

[1]*L. borbonica* seems to be the name accepted by many botanists. However, *L. commersonii* is the name known to horticulturists and to many botanists (including Balfour in *Flora of Mauritius and the Seychelles*). H. E. Moore, Jr. considers *L. commersonii* to be a synonym and *L. borbonica* to be the correct name.

L. LODDIGESII

Differs as follows: **petiole** less broad, less markedly reddish; **segment** blue-gray, instead of gray-green; veins less noticeably red. Bailey states that the petioles and leaves of *L. loddigesii* carry much more tomentum than *L. commersonii*. Personal observation of plants 18–25 years old seems to indicate that the degree of tomentum in all species increases with age and therefore is not dependable for identification.

L. VERSCHAFFELTII

Differs as follows from *L. commersonii:* the petioles and leaf veins are colored with a deep orange, instead of a purplish red. In one old tree at Fairchild Tropical Garden, the deep-yellow orange color on the petiole was still evident, though the plant was 18 years old. Balfour states that the white tomentum on the petioles and leaves of *L. verschaffeltii* is more dense than in either of the two other species. Native to the Mascarene Islands.

I. B. Balfour in *Flora of Mauritius and the Seychelles* describes the petioles of *L. commersonii* as "slightly tomentose," those of *L. loddigesii* as "tomentose," and those of *L. verschaffeltii* as "densely tomentose."

Since most characteristics described above are variable in each species, it is always hazardous to make positive identification. In judging leaf colors, only new leaves should be trusted.

Since the sexes are on separate trees, the possibility of hybrids should be considered.

Cultivation: Plants grow fairly rapidly compared to most palms and are reasonably hardy to cold. Johnston reports seeds germinate readily within 2 months. U.S.P.I. Garden reports that their seeds of *L. verschaffeltii* began germinating in 32 days.

Latania verschaffeltii, the *Latania* with the yellowish petioles.

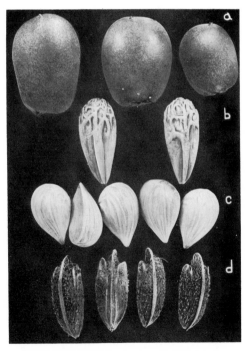

Fruits and seeds of three *Latanias* compared. A. and B. *L. loddigesii.* Three fruits above and two seeds underneath. C. Seeds of *L. commersonii.* D. Seeds of *L. verschaffeltii.* Reprinted from *Gentes Herbarum.*

Young tree in fruit of *Latania loddigesii* in Demerara, British Guiana, South America. Reprinted from *Gentes Herbarum.*

Old well-grown tree of *Latania commersonii* on Trinidad, West Indies. Photo reprinted from *Gentes Herbarum.*

LEOPOLDINIA

Wallace, in his *Palms of the Amazon*, describes and pictures three medium-sized *Leopoldinia* palms with such unusual characteristics that they are included here, although actual specimens are not available in the United States.

Leopoldinia is remarkable for the prominent and interwoven fibers that grow out of the leafbases and completely surround the trunk. The leafbases adhere for long periods so that at least the top half, if not all, of the trunk is so adorned.

These palms always grow near streams in a limited area of the Amazon Valley, within a few degrees of the equator. They never grow far from the water's edge or at an elevation of more than 1,000 feet.

The rough covering of the trunk is a comfortable setting for wild orchids with whose curious blooms they are often adorned.

L. PULCHRA
Latin, beautiful, fair, lovely

Common name: Jara palm. **Origin:** Brazil. **Sex:** Monoecious. **Trunk:** 10–15 ft high, 2 in. thick; covered with prominent, interwoven fibers which, with the old leafbases, adhere to the trunk for years. **Petiole:** 1 ft long; slender; base gives out much closely interwoven fiber. **Leaf:** Pinnate; 4 ft long; leaflets evenly placed and all at same angle. **Leaflets:** Slightly drooping; bright-green, very glossy. **Flowerstalk:** From lower leaves; large; much branched. **Fruit:** Globose; 1 in. diameter; pale greenish-yellow.

LEOPOLDINIA PULCHRA,
HT. 12 FT.

Three sketches reprinted from Wallace's *Palm Trees of the Amazon*. The fibers covering the trunk of *Leopoldinia piassaba* produce large ropes that will not sink in water. *Lepidocaryum tenue* is described by Wallace as being the smallest of all fan palms, with a trunk the size of a finger. Both genera are very rare and are seldom if ever seen in the United States.

OTHER SPECIES

L. major is very similar to *L. pulchra*, but its trunk grows to 30 ft and is 4 in. thick, even wider at the base. The leafbases are not as persistent, so that a greater proportion of the trunk is usually bare. It is often found with the lower part of the trunk actually under water. Native to Brazil.

L. piassaba has very large leaves and a thick trunk, which is usually short, though specimens have grown to 20 ft or more. The fibers coming down from the leafbases are very long, and hang down as much as 5 ft, completely obscuring the trunk and the leafbases, and giving the tree a most curious and remarkable appearance. Native to Brazil.

The filaments of *L. piassaba* are known as piassaba fiber and are an extensive article of commerce. It is said that large ropes or cables of this fiber are particularly favored for marine uses, because they will not sink in water.

LEPIDOCARYUM

Greek, *lepido*, scale, scaly, and *karyon*, nut

This palm is described by Wallace as a "rare and elegant species" and as being the smallest of all the fan palms.

The trunk is about the thickness of a finger and 6–8 ft high. Its small, glossy, palmate leaves are divided right to the stem into only 9–10 dark-green segments, the leaf resembling a small pinwheel. The petioles are proportionately long and are fastened to the trunk by much

LEOPOLDINIA PIASSABA
HT. 20 FT.

LEPIDOCARYUM TENUE
HT. 8 FT.

swollen and lengthened leafbases. The fruits are about the size of a walnut and are covered with handsome scales. Male flowers are found on one tree; female and/or hermaphrodite flowers on another.

This plant must be shade loving, as it grows "in the gloomiest depths of the virgin forest" (Wallace).

LEPIDORRHACHIS MOOREANUM

Bailey considered this palm to be *Clinostigma mooreanum*, under which name it is described in this book. Burret considers it to be *Lepidorrhachis mooreanum*.

The plant is pinnate-leafed and native to Lord Howe Island.

LEPTOPHOENIX

Twelve species of pinnate leafed palms from New Guinea, described by Pichi-Sermolli under the above name, but considered by Burret and Potztal to be part of the genus *Nengella*.

LIBERBAILEYA

A genus of palmate palms, native to Malaya, and little known to cultivation. (Not illustrated.)

The beautiful, undivided, ruffly leaves of *Licuala grandis*, as seen on a specimen in the U.S.P.I. Garden at Coconut Grove, Florida.

Licuala grandis growing in Bogor Botanic Gardens, Java. Photo by T. Satake.

LICUALA*
Molucca name

A genus of more than 70 species of small-growing fan palms. They show a great variety of appearances, all of which are exotic and very suggestive of the tropical equatorial areas to which they are native.

The species best known in the United States is probably *L. grandis*, a palm with a slender, smallish trunk and very unusual round, palmate leaves that remain almost entire, the segments being divided only for about an inch at the very tip.

Most other licualas are clustering palms with multiple trunks, whose leaves produce an exotic appearance in an almost opposite fashion. Deeply divided back to the stem into unequal, square-ended segments of various shapes and sizes, they look like small eccentric windmills.

L. GRANDIS

Common name: None. **Origin:** New Britain Island, north of Australia. **Sex:** Hermaphrodite. **Trunk:** To 6 ft in height, 3 in. diameter or less. **Petiole:** 3 ft long, slender; spines near base and halfway to leaf. **Leaf:** Palmate; 3 by 2 ft; circular appearance, but really more wide than long; not divided, unless split by wind, but notched at tips. M. and R. Foster, in their book, *Brazil*, speak of the leaves as resembling knife-pleated skirts or corrugated roofs. **Segments:** Bright, dark, glossy green; split at ends; very pleated. **Flowerstalk:** Among leaves; same length as leaves. **Flowers:** 1/3 in. long. **Fruit:** Size of pea; glossy crimson.

L. SPINOSA

Common name: None. **Origin:** Malaya. **Sex:** Hermaphrodite. **Trunk:** Multiple; 10–15 ft in height; slender; 2–4 in. thick. **Petiole:** Very long, 4–5 ft; small, brownish spines on edges. **Leaf:** Palmate; nearly orbicular; leaflets parted almost to center, with wide spaces in between. **Segments:** Widest one, 4½–5 in. wide at end, 12 in. long; square and toothed

A large clump of *Licuala spinosa* in Bogor Botanic Gardens, Java. Photo by T. Satake.

Close-up of square-ended leaflets of *Licuala spinosa*. Photo by T. Satake.

at apex; very pleated. About 18 to each leaf. **Flowerstalk:** Among leaves, but much longer, and erect; hence, stands out well beyond leaves. **Flowers:** ⅕ in. long. **Fruit:** Obovoid, ¼ in. long; red, in attractive clusters. **Seed:** Smooth.

OTHER SPECIES

L. peltata (Bengal) is very like *L. spinosa*. Petiole 6–7 ft long, and flowerstalks project several feet beyond the leaves.

Blatter also describes *L. elegans* as similar to *L. peltata* and *L. spinosa*, but leaf segments are cut off more squarely at ends, though still toothed.

Ridley describes 18 species in his *Flora of the Malay Peninsula*.

Cultivation: *L. grandis* is not easy to grow successfully. It seems to prefer shade and it certainly likes warmth. The other species are a little more hardy.

De Leon reports germinating began in seeds of *L. horrida* within 31 days. U.S.P.I. Garden reports seeds of *L. amplifrons* began germinating in 70 days. *L. grandis* seeds did not begin germinating until 122 days had passed.

LINOSPADIX
Greek, linear spadix

A group of small, unarmed, monoecious, pinnate leafed palms from New Guinea.

The best known species is *L. monostachya*, which was at one time quite widely known as *Bacularia monostachya*, under which name it was described by Bailey. In this book, it is described under *Bacularia*. *L. minor* is also described under *Bacularia minor* though it is correctly *Linospadix minor*. All *Bacularia* species are correctly *Linospadix*.

An old specimen of *Livistona australis* (center) in California. Two heavy-trunked specimens in background are *Jubaea spectabilis*. Photo courtesy of Huntington Botanical Gardens.

LIVISTONA*†

Named for Patrick Murray, Baron of Livistone, founder of the Botanic Garden at Edinburgh, Scotland

A group of palms native to Asia, Malaya, New Guinea, and Australia, and widely cultivated in the United States. The species from the less tropical Australian and central China climates are hardy and are much seen in private gardens, and even in highway plantings, particularly in southern California.

The species show great variety, but almost all have spiny, slender, fairly long petioles, with toothed edges, circular palmate leaves, and long-hanging, much-branched fruit clusters. There are often threads among the leaf segments.

The most hardy species of the group is *L. australis*, which Huntington Gardens has found to withstand temperatures as low as 20°.

L. AUSTRALIS

Common name: None. **Origin:** Australia. **Sex:** Monoecious. **Trunk:** To 60 ft or more in height; comparatively slender; covered with brown leafbases and untidy brown fiber until of considerable age. **Petiole:** 5–6 ft long, broad at base; toothed; extends as a rib several inches into leaf. **Leaf:** Costapalmate; 3–4 ft diameter; rib extends from petiole several inches into center of leaf; circular in outline; drooping at tips. **Segments:** Glossy green, with prominent yellow central nerve giving golden-green appearance; soft texture. **Flowerstalk:** Among leaves; at first covered by very woolly spathe, later, long hanging and much branched. **Fruit:** Spherical; ½–¾ in. diameter; reddish-brown.

The interesting trunk of *Livistona mariae*. Photo courtesy of Huntington Botanical Gardens.

L. CHINENSIS
(Synonym, *L. olivaeformis*)

Probably the most popular of all fan palms, as a tub plant for indoor use, *L. chinensis* is also widely grown as an outdoor plant in southern Florida and southern California. It eventually grows, very slowly, to a height of 30 ft or more, but it fruits when the trunk is only a few feet tall. *L. chinensis*, the most widely used of all the livistonas, can usually be recognized when mature by the fringe of drooping leaf tips surrounding the leaves, though this is not true of younger plants.

Common name: Chinese fan palm. **Origin:** Central China. **Sex:** Monoecious. **Trunk:** 20–30 ft in height, 8–10 in. thick; some leafbases adhering near top. **Petiole:** 6 ft long, 6 in. broad; triangular; network of fibers at base; edged with spiny teeth which are more prominent near base; these teeth tend to disappear with age. **Leaf:** Costapalmate (extra rib from petiole extends several inches into center of leaf); this is true only of mature plants; roundish, but more broad than long (4½ by 6 ft); leaflets divided less than half; tip of hastula protrudes outward from leaf about 1 in. **Segments:** Glossy, dark-green, with prominent yellow central nerve giving beautiful golden-green effect. Split for 8 in. at tip into 2 very slender, weak points, which are inclined to droop and form fringe around the leaf. **Flowerstalk:** Among leaves; long; yellowish. **Fruit:** Subglobose; ¾ in. long; dull blue-green, darkening with age; very attractive.

The drooping leaf tips that are so typical of *Livistona chinensis*, the most widely planted of the livistonas. Photo courtesy of Huntington Botanical Gardens.

Livistona decipiens growing in Huntington Botanical Gardens, San Marino, California. Photo courtesy of Huntington Botanical Gardens.

L. ROTUNDIFOLIA
Latin, round-leafed

A palm coming recently into well-deserved popularity in the trade. Young plants are particularly attractive because of their small, perfectly round leaves that look like little footstools. This attractive characteristic can best be retained by limiting plants to tub growth.

Planted outdoors in full sun, the leaves enlarge and lose some of their miniature charm. This can be somewhat retained by planting in shade.

Common name: None. **Origin:** Malaya. **Sex:** Monoecious. **Trunk:** To 50 ft in height, up to 7 in. diameter; slender; brown. **Petiole:** To 6 ft long; toothed, but teeth tend to disappear with age. **Leaf:** Palmate; almost perfectly round; segments grow in perfect circle, completely surrounding the hastula (tip of petiole); young leaves are small, but mature leaves have diameter up to 5 ft. Segments divided only $\frac{1}{3}$ distance to petiole, perhaps split more at maturity. **Segments:** Slightly notched at apex; numerous; green both sides, glossy. **Flower-stalk:** Among leaves; to 5 ft long; bright red. **Flowers:** Yellow. **Fruit:** Spherical; $\frac{3}{4}$ in. diameter; blackish-brown.

OTHER SPECIES

L. robinsoniana is a very attractive plant. Its leaves are like the leaves of *L. chinensis*, but the adhering leafbases and their attached fibers and spikes form a very unique, spiral, striped effect on the trunk. Native to the Philippine Islands.

L. rotundifolia var. *luzonensis* has a trunk with striped markings similar to *L. robinsoniana*, but not quite as marked. Native to the Philippine Islands.

The glossy "footstool" leaves of a young *Livistona rotundifolia*. These leaves maintain their small, roundish appearance longer when grown in shade.

Hertrich's *Palms and Cyclads* briefly describes *L. decipiens* (Australia) with slim trunk, leaves with slender leaflets that are very drooping, and *L. mariae* (Australia), similar to *L. australis*, but with more open crown of leaves; new leaves are reddish; more tender than most Australian species.

Hortus Second describes, among others, *L. humilis* (Australia) with 5–6-ft trunk, small leaves 3 ft diameter, deeply divided. Also, *L. cochinchinensis* (Malaya) with slender trunk to 40 ft high; fruit globose, about ½ in. diameter, blue.

Blatter describes *L. jenkinsiana* (Assam) and quotes Jenkins (for whom it was named) as saying "An indispensable accompaniment of every native gentleman's house, but in some parts, it is rare and the trees are then of great value." The leaves are in universal use for making the peculiar umbrellalike hats of the Assamese.

L. saribus, at Fairchild Tropical Garden, has been observed to have very beautiful bright-blue fruits. In his *World Grows Round My Door* (p. 172), Fairchild stated that this is the only palm he knew of whose fruits are a brilliant blue.

There are many other species of *Livistona* not described here.

Much confusion still exists as to correct species names in *Livistona*. *L. altissima* is considered by *Hortus Second* to be *L. rotundifolia;* however, there are plants offered as *L. altissima* that definitely are neither. *L. hoogendorpii* is considered to be *L. cochinchinensis*. *L. olivaeformis* is considered to be *L. chinensis*. *L. subglobosa* is considered to be *L. chinensis* var. *subglobosa*.

Cultivation: *L. australis* is considered the most hardy, but *L. chinensis* proved to be surprisingly hardy in mid-Florida during the severe winter of 1957–1958. Young plants survived three long freezes in Daytona Beach without the slightest damage. Other *Livistona* species are not as hardy as the two mentioned above.

All *Livistona* seeds germinate readily without any special care and within 6 weeks. The plants, unfortunately, grow very slowly.

U.S.P.I. Garden reports planting one batch of seeds of *L. cochinchinensis* which began germinating in 31 days.

Palm Avenue in Bogor Botanical Gardens lined with trees of *Livistona rotundifolia*. Younger trees on the left; older ones on the right. Photo courtesy A. Dilmy, Bogor Botanic Gardens, Java.

Close-up of trunk of *Livistona robinsoniana* showing interesting pattern formed by fibers on trunk.

A rare species growing in Fairchild Tropical Garden, *Livistona rotundifolia* var. *luzonensis*. Note the very prominently ringed trunk.

LODOICEA
Said to be altered form of Laodice, daughter of Priam

The strange *coco de mer* (sea palm) has many curious characteristics and an even more interesting history.

Its remarkable seed is the largest and heaviest in the whole vegetable kingdom. It looks like a large two-lobed coconut and is commonly called *double coconut*, although the *Lodoicea* palm is not even a distant relative of the genus *Cocos*.

As early as the year 1500, voyagers heard tales of these strange nuts that had been found washed up on the shores of the Indian Ocean. Since no such plant was known, tales persisted that this fruit mysteriously grew on submerged trees. It was said that the trees were clearly visible on calm days, but that they astonishingly disappeared when sailors dived for them.

Their mythical origin, and perhaps their rarity, led to great medicinal values being attributed to the albumen, or white meat, within the nuts. They were particularly credited with being a positive antidote for every form of poison. Princes and potentates of the times, much inclined to the poisoning of their enemies, lived in daily dread of being themselves poisoned. It is not surprising that they were willing to offer large sums for these mysterious objects which they firmly believed could purify any fluid, no matter what poison it contained. Rudolph II of Germany is said to have offered 4,000 florins (about $2,000) for one nut.

A forest of *Lodoicea* palms on Praslin, one of the Seychelles Islands. Reprinted from *Gentes Herbarum*.

A. M. Rothon, in his *Voyage to Madagascar*, states that as late as 1759 it was not uncommon to see these nuts sold for £400 sterling ($2,000).

In 1743 when the Seychelles Islands were first explored, the true source of these nuts was at last discovered. *Coco de mer* trees were found growing in thousands, first on Praslin Island, and then on its near neighbors, Curieuse and Round Hill. Thousands of these nuts, over the years, have been widely scattered by the currents of the Indian Ocean. But for some reason, not one of these floating visitors has been known to germinate on a foreign shore. No lodoicea has ever been found growing wild anywhere in the world except the Seychelles Islands. (The coconut, distributed in a like manner by the ocean, has germinated and become native in so many countries that its true origin is obscure.)

Possession of a lodoicea is rare and, except in its native isles, not many exist, even in the most tropical areas. The particular need of this tree, that can be supplied only in the Seychelles Islands, is as yet unknown. Thousands have been planted, but not even hundreds have survived. After many unsuccessful attempts, a female tree was finally brought to fruit in Kew Gardens, under glass, in 1854. The germinating nuts were sold at public sale, bringing over £10 each ($50)—a tidy sum in 1854; but all of these subsequently died.

The germination and growth of *Lodoicea* are unreasonably slow. The fruit stays on the tree 6 years or more to reach maturity; then, falling to the ground, takes 6 months to a year to germinate. Nine months after germination, it gets its first leaf and, from then on, one new leaf about every 9 months. A tree rarely flowers until it is at least 30 years old.[1] One tree in Jamaica, which was nearly 50 years old, with leaves standing 20 ft high, had not yet developed any trunk. No one can tell how old some of the old specimens are, but it can be conservatively stated that no lodoicea attains its full growth in less than 100 years. A specimen

[1]Waby, in a Kew bulletin, reported that one 13-year-old specimen flowered in Georgetown Botanical Gardens in 1907.

A good crop of fruits of *Lodoicea*, some of them not developed. Photo courtesy of Thomas Man-Cham.

A vigorous young male tree of *Lodoicea* in Jamaica, West Indies. This tree is 39 years old. Note how far the petiole extends into the leaf, forming a midrib. Reprinted from *Gentes Herbarum*.

in Paradeniya Gardens in Ceylon grew for 40 years before showing any trunk, but thereafter grew 7 inches per year.

Another entirely unique characteristic is the large wooden "basin," or socket, in which the trunk grows (see **Trunk** below), which is so durable that it has been found entirely intact 60 years after the removal of an old trunk.

L. MALDIVICA

So many *Lodoicea* nuts were caught in the currents from the Maldive Islands, that Rumphius, supposing them to come from there, named the plant, *Cocos maldivica;* hence, its species name now honors an island where it does not grow.

Common name: *Coco de mer*, double coconut. **Origin:** Seychelles Islands. **Sex:** Dioecious. **Trunk:** Very straight and erect to 90 ft, 1 ft diameter. Base of trunk is bulbous and fits into a natural bowl, or socket, 18 in. deep and 30 in. diameter. Roots penetrate through holes in this socket into the ground, but without being fastened to the socket. This allows a slight play to the trunk when resisting winds. The socket is very hard and durable and has been found entire and perfect 60 years after removal of the tree. **Petiole:** 8–12 ft long; very strong, with rib extending into leaf. **Leaf:** Costapalmate, with rib extending from petiole into leaf, almost to end of leaf. 12–20 leaves on tree. Leaf, 12–18 ft long beyond petiole, 6–12 ft broad. Cut to 1/3 its depth. Full-sized leaves produced by trees at ages of 18–25 years; subsequently smaller. **Segments.** Glossy above, crosslined underneath; very stiff. **Flowerstalk:** From axils of lower leaves; 3–6 ft long; male, single, thick as man's arm. Female, branched, thick as a man's arm, braced by growing bracts to carry weight of fruit. Usually 4–5 fruits on one stalk, but possibly as many as 11 (which would weigh nearly 500 lb). **Fruit:** Very large. Takes one year to reach full size on tree, 5 more years to mature. Covered with rough husk, which turns black and dry at maturity. Tree fruits at 30 years (some say less), though it has

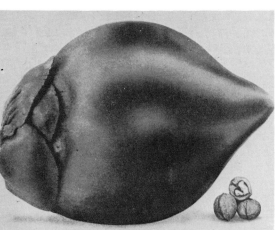

A crop of *Lodoicea* nuts in Demerara, British Guiana, borne near the ground on short, low trees. This is not usual on the Seychelles Islands where the plants are native and prosper. Reprinted from *Gentes Herbarum.*

Front view of *Lodoicea* fruit freshly received from the Seychelles Islands. The three walnuts are for comparison in size. This fruit weighed 30 pounds, was 18 inches long, 12 inches broad, and 9 inches thick. Reprinted from *Gentes Herbarum.*

Lodoicea fruit with shell removed from lower half. The shell is smooth on the outer surface, fibrous on the inside, and forms a covering about 1 inch thick. The seed revealed beneath this covering is the largest seed in the vegetable kingdom. Reprinted from *Gentes Herbarum.*

not yet developed any trunk. **Seed:** Called *double coconut*. Looks like a 2-lobed coconut. There have been pictures published of a 3-lobed seed; 4-lobed and 6-lobed seeds have been recorded. Reaches full size when fruit is 1 year old, at which time shell is lined with thick layer of soft, jellylike albumen and filled with water. At maturity (5 years later), the albumen is hard and solid and completely fills the nut, leaving no cavity.

Where grown: Very rare. Few specimens scattered at botanical gardens throughout the world. New York Botanical Garden has a small specimen in a tub. Private garden of Mrs. Jennings in Miami has two young specimens. Demerara, British Guiana, has fruiting specimens. No specimens at Fairchild Tropical Garden, Chapman Field, or Huntington Gardens.

LOPHOSPATHA

A seldom-cultivated genus of pinnate-leafed palms, native to the Island of Borneo. (Not illustrated.)

LOROMA

A genus founded by O. F. Cook for certain plants growing in California under the name of *Seaforthia elegans*. The name *Loroma* has not been generally accepted by botanists. Plants under this name are usually *Archontophoenix cunninghamiana*, in which case the flowers are lavender and the leaflets green on both sides; or they are *Archontophoenix alexandrae*, in which case the flowers are white and the leaflets are white on the underside.

Those plants not renamed *Loroma* by Cook were still called *Seaforthia elegans*, which has now become *Ptychosperma elegans*.

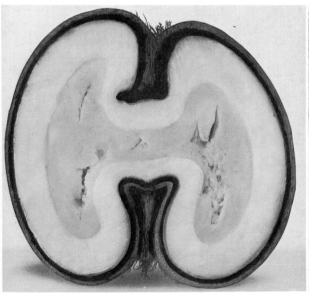

Cross section of the nut. This was a fresh nut from the Seychelles with white flesh, the outer part of which was more dense and more creamy. Reprinted from *Gentes Herbarum*.

Nuts of *Lodoicea* taken up after sprouts have formed and placed bottom up on a *Lodoicea* leaf. Note variation in shape and size of nuts. Reprinted from *Gentes Herbarum*.

LOUVELIA

A genus of three species of pinnate-leafed palms, native to Madagascar and marked by their stout and usually shortish trunks. (Not illustrated.)

LOXOCOCCUS
Greek, *loxos*, oblique, and *cocco*, grain, seed

A one-species genus from Ceylon, where it grows on rocky cliffs, in moist regions at 1,000–5,000-ft elevation. Closely allied to *Ptychosperma*, it is rare in cultivation in the United States. The showy, red fruits are said to be chewed in the same way as the betel nut, *Areca cathecu*.

L. RUPICOLA
Latin, cliff-dwelling

Common name: None. **Origin:** Ceylon (1000–5,000-ft elevation). **Sex:** Monoecious. **Trunk:** Clustered, or single; 30–40 ft in height, 4–5 in. diameter; enlarged at base; topped by small crownshaft. **Petiole:** 1–1½ ft long. **Leaf:** Pinnate; about 10 on tree; each leaf 6–8 ft long, 3–4 ft wide; 12–20 pairs of leaflets. **Leaflets:** Cut off at ends; terminal pair confluent;

Young specimen of *Loxococcus rupicola* in the Botanical Garden at Peradeniya. Reprinted from Blatter's *Palms of British India and Ceylon*.

Fruiting head or crown of *Manicaria saccifera*. It is called the sack-bearing or monkey-cap palm because of the curious sacklike spathes that cover the flowerstalk and remain pendant among the leaves for years. Reprinted from *Gentes Herbarum*.

bright-green above, fuzzy, glaucous underneath. **Flowerstalk:** 12 in. long; below crown-shaft; coral red; branched. **Flowers:** Blood red. **Fruit:** ¾ in. diameter; smooth; blood red. **Seed:** Chewed like betel nut, or sometimes with it.

Cultivation: *Loxococcus* is not common in the United States. De Leon reports seeds of *L. rupicola*, planted with bottom heat, began germinating in 49 days.

LYTOCARYUM

A little-known genus of pinnate-leafed palms, native to Brazil. (Not illustrated.)

MACROPHLOGA

A Madagascar genus name. Burret considers it a valid monotypic genus whose one species, *M. decipiens*, has pinnate leaves. Jumelle, in *Flore de Madagascar*, does not consider *Macrophloga* a valid genus name.

MALORTIEA
(See *Reinhardtia*)

A genus concerning which some controversy exists. In *Gentes Herbarum*, vol. 8, pages 541–576, Moore joins all *Malortiea* species with *Reinhardtia*, eliminating the genus *Malortiea*. He does, however, break the genus *Reinhardtia* into the subgenus *Reinhardtia* and the subgenus *Malortiea*. Within the subgenus *Malortiea* he includes *R. gracilis*, *R. koschnyana* and *R. simplex*, all of which were formerly known as species of *Malortiea*. While he describes other differences, it is interesting to note that all species within the subgenus *Malortiea* have seeds with homogenous albumen while those in the subgenus *Reinhardtia* have seeds with deeply ruminate albumen.

Burret still lists *Malortiea* and *Reinhardtia* as entirely separate, valid genera.

MANICARIA
Latin, *manica*, sleeve, because of the sleeve-shaped spathe

A striking palm with immense, simple, undivided leaves and exposed roots. It is called the *sack-bearing palm*, because of the curious pouchlike spathes that cover the flowerstalk and remain pendant among the leaves for years. These spathes are 2½–3½ ft long, of fine, closely woven texture, and are used by the natives to make soft brown caps without seams or joinings. It is also called the monkey-cap palm, as explained later.

Manicarias grow in dense stands, forming forests, made weird by the old dead leaves that hang down from the easily broken soft petioles.

The flowers are large and fragrant. The fruits are curious hard objects, covered with unique, rough, small protrusions and, when single, are about 1¾ in. in diameter. They may be two-seeded or three-seeded and thus be joined into two or three lobes. They can stay afloat for long periods of time. Nuts of *M. saccifera* (from Brazil) have been picked up on the beaches at Miami Beach, Florida, and Cameron, Louisiana.

The leaves are the largest, entire leaf among all palms and are much used for primitive roofing. A well-made thatch roof of bussu, as it is called by the natives, is said to last as long as 12 years.

M. SACCIFERA
Latin, sack-bearing

Common name: Monkey-cap palm, because spathe, growing like a hood over fruit, resembles a monkey's cap. **Origin:** Tropical South America. **Trunk:** Erect, but sometimes leaning; to 30 ft in height, 1 ft diameter. Mass of roots often present above ground, but horizontal and not stilt roots. **Petiole:** To 4 ft long; deeply channeled; soft not woody; in old leaves, it often breaks in the middle, causing leaves to hang down to the ground. **Leaf:**

Manicaria saccifera. An example of how the wind will tear up the huge, ordinarily solid leaves. Photo by M. B. Foster.

Simple, entire, undivided, except by great age or wind. To 30 ft long, 6 ft broad. Largest entire leaf in palm family; broadly toothed around margins. **Leaflets:** No leaflets, but leaves have many very strong veins, or ribs, which, when used in a thatch roof, form little gutters to carry off the water. **Flowerstalk:** 2½–3 ft; covered, until ripe, with finely woven, soft brown spathe, which eventually bursts open but remains suspended among the lower leaves. **Flowers:** Very large for palms, and decidedly fragrant. **Fruit:** One-lobed, two-lobed, or three-lobed; closely covered with tubercles, or rough protrusions; very hard; floats down rivers for long distances. If single-lobed, spherical, 1¾ in. diameter. **Seed:** One, two, or three per fruit; smooth, not wrinkled.

M. PLUKENETII

A smaller plant; the trunk is erect and 15–18 ft in height. The leaves are pinnate, 3–6 ft long and about 20 in. wide. The spathe is like *M. saccifera*, but smaller (about 18 in. long).

Not grown in the United States at all, except possibly in test cases.

FIG. 27. BROWN CAP sold on the streets of Colon, spathe of *Manicaria saccifera* (×⅜).

A sketch reprinted from *Gentes Herbarum.*

Fruits or nuts of *Manicaria saccifera*. A one-lobed, two-lobed and three-lobed fruit. These nuts can float for long distances. Nuts have been found on Miami Beach, Florida, having drifted from the Amazon area of South America. Reprinted from *Gentes Herbarum.*

MASCARENA*
Named after the Mascarene Islands
(Formerly included in *Hyophorbe*)

A genus, consisting of 3 species; separated from the genus *Hyophorbe*, and named after the Mascarene Archipelago, to which it is native.

Two of the species are much cultivated in southern Florida: *M. verschaffeltii*, (formerly *Hyophorbe verschaffeltii*) and *M. lagenicaulis* (formerly *H. amaricaulis*). Since plants of the two species are sometimes confused, a few of the identifying differences are listed below:

M. verschaffeltii (Spindle palm)	*M. lagenicaulis* (Bottle palm)
Trunk: Diameter is smallest at base and then gradually increases in bulging fashion, until it reaches its widest diameter at crownshaft. 20–30 ft in height, from ground to crownshaft. Shape of trunk triangular in young plants.	Bulging at bottom and irregularly maintains about the same thickness until the middle; then, like a bottleneck, gradually diminishes in thickness until it reaches crownshaft, at which point it again enlarges a trifle. Usually short, 5 ft from ground to crownshaft (perhaps taller in old species).

Flowering specimen of the spindle palm, *Mascarena verschaffeltii*. Note bulge at top of trunk and at bottom of crownshaft. Some flower clusters are open and some are still covered by their spathes. Reprinted from *Gentes Herbarum*.

Petiole: Only 3 in. long; carries a definite yellow stripe on underside; arched and recurved, but not twisted laterally.

Leaflets: 20–30 in. long, 1 in. wide; central nerve prominent on top side, no other nerves of any prominence.

12–18 in. long; reddish, with no yellow stripe; arched and recurved, but also decidedly twisted laterally.

18 in. long, 1½–2 in. wide; central nerve and two side nerves prominent on underside.

M. VERSCHAFFELTII
(Formerly *Hyophorbe verschaffeltii*)

Common name: Spindle palm. **Origin:** Mascarene Islands. **Sex:** Monoecious. **Trunk:** 20–30 ft in height; smallest at ground, gradually and irregularly swelling out until reaching the crownshaft, which is heavy and thick. Lightly ringed, width varying 8–15 in. diameter. **Petiole:** Very short, 3 in. to first leaflet. Definite narrow yellow stripe on underside. **Leaf:** Pinnate; 6–7 ft long (or less); 30–50 pairs of leaflets; only few leaves on tree. **Leaflets:** 12–18 in. long, 1 in. wide; one central nerve, prominent on upper side, few scales, or hairs on central nerve on underside. **Flowerstalk:** Below crownshaft; 27 in. long; branched; spathe 27 in. long, smooth-textured. **Flowers:** Tiny; decidedly fragrant. **Fruit:** ⅞ in. long, ⅝ in. thick; oblong, cylindrical; black, rough surface. **Seed:** Fastened to shell; ⅓ - ⅔ in. long, ¼ in. broad.

Characteristic tree of the bottle palm, *Mascarena lagenicaulis.* Trunk is fat and bulging until near the top. The leaves have decided lateral twist. Reprinted from *Gentes Herbarum.*

M. LAGENICAULIS
(Formerly *Hyophorbe amaricaulis*)

Common name: Bottle palm. **Origin:** Mascarene Islands. **Sex:** Monoecious. **Trunk:** Usually short stature, 5–6 ft high in all mature specimens examined, possibly taller with great age; 18 in. diameter at bottom and at middle, then tapering rather suddenly, like a bottle-neck, to 7 in., enlarging slightly to 9 in. diameter at crownshaft. **Petiole:** 12–18 in. long; reddish when young; bears no yellow stripe; arching and recurving, but also twisted laterally. **Leaf:** Pinnate; 6–7 ft long; 30–50 pairs of leaflets; only few to tree; recurved and twisted laterally. **Leaflets:** 18 in. long, 1½–2 in. broad; stiffer than *M. verschaffeltii* and a little broader (nearer 2 in.); central nerve and 2 side nerves prominent on underside of leaflet. Few scales or hairs on ribs. **Flowerstalk:** 24 in. long; below crownshaft; spathe 24 in. long; smooth-textured. **Fruit:** 1¼ in. long, 1 in. wide; rough surface; irregular shape. **Seed:** Small and flat; spherical; ½ in. long.

M. REVAUGHANII

M. revaughanii, not cultivated in the United States, is similar to *M. lagenicaulis*. From a swollen 18-in. base, the trunk seems to become gradually, but irregularly, smaller and terminates in a very elongated neck. There are sometimes as few as four leaves on the entire tree.

Fruit-bearing tree, *Mascarena revaughanii*, in Mauritius. Its characteristics are the twisted, long, tapering neck, small crownshaft, and the small number of leaves. Reprinted from *Gentes Herbarum*.

Cultivation: Johnston reports that *Mascarena* seeds germinate well within 2 months and without special care. Plants are reasonably hardy, considering their tropical origin.

MASOALA

A one-species genus of pinnate-leafed palms from Madagascar. *M. madagascariensis* has a short trunk (up to 9 ft) with a thickness of 6–7 in. The leaves are 9–12 ft long. (Not illustated.)

A younger specimen of *Mascarena lagenicaulis* at Fairchild Tropical Garden, which shows clearly the characteristic lateral twist of the leaves.

MAURITIA*
Named after Maurice of Nassau, Prince of Orange

A genus native to the Amazon region, where in warm climates it often grows in marshes or in water-covered ground. In some areas, large forests of *M. flexuosa* grow in land too wet for underbrush. The sight of thousands of these smooth trunks rising 80 ft into the air, the view undisturbed by lower leaves or underbrush, is, according to Wallace, more suggestive of a columned temple than a forest. The fruit grows in large clusters, one cluster weighing well over 100 lbs. The leaves of this plant supply the thread the natives use to make their sleeping hammocks.

Among the other species, there is great variety. One has a hairy trunk and one grows only to 8–10 ft in height, slender and spiny. The petioles are always long and the fruit is always covered with characteristic geometric scales.

M. FLEXUOSA
Latin, crooked, pliable

Common name: None. **Origin:** Amazon area. **Sex:** Male flowers on one tree; female, and sometimes hermaphrodite, flowers on another. **Trunk:** To 80–100 ft in height; straight, smooth; 2 ft diameter; sometimes swollen near the middle or toward the top. **Petiole:** 10–12 ft long; base is 1 ft wide; very strong. **Leaf:** Palmate, 10–12 on a tree; rigid; large; cut almost to base; 9–10 ft diameter. **Segments:** Stiff; drooping only at tips. **Flowerstalk:** From among leaves; 4 ft long; much branched. **Fruit:** Spherical; size of small apple; longer than broad; covered with small overlapping scales, forming geometric pattern. **Seed:** Smooth.

Three ponderous trees of *Mauritia setigera*, 60 feet or more tall with heavy palmate leaves and loricate (scale-covered) fruits. Reprinted from *Gentes Herbarum*.

OTHER SPECIES

M. setigera is native to Panama and is quite similar to *M. flexuosa*. The fruit is more broad than long.

M. carana (Amazon) is 30–40 ft in height and 1 ft in diameter. The leafbases adhere, covering large areas of the trunk with long, hairy fibers which are attached to them.

M. pumila (Amazon) is a slender palm, about 8 ft in height, carrying only a few small, palmate leaves on long petioles. The trunk is partly covered with old leafbases and is spiny.

M. gracilis (Amazon) has a trunk 20–30 ft in height; grows close to water's edge; produces great quantities of ovoid fruit.

M. aculeata (Amazon) grows to a height of 40–50 ft.

Cultivation: U.S.P.I. Garden reports that seeds of *M. flexuosa* began germination in 56 days. De Leon reports planting one batch of seeds of *M. flexuosa* that did not begin germinating for 126 days. Mauritia palms are not easy to grow. They require a very warm climate and an abundance of water.

MAURITIELLA

A genus of palmate-leafed palms with spiny trunks, native to Brazil and Colombia. (Not illustrated.)

The loricate (covered with a coat of mail) fruit of *Mauritia setigera*. (At the top is a cut-open seed.) Reprinted from *Gentes Herbarum*.

MAXBURRETIA

A genus of palmate-leafed palms, named by Furtado for the great palm expert, Max Burret of Berlin, Germany; native to Malaya. (Not illustrated.)

MAXIMILIANA

Named after Maximilian Joseph, first king of Bavaria, 1756–1825

A genus distinguished by its long, erect, pinnate leaves. It is very similar to *Attalea*, *Scheelea*, and *Orbignya*, the only dependable differences being in the flowers. The leaves, described by Bailey as being 15 ft long, and by Blatter as "over 15 ft long," would be smaller than those of *Scheelea*, which are up to 30 ft long. However, the descriptions of all these genera are confused and unconvincing. Native to Trinidad and South America. Dahlgren lists nine species.

Cultivation: U.S.P.I. Garden reports seeds of *M. elegans* began germinating in 147 days.

MEDEMIA

Some confusion exists concerning this name. Bailey's *Cyclopedia* lists *Medemia nobilis* as a synonym for *Bismarckia nobilis*, native to Madagascar, the latter being considered the correct name. Jumelle, in his *Flore de Madagascar*, lists *Medemia nobilis* as correct and also states that there are two other species of *Medemia* native to tropical Africa which form the subspecies *Bismarckia*. Wright describes these two species as *Medemia argun* and *Medemia abiadensis*. Burret considers *Medemia* and *Bismarckia* as two separate genera.

METASOCRATEA

A genus of Colombian stilt-rooted palms with pinnate leaves. (Not illustrated.)

Looking up into the head of an old specimen of *Maximiliana caribaea* in Bogor Botanic Gardens, Java. Photo by T. Satake.

The large upright leaves of *Maximiliana caribaea* not yet in fruit. The trunks are covered with epiphytes. Reprinted from *Gentes Herbarum*.

METROXYLON
Greek, *metra*, heart of a tree, *xylon*, wood
(Evidently refers in some way to the large amount of pith)

Metroxylon was originally a large-fruited genus of pinnate palms, all species of which were monocarpic (fruit once and then die).

The genus *Coelococcus* was later joined with *Metroxylon*. All *Coelococcus* species, including *C. amicarum*, automatically became species of *Metroxylon*. All these species fruit normally and are not monocarpic. Hence, the genus *Metroxylon* is now one in which some species are monocarpic and others (formerly *Coelococcus*) are not monocarpic.

M. AMICARUM
(Formerly *Coelococcus amicarum*)

M. amicarum is known as the Caroline ivory nut palm. It is not to be confused with *Phytelephas macrocarpa*, the ivory-nut palm, although the hard albumen of the seeds of both palms supply vegetable ivory, which is used for buttons and other commercial products.

Common name: Caroline ivory-nut palm. **Origin:** Caroline Islands. **Sex:** Monoecious. **Trunk:** To 60 ft in height (some claim much higher), 12–15 in. thick; brown and corky with small, spiny, incipient roots; upper part covered with stubs of old flowerstalks. **Petiole:** 10 in. long, expanding below into sheath 2 ft long, which is marked with peculiar wartlike ridges which carry a few spines. **Leaf:** Pinnate; 15 ft long; 85 pairs leaflets. **Leaflets:** 1–2 in. wide, 2–3 ft long; irregularly set on rachis. **Flowerstalk:** New ones among leaves; those with mature fruit, below leaves; to 4 ft long; branched. **Fruit:** Ovoid; large, 3–4 in. long; covered with glossy scales. **Seed:** Spherical; filled with very hard, ivorylike solid albumen. One shipment of 100 seeds with shells removed received by Vero Beach Nursery weighed 126 lbs, averaging 1.26 lbs per seed after shells were removed.

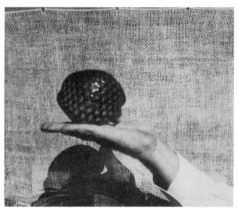

Close-up of the polished fruit of *Metroxylon amicarum*, the Caroline ivory-nut palm, dressed in its coat of mail. Photo by A. C. Langlois.

The Caroline ivory-nut palm, *Metroxylon amicarum*, showing the large fruit which yields vegetable ivory. Reprinted from *Gentes Herbarum*.

OTHER SPECIES

M. rumphii and *M. laeve* (synonym *M. sagus*) are known as the sago palms, because the sago of commerce is derived from the pith in their trunks. These plants furnish the staple food for millions of people in the Far East, from Siam to New Guinea. The trunk of one tree yields 600–800 lbs of sago, which is collected just before the tree begins to show its large terminal flowerstalk.

These two species are monocarpic. They fruit but once, and die. If the fruits were allowed to develop to maturity, which takes about 2 years, the tree would perish and the pith of the center would be found to be dried up.

M. RUMPHII

Common name: Sago palm. **Origin:** Malaya, New Guinea, Fiji Islands. **Sex:** Monoecious monocarpic. **Trunk:** 25–30 ft in height, 15 in. thick; suckering. **Petiole:** 4 ft long; deeply channeled; heavy; strong. **Leaf:** Pinnate; 20 ft or more long. **Leaflets:** 2–4 ft long, 1–3 in. broad. **Flowerstalk:** Above leaves (terminal); 12–15 ft long; covered with black spines. **Fruit:** Globular; 2 in. diameter; dull yellow; covered with glossy scales in attractive geometric pattern. **Seed:** Globose; albumen solid and bony.

M. sagus is very like *M. rumphii*, but does not have spines on the flowerstalk.

Metroxylons are not known to be grown in the United States, except for some few seedlings under test in southern Florida. There are no mature specimens in botanical gardens in Florida or California.

Cultivation: Johnston reports that seeds of *M. amicarum* are very large and slow to germinate. The seeds should be soaked in warm or hot water for one week before planting. Plants do not like cold. U.S.P.I. Garden records show one batch of seeds of *M. amicarum* began germinating in 94 days.

MICROCOELUM

A genus of pinnate palms, native to Brazil and little known to cultivation. (Not illustrated.)

MICRONOMA

A little-known genus included in Max Burret's list of valid genera. No further information available. (Not illustrated.)

MISCHOPHLOEUS

The beautiful palm pictured was planted and grown anonymously, but was later identified as probably a species of *Mischophloeus*. Its species name has not been definitely identified, but

Mischophloeus sp. believed now to be a species of the genus *Areca*. Photo by A. C. Langlois.

The spines form an unusual pattern on the trunk of *Myrialepis scortechinii*. Photo by A. C. Langlois.

the photograph sent in by Mr. and Mrs. Langlois shows such an unusual and highly tropical palm, that it is included here. It should perhaps more correctly appear under *Areca*.

Furtado, after studying *Mischophloeus*, decided that it should not be a separate genus but merely a subdivision of the genus *Areca*, with which H. E. Moore, Jr. of the Bailey Hortorium concurs. Burret does not recognize *Mischophloeus* as a valid genus.

MORENIA

H. E. Moore, Jr. feels that *Morenia* belongs in *Chamaedorea* and that it will soon be transferred to that genus. *M. latisecta* would then be *Chamaedorea latisecta;* and *M. corallina* would then be *Chamaedorea corallina*.

Burret considers *Morenia* to be a separate valid genus of smallish, pinnate-leafed palms, allied to *Chamaedorea* and *Geonoma*, native to the Andes of South America.

MYRIALEPIS SCORTECHINII

A genus of spiny, climbing, pinnate palms, related to *Plectocomiopsis*, from which it differs by having the minute scales on the fruit arranged without order. Not cultivated in the United States and not widely known.

It is included here because of the photograph sent in under that name by Mr. and Mrs. Langlois of Nassau. The attractive design of the spikes on the stem and the sparse arrangement of the few pinnate leaflets are unique. Native to Perak, Malaya.

NANNORRHOPS*

Greek, *nanos*, dwarf, and *rhops*, bush, shrub

A low bristly shrub with leaves springing from an underground much-branched trunk, 8–10 ft long.

In sheltered conditions, the trunk sometimes turns upright and has been known to reach a height of 20 ft.

It grows in the mountains of northern India and Afghanistan at elevations from 2500–5000 ft. In some of these cold arid areas, the plant is often covered with snow in the winter.

On a trunk that is about to flower, the last few leaves produced are progressively reduced in size and length, the final leaf being very small. Although most descriptions ignore the subject, it is probable that each trunk dies after fruiting, as does the talipot palm, *Corypha*, to which *Nannorrhops* is related.[1]

N. RITCHIEANA

Common name: None. **Origin:** Mountains of Afghanistan. **Sex:** Polygamous; male and hermaphrodite. **Trunk:** Usually subterranean and branching; 8–10 ft long; under ideal conditions, it sometimes turns upward and reaches a height of as much as 20 ft. One trunk at Fairchild Tropical Garden is already 5 ft above ground. **Petiole:** Short, 6–12 in. long; no spines, but margins have tiny teeth; covered with rust-colored wool. **Leaf:** Palmate; 2–4 ft long; 8–15 leaflets; cut more than halfway, but outer ends are stiff and protruding. **Segments:** Rigid, 12–15 in. long; split at apex; powdery grayish-green. **Flowerstalk:** From tip of trunk, but projecting beyond leaves. **Flowers:** Polygamous (male and hermaphrodite); creamy white. **Fruit:** Size of grape; minutely wrinkled. **Seed:** Very hard; with homogenous albumen and edible pulp.

[1]Loomis reports that in plants at Chapman Field, Florida, the stems that have flowered have several dead leaves at the top, but that the lower leaves are green. These stems are still alive two years after flowering. However, although they flowered, they have never borne fruit and perhaps this makes a difference.

The dwarf bush from the mountains of Afghanistan, growing at U.S.P.I. Garden in Florida, *Nannorrhops ritchieana.*

NEANTHE BELLA*
(See *Collinia elegans*)

NENGA
Malayan name

A few species of slender, pinnate, cluster-forming palms allied to *Pinanga*. They are native to Malaya and are distinguished by the purplish streaks that are found on the spathes and on the small crownshaft. They are not widely cultivated and are not well known in the United States.

N. WENDLANDIANA

Common name: None. **Origin:** Java. **Sex:** Monoecious. **Trunk:** Clustered; to 20 ft in height; only 1½–2 in. thick; with small crownshaft which is often tinged with purple. **Petiole:** Slender, short; tinged with purple near base. **Leaf:** Pinnate; 8–9 ft long. **Leaflets:** 2½ ft long, ½–1½ in. wide; leathery; bright green. **Flowerstalk:** Below crownshaft; short peduncle; slender; pendant branches. **Flowers:** White, fragrant. **Fruit:** Ellipsoidal; 1 in. long; smooth; purplish-claret; very handsome.

OTHER SPECIES

N. schefferiana is found in Bogor Botanical Gardens in Java. Ridley describes one additional species in Malaya, *N. macrocarpa*.

NENGELLA

A genus of seven pinnate-leafed species, all native to New Guinea and Malaya and little cultivated elsewhere. (Not illustrated.)

Close-up of crown of *Nenga schefferiana.* Notice the very small crownshaft. Photo by T. Satake.

Nenga schefferiana in Bogor Botanic Gardens, Java. These trunks are less than 2 inches in diameter at their thickest part. Photo by T. Satake.

NEODYPSIS*
Greek, *neo*, new, and *dypsis*, another genus name (which it little resembles)

A large genus of over 15 species, native to Madagascar and little known elsewhere.

Three beautiful specimens of *Neodypsis decaryi*, growing in Fairchild Tropical Garden, may possibly be the only palms of this rare genus in the United States, or even in the Western Hemisphere.

N. decaryi is distinguishable at a glance from all other *Neodypsis* species and all other palms by the three-sided appearance of the trunk, caused by the odd placement of the bulging leafbases in three vertical ranks. The sharply ascending leaves continue the general triangular appearance.

N. DECARYI
Named in honor of Decary, a French botanist and collector, who specialized in the plants of Madagascar

Common name: None. **Origin:** Madagascar. **Sex:** Monoecious. **Trunk:** Single; 9–18 ft in height, 12–16 in. thick. **Petiole:** The wide protruding petiole bases are attached to the

The surprising arrangement of the leaves of *Neodypsis decaryi*. They are in three distinct ranks. The three trees of this species at Fairchild Tropical Garden are believed to be the only ones in the United States. Photo by H. F. Loomis.

tree in three vertical rows, producing a unique triangular appearance. Bases are partly covered with stiff, brownish-black, woolly fuzz. Petiole without base 10 in. **Leaf:** Pinnate; 8 ft or more long; ascending gracefully; recurving at ends; 55–60 pairs of leaflets. **Leaflet:** Gray-green; regularly spaced; erect on rachis, lower ones prolonged into hanging ribbons, which originally surrounded and tied together the tips of all the new leaflets. **Flowerstalk:** From lower leaves; branched. **Fruit:** Ovoid; ½ in. long.

Neodypsis is very rare in the United States. It grows on the north coast of Madagascar, where droughts are frequent. Jumelle, in *Flore de Madagascar* describes 14 species of *Neodypsis*, but only *N. decaryi* produces the odd triangular effect described above.

NEONICHOLSONIA

Named in honor of the late George Nicholson, curator
at Kew, author of the *Dictionary of Gardening*

Two species of monoecious, pinnate-leafed palms, allied to *Calyptrogyne*, and native to Costa Rica.

They are trunkless palms, which are not widely cultivated, and not believed to have been introduced into the United States. (Not illustrated.)

NEOPHLOGA

A very large genus of pinnate-leafed palms, native to and fairly common in Madagascar and surprisingly little known or cultivated elsewhere. They are small, slender palms, seldom exceeding 15 ft in height. The graceful small leaflets are often of unusual and attractive shapes. Thirty species are fully described by Jumelle in *Flore de Madagascar*. (Not illustrated.)

Showing the odd three-sided appearance of the trunk on which the leaf bases are arranged in three definite vertical ranks. *Neodypsis decaryi.*

A close-up of the trunk from another angle. *Neodypsis decaryi.*

NEOVEITCHIA

A genus of pinnate-leafed palms, native to the Fiji Islands and not often cultivated elsewhere. (Not illustrated.)

NEPHROSPERMA

Greek, *nephros*, kidney, and *sperma*, seed
(referring to the shape of the seed)

A monotypic genus, native to the famous Seychelles Islands, where it is found in soil pockets on rocky cliffs, also in open places and by the sides of streams, at elevations not over 1,000 feet.

N. VAN HOUTTEANA

Common name: None. **Origin:** Seychelles Islands. **Sex:** Monoecious. **Trunk:** Single; 20–55 ft in height, 4–6 in. thick; enlarged at base; surmounted by a closely packed cylinder of glossy green leafbases, called a *crownshaft*. **Petiole:** 1 ft long; green; smooth; leafbase 1½–2 ft long; woven and sparsely spiny. **Leaf:** Pinnate; 5–7 ft long; arching and drooping. **Leaflets:** 3–3½ ft long, drooping; narrow ones alternating irregularly with wider ones; terminal pair confluent. **Flowerstalk:** From below crownshaft; 4–8 ft long; branched. **Fruit:** Globose; ½ in. long; orange-red. **Seed:** Wrinkled; tiny.

Cultivation: Johnston reports that the tiny seeds germinate readily within a few weeks. Plants are very tender to cold.

Young specimen of *Nephrosperma van Houtteana*, Victoria Gardens, Bombay. Reprinted from Blatter's *Palms of British India and Ceylon*.

The Australian plume palm, *Normanbya normanbyi*. The leaflets are in clusters united at the base. Photo by A. C. Langlois.

Nypa fruticans, the palm that seems to thrive only in brackish water. One stand in the Philippine Islands covers 20,000 acres. Photo by H. F. Loomis.

NORMANBYA*
Named for the Marquis of Normanby

A monotypic genus, notable for the feathery, plumed appearance of the pinnate leaves. The clustered leaflets are united at the base, as if one leaflet were split into several, each tip being square-ended and jagged. The trunk is dark-colored and very hard.

N. NORMANBYI

Common name: Black palm. **Origin:** Queensland, Australia, in rain forests. **Sex:** Monoecious. **Trunk:** To 60 ft tall; slender; slightly enlarged at base; wood is very hard and dark, almost black, marked with small red specks; trunk surmounted by crownshaft. **Petiole:** Short, or none. **Leaf:** Pinnate; 6–8 ft long; leaflets arranged in groups of two or more; attached at the base, but divided and spreading from the base outward. **Leaflets:** 18 in. long; cut off and jagged at apex; dark-green, whitish beneath. **Flowerstalk:** Below crownshaft; much branched. **Fruit:** 1½ in. long; pear-shaped; color of peach; fleshy. **Seed:** Broadly ovoid; ¾ in. diameter; roughly ridged.

Cultivation: Johnston reports seeds hard to secure and germination difficult. Fairchild lists their specimen as hardy at F.T.G.

NYPA*
Native name in Molucca; spelled *Nipa* by some authorities

A one-species genus of low, shrubby palm, that thrives only with its base at least partially submerged in brackish water. Hence, it grows only in tidal lands near the sea.

Spreading by means of a thick prostrate branching, subterranean rootstock, it fills huge areas in the Philippines, Burma, northern Australia, and Ceylon. One *Nypa* marsh in the Philippines covers 20,000 acres.

The odd fruits are the size of a man's head and are composed of many rough carpels, the larger ones each containing an egg-sized seed filled with a hard, white albumen.

Large quantities of sweet sirup can be extracted from the trunk if the flowerstalks are cut off at the proper time. One acre of *Nypa* will yield 3,200 gallons of this inexpensive source of sugar, vinegar, and, particularly, alcohol. In 1919, 2¼ million gallons of alcohol were produced from *Nypa* juice.

Nypa could be used in the United States and elsewhere to fill salt-marsh areas in which most plants will not grow. The bright-yellow, male flowers are an impressive sight during the few days the plant is in flower. Although quite different from each other, *Nypa* and *Phytelephas*, because of their inflorescence and fruit, seem to stand almost as separate divisions of the palms. Blatter felt that they exhibited affinities to *Pandanus*.

N. FRUTICANS
Latin, bushy

Common name: Nypa palm. **Origin:** Philippines, India, and Malaya. **Sex:** Monoecious. **Trunk:** Prostrate, usually under water; branching; actually just rootstock about 1½ in. diameter, but sometimes more. **Petiole:** 4–5 ft long, very stout; from end of rootstock. **Leaf:** Pinnate; 10–30 ft long; erect and recurved. **Leaflets:** 3–4 ft long; rigid; shiny bright green, powdery white beneath. **Flowerstalk:** Direct from rootstock; 4–7 ft long; covered with many papery spathes. Male flowers on long, slender, brown stem, terminating in a catkin, covered with bright-yellow flowers; very showy. **Fruit:** 12 in. diameter; spherical; actually a closely packed clump of carpels, each about 3–4 in. long. **Seed:** Hard; white; edible; size and shape of a small hen's egg.

Bailey's *Cyclopedia of Horticulture* states that *Nypa* grows successfully in brackish water in southern Florida, although often destroyed by land crabs.

Fairchild Tropical Garden has one clump that has never flowered. Chapman Field has one that has flowered but never fruited. A private garden in Miami has one planting that has both flowered and fruited.

Nypa fruticans in flower in Bogor Botanic Gardens, Java. Photo by T. Satake.

The odd fruit of *Nypa fruticans* with its many, closely packed carpels. A sweet sirup can be extracted from its flowerstalks. One acre of *Nypa* plants will yield 3,200 gallons of this inexpensive source of sugar and alcohol.

OENOCARPUS

Greek, *oinē*, vine, and *karpus*, fruit

A few species of pinnate South American palms, seldom encountered in the United States, but numerous in the Amazon regions of tropical South America and in Panama. The fruits of some species yield a beverage.

The tall, slender trunks are very smooth, whether single or clustered, and have widely spaced rings which much resemble bamboo.

Plants of this genus grow in dry, and rather elevated forest land.

O. PANAMANUS

Common name: None. **Origin:** Panama. **Sex:** Monoecious. **Trunk:** To 60 ft in height, 5 in. diameter; clustering; ringed and jointed, resembling bamboo; with crownshaft; dark-green. **Petiole:** 2–3 ft or longer; slender. **Leaf:** Pinnate; 6 ft long; 60 pairs well-spaced narrow leaflets. **Leaflets:** 30 in. long, ½–1½ in. wide; split at apex. **Flowerstalk:** Below crownshaft; 9 in. long; branched and hanging. **Flowers:** Numerous; tiny. **Fruit:** Ovoid; 1

Colony of *Oenocarpus panamanus*. The trunks are smooth and banded and somewhat resemble bamboo. Reprinted from *Gentes Herbarum*.

in. long, ¾ in. broad; short; black and hard; formed only on upper half of spadix branches. **Seed:** Single; enclosed in hairs.

OTHER SPECIES

Wallace describes *O. baccaba* and *O. minor* from the Amazon region. He also describes the following two Amazon species with unique characteristics:

O. batawa: Very old trees have smooth trunks, but younger trees, and those grown in forest shade, are covered with old leafbases. These leafbases carry long black spines of very singular character. They are from 1 to even 3 ft long and, projecting from the trunk, give it a generally porcupine appearance. These long spines were once much sought after by the Indians to make arrows for their blowguns.

O. distichus: Distinctive because the leaves are arranged nearly on one plane on both sides of the tree, giving the plant a peculiarly flat aspect, very unlike most palms.

Cultivation: De Leon reports that seeds germinate in approximately 2 months. Believed to be a strictly tropical plant but small plants have been recently introduced in southern Florida.

ONCOCALAMUS
Greek, *onkos*, tumor, swelling, and Latin, *calamus*, reed

A genus of West African climbing palms with pinnate leaves. (Not illustrated.)

Fruit cluster of *Oenocarpus panamanus*. Reprinted from *Gentes Herbarum*.

A characteristically tall specimen of the genus *Oncosperma filamentosum* growing in Bogor. Photo courtesy A. Dilmy, Bogor Botanic Gardens, Java.

ONCOSPERMA

Greek, *onkos*, tumor and *sperma*, seed

A genus of tall, monoecious, very spiny, pinnate-leafed palms from tropical Asia, little known in the United States. A few young plants have recently been introduced to southern Florida.

Blatter, in his *Palms of British India and Ceylon*, describes three species:

O. fasciculatum (Ceylon): Trunks in clusters, reaching 30–50 ft in height, with a diameter of 5–6 in., and covered with long, black spines. Leaves 8 ft long; pinnate. Leaflets 12–18 in. long, 1–1¾ in. broad, with drooping tips. The petioles are spiny, but the flowerstalks are not. Fruit like large, black currants.

O. filamentosum spelled *filamentosa* by Ridley (Malaya): Trunks multiple, 30–80 ft in height, 6 in. through, armed with long, black spines. Leaves 10–12 ft long, drooping. Leaflets 2 ft long and leathery. Petioles, spathes, and spadices all armed with spines. Fruit ¼ in. diameter. Grows in damp ground near tidal rivers.

O. horridum spelled *horrida* by Ridley (Malaya): Trunk single, to 40 ft, prominently ringed. Spaces between rings strongly armed with spines. Petiole very short. Leaves 14–16 ft long, 5 ft wide, spreading. Leaflets 2–3 ft long, dark-green, leathery. Petioles, spathes, and spadices all strongly armed with spines. Fruit spherical and large, up to 1 in. diameter, purplish-black.[1]

There are numerous other species which are not described here.

Cultivation: Johnston reports seeds are available to him but that they often lose viability before arriving. Plants are tender and not easy to raise in Florida. De Leon reports seeds of *O. fasciculatum* began germinating in 46 days; seeds of *O. tigillaria* in 44 days.

OOTHRINAX*

(See *Zombia*)

[1]Blatter and Brown describe *O. horridum* with a single trunk. Ridley, in his *Flora of the Malay Peninsula*, describes *O. horrida* as having multiple trunks. Our photograph from Bogor Gardens shows multiple trunks.

Close-up of spiny trunk of *Oncosperma fasciculatum*. Photo by T. Satake.

OPSIANDRA*

A one-species genus of pinnate-leafed palm from Guatemala, grown to some extent in southern Florida and distinguished by its strange manner of flowering.

Flowerstalks are produced from the lower trunk in its early life, but do not produce flowers until several other spikes appear above them. Then, the various flowerstalks begin flowering in order. It is not uncommon to see a tree with as many as 17 flowerstalks on the trunk at one time in various stages of development, ranging from young flowers to ripe-red, cherrylike fruits. The effect produced is curious and spectacular.

The fruits contain stinging crystals and are not edible.

O. MAYA

Common name: None. **Origin:** Guatemala. **Sex:** Monoecious. **Trunk:** To 60 ft in height, 6 in. diameter; topped by short crownshaft and often covered with flowerstalks.

Opsiandra maya in full flower in British Honduras. A thriving tree will sometimes carry as many as 19 flowerstalks at one time in varying stages of development.
Photo by A. C. Langlois.

Petiole: Channeled. **Leaf:** Pinnate; to 9 ft long. **Leaflets:** To 2 ft long; very numerous. **Flowerstalk:** 2–3 ft long; below the foliage, all along the trunk, even almost to bottom. **Fruit:** Globular; ¾ in. thick; cherry red.

Cultivation: Johnston reports seeds germinate easily and well within 2 months. Plants are tender to cold.

ORANIA

A genus of several species of tall, pinnate-leafed palms from Malaya and the Philippines, which somewhat resemble the coconut in general appearance. The large round fruits of about 1¾ in. diameter are very poisonous and are said to have been used by the natives in concocting their arrow poisons. This unpleasant fruit may account for oranias being so rare in cultivation in the United States.

Brown describes the following species in the Philippines: *O. palindan, O. paraguanensis, O. decipiens,* and *O. rubiginosa.*

Ridley describes only *O. macrocladus* in Malaya.

Cultivation: Johnston reports that *Orania* seeds are not easily acquired and plants are not easily raised. The seed throws out a shoot which goes straight down for some distance before producing leaves above ground.

De Leon reports seeds will germinate in 3 months with bottom heat.

Orania aruensis. The large fruits are very poisonous and are said to have been used for arrow poison. Photo taken in Bogor Botanic Gardens, Java, by T. Satake.

ORBIGNYA*

Named for A. D. d'Orbigny (1802–1857) a French naturalist whose palm collection
was studied by Martius

A South American genus whose many species are often confused with those of *Attalea*,
Maximiliana, and *Scheelea*.

It has the characteristic tall, erect leaves of these genera and differs only in details of the
flowers. Since the flowers are not always present for planters and students to observe, its
nomenclature is not dependable.

The most famous *Orbignya* is the cohune palm, *O. cohune*, but some confusion exists as to
whether this cohune palm is *O. cohune* or *Attalea cohune*. H. E. Moore Jr. considers it to be *Orbignya cohune*. *Orbignya* is omitted from *Hortus Second*. Blatter describes *Attalea cohune*. For
description in this book, see *Attalea cohune*.

Cultivation: Johnston reports that the large seeds are surprisingly easy to germinate, if
fresh. Plants seem to be reasonably cold tolerant. The only seed report is of one batch of *O.
phalerata* planted at the U.S.P.I. Garden which began germinating in 71 days.

OREODOXA

(See *Roystonea*)

A fine specimen of *Orbignya cohune* in Bogor
Botanic Gardens, Java. It is believed that most
plants introduced into the United States under
this name are really *Attalea cohune*. Photo by T.
Satake.

A typical fruit cluster of *Orbignya cohune*. Photo
by T. Satake.

PARAGULUBIA

A monotypic genus of pinnate-leafed palms, native to the Solomon Islands. (Not illustrated.)

PARAJUBAEA

A genus of pinnate-leafed palms, native to Brazil and little known elsewhere.

PARALINOSPADIX

A pinnate-leafed genus, closely related to *Calyptrocalyx*. It is native to New Guinea and not very widely known to cultivation. The plant illustrated is growing in Bogor Gardens, Java.

Parajubaea sp. growing in Northern Ecuador. Photo courtesy of Dr. Eva Potztal.

Paralinospadix petrickianus in Bogor Botanic Gardens, Java. Photo courtesy A. Dilmy, Bogor Botanic Gardens, Java.

PARASCHEELEA

A genus of pinnate-leafed palms, native to Colombia and tropical South America. It is notable for the huge boat-shaped spathe that surrounds its flowerstalk. Not widely known to cultivation.

PAUROTIS*†
(Formerly *Acoelorraphe*)

A cluster palm, native to the Florida Everglades, with an appearance as exotic and tropical as any species from equatorial regions.

Given plenty of room and plenty of water, it forms a dense clump, the leaves from younger trunks hiding most of the interesting older trunks. A few slender trunks are sometimes seen reaching out above the clump. Each trunk is wrapped in an intricate attractive network of closely woven fibers.

Paurotis wrightii thrives in low, damp soil. Planted on higher ground, it will survive, but its growth is very slow.

P. WRIGHTII

Common name: None. **Origin:** Southern Florida, West Indies, and Central America. **Sex:** Monoecious. **Trunk:** Several to many in clump; to 40 ft tall, usually much less; slender; wrapped in handsome matting, which is red-brown when new, fading to gray.

Parascheelea anchistropetala, with its huge spathe covering the flower, growing in Colombia. Photo courtesy of Dugand.

Petiole: Long; to 3 ft; slender; orange-colored saw teeth on edges. **Leaf:** Palmate; 2–3 ft or more in diameter; nearly round in outline; divided more than halfway. **Segments:** Pointed, stiff; split at apex; light green above, silvery underneath. **Flowerstalk:** From among leaves; slender, long and branched; projecting beyond leaves. **Fruit:** Size of garden pea; handsome, orange, finally ripening to a shiny, jet black. **Seed:** Smooth, round, hard. **Oddities:** Young plants have simple, entire, pinnately veined leaves for several years before the palmate character leaves appear.

Cultivation: Johnston reports seeds germinate readily within 2 months. Plants are easy to raise and grow readily in moist low soil. Plants will survive in dry land but grow slowly there. Huntington Gardens reports receiving three young plants in 1928 from the U.S.P.I. Gardens labeled "*Paurotis* sp., grown from seed received from Georgetown British Guiana." These plants 12 years later had not grown perceptibly—perhaps an example of the inability of *Paurotis* to grow where it is dry.

A large clump of *Paurotis wrightii* in Palm Beach, Florida.

PELAGODOXA

A very unusual palm that is rare not only in cultivation but also in its native habitat: three small islands in the Marquesas, 700 miles north of Tahiti.

Its graceful, 6-ft leaves are not divided except for a deeply toothed margin. They are pinnately veined and unless protected from the wind tend to tear into frayed segments that resemble pinnate leaflets.

The most beautiful specimens found were in complete shade and in very humid atmosphere, such as is found near rivers and waterfalls.

It is so delightful a palm that it would be well worth any special treatment required to grow it in the United States.

Its odd, bumpy, round fruit and simple, entire leaf suggest a possible relationship with the genus *Manicaria*.

Photograph showing the big, simple, undivided, pinnately veined leaves of *Pelagodoxa henryana*. The older lower leaf is showing signs of being divided into segments by the wind. Photographed at Summit Garden in Panama.

A mature tree of *Pelagodoxa henryana* in Bogor Botanic Gardens, Java. Photo by T. Satake.

P. HENRYANA
Named for Charles Henry

This description is of specimens in Summit Gardens, Panama Canal Zone.
Common name: None. **Origin:** Three small islands in the Marquesas—Nukuhiva, Hivaoa, Tahuata. **Sex:** Monoecious. **Trunk:** To 24 ft in height; brown; 6–8 in. thick. **Petiole:** Short; stiff; yellowish, with white felt on underside. **Leaf:** Simple, with little indented margins, pinnately veined; 6 ft long, 3 ft wide; undivided, unless split by wind; green above, silvery underneath. **Leaflets:** None. **Flowerstalks:** Among leaves. **Flowers:** Yellow. **Fruit:** Spherical; 3–4 in. diameter; covered with large tubercles (rough projections) in a geometric pattern. **Seed:** Round; smooth.

P. macrocarpa has been described as another species but cannot be verified at this time.

PHLOGA

A two-species genus of pinnate-leafed palms related to *Neodypsis*. They are small palms with very slender trunks. *P. polystachya* has a trunk 6–10 ft high and about 1 in. in diameter. The trunk of *P. gracilis* grows up to 20 ft high but is still little more than 1 in. thick. Native to Madagascar. (Not illustrated.)

PHOENICOPHORIUM

L. H. Bailey and some other authorities preferred the name of *Stevensonia* for this plant. See *Stevensonia* for description. Max Burret considers *Phoenicophorium* to be the only correct name for this genus.

Looking up into the crown of a *Pelagodoxa henryana*. Note the large attractively covered fruit. Plant in Bogor Botanic Gardens, Java. Photo by T. Satake.

Young tree of *Pelagodoxa henryana* in Summit Garden in Panama, 1949. Photo by A. C. Langlois.

PHOENIX*†

Greek, *phoenix*, date palm. It is also possible that this ancient plant was named for the phoenix, the mythological bird of Egypt, or after Phoenicia, an ancient country on the coast of Syria, where date palms grow abundantly.

Native only to tropical Africa and Asia, the various species of the *Phoenix* genus are now cultivated throughout the tropical world.

The fruit has been an important part of the diet of Arabia and nearby areas from remotest antiquity. Its cultivation and uses are described in the murals of the ancient Assyrians. Date palms are believed to have been grown 8,000 years ago in Babylonia and to be the palms mentioned in the Bible in connection with Palm Sunday.

Planted for ornament, the luxurious spreading crowns and the curiously marked trunks, often covered with ferns, seem to transform the scene and to bring to it the exotic charm of the tropics.

Phoenix is easily recognized by two characteristics that are always present in the genus:

1. The lower few, basal leaflets of each leaf are long, green spines.

2. The leaflets are always folded into their stems in such a way that the edges turn upward, the inside of the pleat facing the sky. This is known botanically as *induplicate in vernation*, a condition that is rare in pinnate palms and is to be found only in the following genera: *Phoenix, Caryota, Arenga, Didymosperma,* and *Wallichia.*

It is difficult to identify the exact species of any *Phoenix*. The surest identifying characteristics are in the male flower and in the fruit. Since trees are unisexual, these two parts are not found on any one plant.

Except in areas where only one species occurs, or where special precautions are taken, cross-pollination is frequent and there will be more hybrids than thoroughbreds. There are several recognized species that are well established in cultivation in the United States and some of these are described in this volume.

P. CANARIENSIS

This native of the Canary Islands is probably the *Phoenix* species with the most markedly tropical appearance.

The heavy trunk, in younger specimens, is usually covered with old leafbases, forming a rough mass about 4 ft thick, which is often covered with attractive air plants and ferns.

Bailey says, "The only species easily recognized everywhere, and by everybody is *P. canariensis*, the gem of the genus."

Common name: Canary Island date palm. **Origin:** Canary Islands. **Sex:** Dioecious. **Trunk:** 50–60 ft in height; very stout; leafbases adhere for many years, forming a mass 4 ft in diameter. **Petiole:** Short; strongly ascending; spiny (see **Leaflet**). **Leaf:** Pinnate; forming dense crown of about 200 leaves; leaves 17–20 ft long, strongly ascending, but lower ones hanging with age; 150–200 pairs of leaflets; leaflets in several ranks, i.e., leaving the stem at various angles. **Leaflets:** Short and narrow; long-pointed; light-green; induplicate; straight, not drooping; spines at base of leafstalk gradually become longer and are followed by small leaflets which then become full-sized leaflets. **Flowerstalk:** Between the leaves; 6 ft long; much branched. **Fruit:** In heavy clusters; globose ovoid; 1 in. diameter; orange. **Seed:** Wrinkled.

Only *Phoenix* leaves have spikes instead of leaflets at their lower end.

A *Phoenix* leaf showing leaflets folded into their stems with the edges turned upward, a rarity in pinnate palms.

Phoenix canariensis in a garden in Florida.

P. DACTYLIFERA
Latin, finger-bearing

P. dactylifera, the true date palm, has a tall slender trunk, which is either covered with persistent leafbases or, in later years, with their scars, which form an easily recognized geometric pattern. The base is usually surrounded with a mass of suckers until the tree has reached a certain age, when it no longer produces suckers. The crown forms a rather sparse fan-shaped head, containing as few as 20 leaves and sometimes even less. It is the only *Phoenix* species which bears commercial dates.

The date is the staple food of millions in Arabia, Persia, Egypt, and nearby countries, where hundreds of varieties of all sizes and flavors are grown commercially. The best quality "soft dates" have a sugar content of over 60 per cent.

Phoenix dactylifera growing at Fairchild Tropical Garden. This species is the source of the commercial date. Suckers have been removed.

The date groves around the city of Marrakesh alone are said to contain well over 1 million plants. Dates are also grown commercially in California and Arizona.

P. dactylifera prefers warm dry zones in latitudes between 15° and 30°N, where it usually fruits every year. It is found in zones farther north, where it fruits indifferently, and in zones still farther north, where it grows well enough but without ever flowering or fruiting.

Common name: Date palm. **Origin:** West Asia and North Africa. **Sex:** Dioecious. [1] **Trunk:** To 100 ft or more; slender; suckering at base; covered for years with old leafbases; later covered with scars which form a recognizable pattern. **Petiole:** Long; slender; almost flat; gray. **Leaf:** Pinnate; to 20 ft long; upper ones ascending, lower ones down-curving, forming a rather sparse head of perhaps 20–40 leaves. **Leaflets:** 18 in. long or less; gray-green, glaucous; rigid; sharp-pointed; in several ranks, i.e., attached to rachis at various angles; leaflet induplicate. **Flowerstalk:** Between leaves; to 4 ft long; hanging with weight of fruit. **Flowers:** White and fragrant. **Fruit:** Oblong ovoid; 1–3 in. diameter; deep orange when ripe; edible, very sweet. There are many varieties.

[1] Bailey's *Manual of Cultivated Plants* states that "sometimes a tree is apparently bisexual."

Phoenix dactylifera, a specimen growing in California which clearly illustrates the suckering habit. The suckers have not been removed from this tree. Photo courtesy of Huntington Botanical Gardens.

Where grown: Prefers warm, dry climate of 15–20° latitude. The drier and hotter the climate, the better the fruit. Excessive humidity probably tempers the sun and causes fermentation in the fruit. The plant must have direct sun and will not grow in shade, even when young. It can survive a temperature of 20°F but requires a mean temperature well over 65°F in order to flower and fruit.

Propagation is best by suckers. The sucker of a female plant will be a female and bear about the same quality fruit as its parent. One male tree suffices to pollinate 100 female trees. Date palms will not produce abundant crops of fruit in soil in which the alkali content is more than ½ of 1 per cent.

P. dactylifera usually suckers at from 6–16 years of age; it flowers in about 8 years from seed and in about 5 years from suckers.

All the dates on one stalk do not ripen at the same time, but if the stalk is cut off the tree when first fruits are ripe, fruits will continue to ripen.

In very rare qualities, the dates are picked individually as they ripen.

P. RECLINATA
Latin, reclining, bent back
(Synonyms: *P. natalensis, P. senegalensis, P. spinosa*)

A very handsome African cluster palm, with slender, often inclined trunks and bright-green, recurved leaves. If all suckers are removed, the remaining single trunk will usually grow taller than otherwise.

Common name: Senegal date palm. **Origin:** Tropical Africa. **Sex:** Dioecious. **Trunk:** Multiple; to 25 ft tall, 4–7 in. thick; usually free of leafbases; suckering freely; trunk usually

A grove of commercial dates in Egypt. Suckers will continually be removed from these trees and planted elsewhere. The date is the staple food of millions in Arabia, Persia, and Egypt. Photo by T. Satake.

leaning at an angle. **Petiole:** Short. **Leaf:** Pinnate; to 20 ft long, narrow (2 ft); recurving (the ends curved downward); lower leaflets are long spines; leaflets in several ranks, each rank attached to rachis at a different angle. **Leaflets:** Narrow, short (1 ft); sharp, stiff points; young plants have white wool on under surface; old plants somewhat scaly underneath; lower leaflets much smaller and finally become long spines; induplicate. **Flowerstalk:** From leaf axils; 3 ft long; very branched; covered by boat-shaped spathes. **Fruit:** ¾ in. long; egg-shaped; astringent; brown or reddish. **Seed:** Ovoid; rounded at extremities.

P. PUSILLA
Latin, *pusilla*, very small
(Synonym, *P. farinifera*)

A shrubby, cluster palm with very short bulbous trunks entirely covered by persisting leafbases.

The short trunks are filled with a soft pith, which is said to yield a type of meal or flour, which is used by natives only in times of scarcity. The foliage is said to be so spiny that it is impossible to walk through clumps of it.

This plant is very incompletely understood and is seldom seen in the United States.

Common name: None. **Origin:** Southern India and Ceylon (near the sea). **Sex:** Dioecious. **Trunk:** Clustered; very short, usually 1 ft (at most 4 ft) tall; completely covered with leafbases; filled with a flour-yielding pith. **Petiole:** Short. **Leaf:** Pinnate; rigid; lower leaflets are spines; pale-green. **Leaflets:** Rigid; sharp-pointed; lower leaflets are spines; attached to rachis in four planes; induplicate; pale-green. **Flowerstalk:** Among leaves; 8–12 in. long. **Fruit:** ½ in. long; dull, purple-black.

The clustered trunks of *Phoenix reclinata*. Photo courtesy of the U.S. Agricultural Experimental Station at Gainesville, Florida.

P. RUPICOLA
Latin, cliff-dwelling

P. rupicola is the least bristly, and the most graceful of all the species of *Phoenix*.

Its single trunk, naked of leafbases, is slender and grows only to medium height.

The leaflets are of soft texture and lie flat and limp, being all attached to the rachis on the one plane.

The bright yellow fruits are a picturesque feature.

The true *P. rupicola* is quite rare, although many plants are offered for sale by that name.

Common name: Cliff date. **Origin:** India. **Sex:** Dioecious. **Trunk:** Solitary; to 25 ft tall, 6–10 in. diameter, naked of leafbases. **Petiole:** Short; spiny. **Leaf:** Pinnate; 10 ft long; flat appearance because leaflets are all on the horizontal plane; lower leaflets are replaced by long spines; glossy green. **Leaflets:** 18 in. long; soft-textured; bright-green; lower ones become spines; induplicate. **Flowerstalk:** Among leaves. **Fruit:** Oblong ovoid; ¾ in. long; shiny yellow.

The flowering head of *Phoenix rupicola*. Photo courtesy of Huntington Botanical Gardens.

P. ZEYLANICA
Latin, of Ceylon

A moderate-sized, very stern and forbidding-looking species indigenous to Ceylon.

The trunk is easily recognized by the closely packed leafbases which cover it. The leaves and leaflets are shorter than those of other species.

Although native to the moist low regions of Ceylon, it seems to thrive in southern California.

Common name: Ceylon date palm. **Origin:** Ceylon. **Sex:** Dioecious. **Trunk:** Single; to 20 ft; densely covered with many leafbases, packed closely together. **Petiole:** Short; spiny. **Leaf:** Pinnate; short; many leaflets in several ranks on rachis. **Leaflets:** 7–10 in. long; rigid; with sharp points; basal ones becoming long spines; induplicate; bright-green. **Flower-stalk:** Among leaves; 1 ft long or more; branched. **Fruit:** ½ by ¼ in.; obovoid oblong; ripens from red to violet-blue. Pulp is sweet and said to be eaten by some.

Close-up of the leaf of *Phoenix rupicola*, showing the leaflets in only two ranks, forming a flat leaf. Note that the pleats of the leaflets are facing skyward, whereas in most pinnate genera the pleats face downward.

Small specimen of *Phoenix rupicola* at Fairchild Tropical Garden. This is the only *Phoenix* with flat, limp leaves. Other *Phoenix* species have leaflets leaving the stems at several different angles.

P. ROEBELENII
(Synonym, *P. lourelei*)

A fine-leafed dwarf variety seldom growing to more than 6 ft.

The very slender soft leaflets produce a fragile but graceful effect.

The origin and present standing of this interesting palm (no doubt at one time a hybrid) is confused and requires further study.

Common name: Dwarf date palm. **Origin:** Possibly Cochin China. **Sex:** Dioecious. **Trunk:** Single or clustered; from 2–6 ft tall; covered near top with leafbases. **Petiole:** Slender; short. **Leaf:** Pinnate; 12–18 in. long; curving and drooping. **Leaflet:** 5–8 in. long; very narrow and numerous; replaced at base by slender, weak spines; dark-green, with some powdery white covering. **Flowerstalk:** Among leaves; a 12-in. stem ending in many branches. **Fruit:** Obloid; ½ in. long.

Blatter makes *P. roebelinii* a synonym for *P. humilis* var. *lourelei*.

The dwarf date palm, *Phoenix roebelenii*, growing at Fairchild Tropical Garden. The *P. roebelenii* trunks are rarely more than 6 feet high.

P. SYLVESTRIS
Latin, of woods or forests

An attractive large palm with a trunk almost as stocky as *P. canariensis*. It grows faster than *P. canariensis* and becomes a tall impressive tree within a fairly short time. The leaves are gray-green, sometimes almost bluish.

Date sugar, a valuable commercial product in India and in the East Indies, is obtained from its sap. The boiled-down sap is sold to sugar refiners for manufacture into various grades of sugar.

P. sylvestris is supposed by some to be the parent stock of all the species of *Phoenix*.

Common name: Wild date palm, silver date palm. **Origin:** India. **Sex:** Dioecious. **Trunk:** 30–50 ft in height; single; covered with leafbases; at advanced age, trunk is set on a mass of exposed rootlike structures several feet high. **Petiole:** Short; spiny. **Leaf:** Pinnate; 10–15 ft long, 2½ ft wide; very heavy crown of leaves; many leaflets attached to rachis in several different planes. **Leaflets:** 6–18 in. long; with sharp points; dark gray-green with whitish bloom; lower ones becoming smaller; finally becoming spines; folded into stem with edges turned upward (induplicate). **Flowerstalk:** 2–3 ft long; erect; covered with two leathery, boat-shaped spathes. **Flowers:** White; scented. **Fruit:** 1–1¼ in. long; olive-shaped; astringent; orange-yellow. **Seed:** ⅔ in. long; rounded at ends.

Phoenix sylvestris. A handsome, large *Phoenix* whose sap yields date sugar, a commerical product in India. The leaves are gray-green. Photo courtesy of Huntington Botanical Gardens.

P. HUMILIS
Latin, short stature

A medium-sized palm whose trunk is closely covered with leafbases arranged in a very definite spiral pattern.

A species whose origin is confused and whose present identification is always doubtful. **Common name:** None. **Origin:** India to Central China. **Sex:** Dioecious. **Trunk:** 6–12 ft in height; covered with spirally arranged leafbases, giving a checkered appearance. **Petiole:** Short; spiny. **Leaf:** Pinnate; 3–5 ft long; basal leaflets are spines. **Leaflets:** Stiff; in many ranks; rather short; lower ones transformed to spines; glaucous; green. **Flowerstalk:** Among leaves; 2 ft or more long. **Fruit:** Red, turning to blue-black; ½ in. long.

OTHER SPECIES

P. paludosa (Bengal) is a species somewhat similar to *P. reclinata*. The trunks are 8–20 ft in height, 5½ in. diameter. The plants form heavy, impenetrable, but elegant clumps. The pinnate leaves are 10–12 ft long, with light-green leaflets about 12 in. long, soft and pliable in texture. Not much cultivated in the United States, although there is a specimen at Huntington Gardens.

P. acaulis is a trunkless, spiny, bushlike species from North and Central Bengal, not believed to be cultivated in the United States.

P. natalensis = *P. reclinata*.

P. senegalensis = *P. reclinata*.

P. spinosa = *P. reclinata*.

P. lourelei = *P. roebelenii*.

Phoenix humilis growing in Bogor Botanic Gardens, Java. Photo courtesy A. Dilmy, Bogor Botanic Gardens, Java.

P. humilis var. *loureirii* = *P. roebelenii.*

P. ouseleyana = *P. humilis.*

P. farinifera = *P. pusilla.*

There are many other species of *Phoenix*, including hundreds of hybrids.

Cultivation: Most *Phoenix* species are very hardy for palms. *P. canariensis* is probably the most hardy, being found throughout California and Florida and on the coast of the Gulf of Mexico. *P. sylvestris* is almost, but not quite, as hardy. *P. roebelenii* is perhaps the least hardy. *P. sylvestris* grows more rapidly than the others. *P. canariensis* and *P. dactylifera* grow slowly. All can be grown outdoors in southern California as well as in southern and central Florida.

All *Phoenix* seeds germinate easily and rapidly, well within 2 months.

U.S.P.I. Garden records planting three batches of seed of *P. abyssinica*, one of which began germinating in 31 days; another in 34 days and another in 49 days. At the same establishment, seeds of *P. reclinata* began germinating in 42 days.

For further details on the cultivation of *P. dactylifera*, see **Where grown** under *P. dactylifera*, p.

PHOLIDOCARPUS

Greek, *pholido*, scale, and *karpos*, fruit, referring to the scaly coat of the fruit

These are palms of the Oriental tropics, little known in the United States. They are lofty palms with stout trunks, large palmate leaves, spiny petioles, and very large, scale-covered fruits. There are about 5 species, all from Malaya. Bailey says leaves resemble *Borassus*.

The characteristics mentioned below are from descriptions in Ridley's *Flora of the Malay Peninsula*.

Pholidocarpus mucronata growing in Bogor Botanic Gardens, Java. Photo courtesy A. Dilmy, Bogor Botanic Gardens, Java.

P. macrocarpus[1] (Greek, large fruited): Trunk about 50 ft tall; leaf palmate, very large, divided into 5 or 6 segments; petioles spiny; flowerstalk, 5 ft long, very thick, with many branches; fruit, ovoid, 6 in. long, 4 in. wide; brown; covered with attractive scales; containing 4 or 5 seeds.

P. kingianus[2]: Trunk 40–80 ft, 8–12 in. through, covered with leafbases and with a brown network of fibers; petiole, 6–7 ft long, 1 in. thick; green, with two yellow bands. Leafbase is swollen, black, and fibrous. Leaf, palmate, 3–5 ft long, cut to base into wide segments (3 in.); flowerstalk, to 6 ft long, orange-brown; fruit, dark-green, 2 in. diameter; covered with rough scales. Seed, 1-in. diameter; covered with scales. The plant illustrated is *P. mucronata*.

Where grown: Both species grow in low, swampy woods in Malaya. Not believed to be cultivated in the United States or to be widely known except in its native land.

PHOLIDOSTACHYS

A delicate, slender, pinnate-leafed palm native to Costa Rica and little-known elsewhere. It is not known to have been introduced in the United States.

P. PULCHRA
Latin, beautiful

The few characteristics mentioned below are taken from the descriptions found in Standley's *Flora of Costa Rica*.

Trunk, single, unarmed; 18–30 ft tall, 2 in. thick; leaves, pinnate; 6 ft long; leaflets 18 in. long, 1–2 in. wide; flowerstalks, pendant; between the leaves, 18 in. long.

[1]Ridley spells it *macrocarpa*.
[2]Ridley spells it *kingiana*.

Pholidostachys pulchra, a Malayan species. The tree has been cut in a forest and brought out to photograph. Photo by A. C. Langlois.

PHYSOKENTIA

A little-known monotypic genus of pinnate-leafed palms, native to New Guinea. (Not illustrated.)

PHYTELEPHAS

Greek, *phyton*, plant, and *elephas*, elephant, ivory, referring to the hard, white seeds
that can be worked like ivory

A curious genus of dioecious feather palms of tropical South America, which includes the ivory-nut palm (not to be confused with the Carolina ivory-nut palm (*Metroxylon amicarum*) which also produces vegetable ivory).

The trunk is always creeping, or leaning, pulled down partly by its own weight and partly by its aerial roots, so that while it may be as long as 20 ft over all, the erect portion is usually 6–7 ft or less above the ground.

Male trees have strange, unbranched flowerspikes that look like long, furry catkins.

Female trees bear a fruit as large as a man's head, composed of 6–7 berrylike parts, each containing a hard white seed. At first these seeds contain an albumen that is milky and edible; but at full maturity this becomes very hard and so much resembles the ivory obtained from elephants that it has frequently passed for such. This albumen is almost chemically pure cellulose and, as vegetable ivory, has been exported from South America since 1826, for use in the making of buttons and similar objects.

Phytelephas and *Nypa* are considered to differ from all other palms (and from each other) in their inflorescence, flowers, and fruit. Blatter seemed to feel that they exhibit affinities to *Pandanus*.

The male ivory-nut palm, *Phytelephas macrocarpa*, at the botanical gardens in Peradeniya, Ceylon. Note the unbranched fluffy flowerstalks, covered with their flowers. Photo reprinted from Blatter's *Palms of British India and Ceylon*.

P. MACROCARPA
Greek, large-fruited

Common name: Ivory-nut palm. **Origin:** Colombia, Ecuador. **Sex:** Dioecious. **Trunk:** Creeping or leaning with an erect portion seldom more than 6 ft above ground. Male trunks said to be usually higher and heavier than female. Furnished with aerial roots. **Petiole:** 1–2 ft long. **Leaf:** Pinnate; very erect; 12–20 in number; 18–20 ft long; 80 pairs of leaflets. **Leaflets:** 3 ft long, 2 in. wide; many-nerved; stiff. **Flowerstalk:** The male spadix is unbranched and forms a very strange, long, fluffy cylinder, crowded with tiny flowers; cylinders may be up to 10 in. diameter. The female spadix is also unbranched but is shorter than the male; it carries large white flowers in clusters, which ripen into a strange aggregation of fruits. **Fruit:** A large cluster of 6–7 drupes huddled together, each covered with hard woody protuberances and containing 6–9 seeds; the plant may carry 6–7 of these clusters at one time, each weighing about 25 lb. **Seed:** Size and shape of hen's egg; strong; hard; containing under several layers an albumen which resembles ivory.

Cultivation: Always found in damp locations in South America, but sometimes at more than 3,000 ft elevation. Not grown in the United States, except perhaps in a few collections.

De Leon reports seed begins germinating in 3–4 months. Young plants must have protection and shade.

The female ivory-nut palm, *Phytelephas macrocarpa*, in Ceylon. The albumen of the fruit is the so-called vegetable ivory. Reprinted from Blatter's *Palms of British India and Ceylon*.

PIGAFETTA
Named after Antonio Pigafetta, historian of Magellan's trip around the world

David Fairchild, in his *Garden Islands of the Great East*, speaks of *Pigafetta* as his favorite palm and shows several illustrations from the island of Celebes. He speaks of one palm as being "80 ft high and as straight as an arrow." If the nearby villagers were correct in saying the tree was only 20 years old, it must grow very rapidly for a palm. He also shows a photograph of a tree 15 years old that one might estimate to be 30 ft high, with perhaps 10 ft of trunk.

One specimen, actually examined by the author at Summit Gardens in Panama, was growing in close among other trees. The trunk was about 6–8 in. thick. It was a rich dark green, marked at wide intervals with light-gray rings and looked much like a very stout bamboo. Fairchild says that with time the lower half of the trunk becomes dark gray, but this specimen, which looked about 60 ft tall, seemed to have retained its green trunk throughout.

Pigafetta elata in Sibolangit, Sumatra. Photo courtesy of New Crops Research Branch, U.S. Department of Agriculture.

P. ELATA

Common name: None. **Origin:** Malaya. **Sex:** Polygamo-monoecious. **Trunk:** To 120 ft in height, with gray rings about every 7 in.; resembles a heavy bamboo shoot; very straight, wood very hard; rich, glossy, dark-green. **Petiole:** 3–4 ft long; thick, with long bristles that become spines with age; base covered with yellow spines. **Leaf:** Pinnate; to 20 ft long; somewhat arching; rachis covered with golden spines. **Leaflet:** Dark green. **Flowerstalk:** Branching; hanging from lower leaves. **Fruit:** Globose; 2 in. diameter; covered with overlapping scales; brown. **Seed:** Black.

OTHER SPECIES

Bailey mentions 5 species, but *P. elata* is the only one described. Hawkes mentions *P. filaris*, *P. filifera*, and *P. papuana*.

Cultivation: Seeds were sent by Fairchild to Coconut Grove, Florida, but they did not germinate. According to him, some seeds from Sumatra did germinate in Florida years ago, but he does not mention what became of them. If there are any plants in the United States, they are only in very rare collections.

Fairchild once called this his favorite palm. *Pigafetta elata* growing in Bogor Botanic Gardens, Java. Photo by T. Satake.

A close-up of the crown of *Pigafetta elata*. The trunk is straight as an arrow and is marked somewhat like bamboo. Photo by T. Satake.

Pigafetta is evidently one of the fastest growing palms. Fairchild, in *Exploring for Plants*, speaks particularly of one specimen in the Sibolangit Garden in Sumatra which was about 60 ft tall and said to be only 6½ years old, which seems incredible. It had grown to more than double the height of some royal palms that were planted at the same time.

PINANGA*

Malay, pinang, palm

A group of 60 or more Indo-Malayan palms of medium size and very tropical appearance. The slender trunks, single or multiple, are sometimes as little as ¼ in. thick, and ringed and jointed like bamboo. The leaflets are always unusual and of eccentric and varied shapes, generally wider and shorter than other pinnate leaflets and are often separated by several inches of naked stem. Some few species of *Pinanga* have simple, undivided leaves, pinnately veined.

Plants of *P. kuhlii* have recently been introduced into southern Florida. It is to be hoped that some of the even more exotic species will soon be introduced into the United States.

Seeds of *Pigafetta elata* on the ground under the mother tree and seedling palms growing up from some of them. Photo courtesy of New Crops Research Branch, U.S. Department of Agriculture.

Pinanga kuhlii var. *sumatrana* growing in Bogor Botanic Gardens, Java. The slender trunks are ringed and jointed like bamboo and are sometimes as little as ¼ inch thick. Photo by T. Satake.

P. KUHLII

Common name: None. **Origin:** Sumatra and Java. **Sex:** Monoecious. **Trunk:** Several; to 30 ft in height, often much less; topped by crownshaft which has a diameter greater than the trunk. **Petiole:** Variable; scurfy. **Leaf:** Pinnate; 3–4 ft long, 2–3 ft wide. **Leaflets:** 1–2 ft long, up to 4 in. wide; very varied; lower ones narrow and pointed, upper and terminal ones, wide and blunt; about 6 pairs in all. **Flowerstalk:** Among leaves; 1 ft long; simply branched; coral red. **Fruit:** Obovoid; ½ in. long; smooth; lacquer red. **Seed:** Wrinkled.

OTHER SPECIES

Hawkes describes *P. paradoxa*, with 12-ft clustered trunks, only ¼ in. thick, leaves only 18 in. long, with wedge-shaped leaflets only 5 in. long, and bright, glossy red fruit. Malaya. He also mentions *P. maculata*, *P. coronata*, *P. distichya* and *P. furfuracea*.

Brown describes over 24 species growing in the Philippines.

Ridley describes 21 species growing in Malaya.

Fairchild speaks of one unidentified species of *Pinanga* growing on Wowoni, one of the Spice Islands (the Moluccas) whose crownshaft is claret-red with pink flowerstalks and ivory-white flowers that turn to red!

Bailey mentions *P. maculata* (with apparently variegated leaves), also *P. malaiana*, *P. micholitzii*, *P. patula*, *P. gracilis*, *P. ternatensis*.

Hortus Second mentions *P. decora* (Borneo) and *P. patula* (Sumatra).

Blatter describes *P. hexasticha*, *P. gracilis*, *P. griffithii*, *P. manii*, *P. dicksonii*, *P. hookeriana*, and *P. hymenospatha*.

Cultivation: Johnston reports that *Pinanga* seeds germinate readily within 2 months. The seedlings, however, are very susceptible to cold and prefer shade.

Pinanga sp. *FTG 192* growing in the garden of Mr. and Mrs. A. C. Langlois in Nassau, Bahamas, who kindly supplied the photograph. Seed for this plant was brought to the Langlois by Dr. Fairchild after his expedition to the Moluccas.

Close-up of the odd-shaped and greatly varied leaflets of *Pinanga kuhlii* var. *sumatrana*. Photo by T. Satake.

PLECTOCOMIA
Greek, plaited hair

Six species of unisexual East Indian, pinnate-leafed palms that climb by means of peculiar, handlike claws. They fruit once and then die, having produced globular fruits from 1–1½ in. long, covered with glossy, brown, overlapping scales. The leaves are very long (10 ft), with leaflets 1 ft long, 3 in. wide, in distinct clusters of 2 or 3. The flowerstalks are very long (6 ft) and carry medium-sized loricate (scale-covered) fruits with a recurved point.

Like its relative *Calamus*, the mature climbing habits of *Plectocomia* are not suited to most gardens; but before reaching greatly elongated proportions, *Plectocomia* species are singularly attractive and interesting. They are little known in the United States.

P. ELONGATA
Latin, elongated, lengthened

Common name: None. **Origin:** Penang, Sumatra, Java, where it forms immense thickets. **Sex:** Dioecious; monocarpic (flowers once and then dies). **Trunk:** To 150 ft in height; slender at bottom; size of man's arm farther up; suckers freely. **Petiole:** Short. **Leaf:** Pinnate; 12 ft long, 3 ft wide; end of rachis carries special claws with a yellow portion that

Plectocomia elongata, an East Indian climbing palm whose peculiar handlike claws will take it up through the trees as high as 105 feet. Photo reprinted from Blatter's *Palms of British India and Ceylon.*

looks like the palm of the hand and with long, black spines for fingers. **Leaflets:** 18 in. long, 3 in. wide; short; pointed; glossy green above, powdery white beneath. **Flowerstalk:** To 4 ft; hanging. **Fruit:** 1 in. diameter; brown; covered with overlapping scales; fuzzy. Each plant dies when it has fruited.

OTHER SPECIES

P. khasyana (sometimes erroneously called *P. assamica*) has leaves 30 ft long, the upper halves of which are just whiplike extensions for climbing. The stem has a 4-in. diameter and grows to a length of 80 ft. Other characteristics are much like *P. elongata*. Native to the Himalayas, at quite high altitudes.

Blatter mentions *P. machrostachya*, and *P. bractealis* (both of India).

Plectocomia was offered for sale in the United States in 1890, but it is not much cultivated today.

PLECTOCOMIOPSIS
Greek, like *Plectocomia*

A genus very similar to *Plectocomia*, as the name implies, differing only in floral details. Native to Tenasserim, Borneo, and Sumatra.

Blatter describes *P. geminiflorus*, and *P. paradoxus*.

Ridley describes *P. geminiflorus*, *P. wrayi*, *P. dubius*, *P. annulatus*, *P. ferox*, *P. scortechinii* (probably *Myrialepis scortechinii*), all growing in Malaya. (Not illustrated.)

PODOCOCCUS

Two species of pinnate-leafed palms from tropical Africa distinguished by their very slim trunks, odd wedge-shaped leaflets, and unbranched flowerstalks.

The following description is from that written by C. H. Wright in *Flora of Tropical Africa*. No plants were available for study or photography. *Podococcus* is little known outside its native land.

P. BARTERI

Common name: None. **Origin:** Equatorial Africa. **Sex:** Both on one tree. **Trunk:** To 8 ft in height; smooth; ringed; slender. **Petiole:** 1 ft long; fuzzy with red scurf. **Leaf:** Pinnate; 6 ft long. **Leaflets:** Varied—6 in.–1 ft long, 4–8 in. broad; wedge-shaped; terminal pair confluent; glaucous green. **Flowerstalk:** Male on one stalk, female on another; both unbranched; 2 ft long; from lower leaves. **Fruit:** Cylindrical; 1 in. long; red.

POLYANDROCOCOS

P. CAUDESCENS
(Formerly *Diplothemium caudescens*)

This palm was introduced into the United States as *Diplothemium caudescens*. It has since been found to belong in the genus *Polyandrococos* but will often be encountered under its former name.

A medium-sized palm, with a heavy dense crown of stiff, pinnate leaves.

The bright-yellow flowers are unusually large and showy for palm flowers and are followed by attractive, large, cylindrical clusters of deep orange fruits.

Common name: None. **Origin:** Brazil. **Sex:** Monoecious. **Trunk:** 12–20 ft in height, 10–12 in. thick; ringed; often swollen in the middle. **Petiole:** Short. **Leaf:** Pinnate; 9–12 ft long; 70–90 pairs of leaflets. **Leaflets:** 24–28 in. long, 1¾ in. wide; green above; back of leaflet has a whitish appearance which on close examination proves to be a coat of fine white hairs. Obtuse at apex; stiff. **Flowerstalk:** 4 ft long; hanging with weight of fruit. **Flowers:** Large; yellow; very showy. **Fruit:** 1¼ in. long; globular; deep orange; edible. **Oddities:** Young plants have simple, or undivided, leaves for first 12–18 months.

Where grown: Not well known in the United States, though some young plants are beginning to appear in southern Florida.

Polyandrococos (formerly *Diplothemium*) *caudescens* in the Royal Botanical Garden, Trinidad, West Indies. Its yellow flowers are unusually large and showy for palms. Photo by A. C. Langlois.

Polyandrococos caudescens in Rio de Janeiro. Photo by M. B. Foster.

PONAPEA [1]

Four species form this genus of pinnate-leafed palms, native to the Islands of Ponape and two nearby islands. (Not illustrated.)

PRESTOEA

Named for H. Prestoe of the Botanical Gardens of Trinidad, superintendent from 1864–1886

A genus closely related to *Hyospathe* but separated on floral characteristics alone.

A relationship with *Euterpe* has been mentioned but, according to Bailey, the absence of a crownshaft in *Prestoea* made separation from *Euterpe* simple and definite. Max Burret disagrees and retains *Prestoea* in *Euterpe*.

A few species of slender, dwarf palms, with prominently ringed trunks. The one species described below has been seen in a juvenile state in southern Florida. It is not believed to be cultivated in the United States except for a few experimental plants.

P. PUBIGERA

Common name: None. **Origin:** The mountains of Trinidad. **Sex:** Monoecious. **Trunk:** 10–12 ft in height, 1½ in. diameter; slender; reedlike; no crownshaft. **Petiole:** Slender; 1½ in. diameter. **Leaf:** Variable from simple to irregularly pinnate; 3–4 ft long. **Leaflets:** Terminal ones unite to form a large oblong blade deeply indented at end; bright green with yellow veins. **Flowerstalk:** 18 in. long; among leaves. **Flowers:** Tiny; insignificant. **Fruit:** ½ in. diameter; globular; fleshy; reddish to purple-black.

OTHER SPECIES

Gentes Herbarum describes *P. montana*, from the island of Grenada, British West Indies, *P. carderi* from Guatemala, and *P. sejuncta* of Panama.

[1]Several species of *Ponapea* were joined with *Ptychosperma* by Moore and Fosberg in *Gentes Herbarum*, vol. 8, page 468. Burret retains *Ponapea* as a separate species.

Growing in the rain forest of Trinidad, at 2,000-feet elevation, this *Prestoea pubigera* (left background) was hard to photograph. Photo by A. C. Langlois.

The same tree has been cut off and brought out into the open for photograph. *Prestoea pubigera*. Photo by A. C. Langlois.

PRITCHARDIA*
Named for W. T. Pritchard, British Consul to Fiji in 1860
(Formerly *Eupritchardia*)

This is the only palm genus native to Hawaii and is one of the most handsome and exotic of all palms. The big, erect, pleated, fan-shaped leaves carry a look of the South Seas wherever they are planted. In young plants with only a short trunk, these leaves are very large and completely dominate their surroundings. On taller trees, in Florida, the leaves seem smaller, but they retain their Polynesian appearance. Nothing can surpass the magnificent *P. pacifica* as an ornamental palm.

Pritchardia pacifica at U.S.P.I. Garden at Coconut Grove, Florida. The fruitstalks are short and stay in among the leaves. Photo by H. F. Loomis.

P. PACIFICA

Common name: Fiji fan palm. **Origin:** Fiji Islands and islands of the Pacific. **Sex:** Monoecious. **Trunk:** To 30 ft in height, usually less; 10–12 in. diameter; smooth; straight. **Petiole:** Unarmed; 3 ft or more long; base covered with mass of brown fibers. **Leaf:** Palmate; up to 5 ft long, 4 ft wide; about 20 on one tree; not divided except at tips; shaped like large fan; deeply folded like a corrugated roof; very large when tree is only a few years old, getting smaller as trunk grows taller; easily injured by the wind. **Segments:** Covered with a light, tawny down when young, which later disappears; texture is heavy and leathery but not stiff. **Flowerstalk:** From axils of leaves; 3 ft long; stiff; straight. **Flowers:** Numerous; tiny; brownish-yellow. **Fruit:** Perfectly round; ½ in. diameter; black.

OTHER SPECIES

P. thurstonii (named for J. B. Thurston, once governor of Fiji) is very similar to *P. pacifica*, but smaller in every way. The trunk is more slender; the petioles and leaves are smaller; the flowerstalk is much longer, up to 10 ft. The fruit is smaller, ¼ in. long. (As a memory trick, *P. thurstonii* is the species that *thrusts* its fruit out well beyond the leaves.) *P. thurstonii* is not nearly as common in the United States as *P. pacifica*. Native to Fiji Islands.

Pritchardia pacifica in Bogor Botanic Gardens, Java. Photo by T. Satake.

Pritchardia thurstonii at U.S.P.I. Garden. The flowerstalks thrust themselves well out beyond the leaves. Photo by H. F. Loomis.

Young *Pritchardia* species growing in Palm Beach, Florida.

P. gaudichaudii does not grow over 20 ft tall and has a spherical fruit 1¾ in. long.
P. martii grows only 12 ft tall and has a 1¾-in. fruit.
Both above are the large-fruited species that are native to the Hawaiian Islands.
There are several other species not described here and not very widely cultivated.

Cultivation: *Pritchardia* seeds germinate readily within 2 months. The plants will not tolerate much cold. Unfortunately, most people do not dependably know the species name of the *Pritchardia* plants in their gardens. After the abnormally cold winter of 1957–1958 in the Palm Beach, Florida, area, however, it seems safe to say that the large-leaf species, *P. pacifica* is far more tender than *P. thurstonii*. Plants in that area, believed to be *P. pacifica*, were badly hurt and lost most of their leaves, while plants believed to be *P. thurstonii* showed less injury. Fairchild Tropical Garden lists all its *Pritchardia* species as tender in southern Florida. U.S.P.I. Garden reports seeds of *P. cowreyana* began germinating in 45 days.

PRITCHARDIOPSIS

A genus of palmate-leafed palms, native to New Caledonia and little known to cultivation. (Not illustrated.)

PSEUDOPHOENIX*
Greek, false phoenix

Several species of attractive palms, somewhat resembling small royal palms, but distinguished by their trunks, which are more smooth and glossy. The rings on the trunks are usually more prominent and closer together than those found on trunks of the royal palm.

P. sargentii was discovered by Charles Sprague Sargent in the wilds of Elliott Key in Florida in 1886. It was considered a new genus because it was the first palm found growing wild in North America that bore bright-red fruits. From specimens sent to him in Hanover, Germany, Wendland named it *Pseudophoenix.*

Specimens of this species were subsequently found on various islands in the Bahamas and other species of the same genus were found elsewhere in Cuba and Hispaniola.

P. vinifera was once very common in Haiti, but many of the trees have been destroyed by the natives, who extract a sweet juice for making wine from the bulging part of the trunk.

Two relatively young specimens of *Pseudophoenix vinifera*, (one in flower) at U.S.P.I. Garden at Coconut Grove, Florida. Photo by H. F. Loomis.

P. VINIFERA
Latin, wine-bearing

Common name: Cherry palm. **Origin:** Cuba, Haiti, and San Domingo. **Sex:** Monoecious. **Trunk:** To 30 ft or more in height; 10–12 in. thick at base; prominently ringed; space between rings gray-green and smooth. Young trees bulged in various ways. Mature trees narrowest at base, widest near top, and then constricting rather suddenly to meet crownshaft. **Petiole:** 18–24 in. long; firm; yellow-green; base clasping trunk to form crownshaft. **Leaf:** Pinnate; 4–6 ft long, 3 ft wide; arching, or downward curved. **Leaflets:** 12–18 in. long, up to 1¼ in. wide; clustered in groups of 2 or 3 on rachis; many veins or nerves; stiffish; yellow-green. **Flowerstalk:** 6 ft long; among leaves, very heavy with fruit, not very widely branched. **Fruit:** Size of large cherry; 1–1½ in. diameter; globular; bright-red; covered with waxy bloom, 1-lobed or 2-lobed, rarely 3-lobed. **Seed:** Globular; ⅝ in. diameter.

A tall specimen of *Pseudophoenix vinifera* at Mrs. Jennings' garden in Florida.

OTHER SPECIES

P. sargentii, similar to *P. vinifera*, but has a shorter trunk—to 25 ft tall, usually much less; bulging, but not as much as *P. vinifera*. The flowerstalk is shorter (3 ft), but its branches spread out to form a much wider cluster. The bright-red fruit is much smaller (about ½ in. diameter). The leaflets are more blue-green. Grows native in Florida on Elliott Key and Long Key. Grows more slowly than *P. vinifera*.

P. ekmanii (Santo Domingo): Short, 15 ft; 8 in. at base, bulging out to 36 in., narrowing to 6 in. at crownshaft; flowerstalk 3 ft long.

P. gracilis (Gonave Island in Gulf of Gonaives, on west coast of Haiti): Trunk erect and slender, 4 in. wide at base and bulging only slightly. Leaflets pale-green above, waxy white beneath. Fruit always 1-lobed.

Further study is needed to establish *P. ekmanii* and *P. gracilis* (mentioned by Bailey) as valid species.

P. saonae (Island of Saona, Santo Domingo): A species very similar to *P. sargentii*. It is not yet officially decided whether certain young plants at Fairchild Tropical Garden represent a separate species or whether they belong in *P. sargentii*. One specimen, believed to be *P.*

A small, but very handsome, specimen of *Pseudophoenix vinifera* at Fairchild Tropical Garden. The trunk is smooth and beautifully striped.

saonae, was examined there in January, 1958. The trunk was 3 ft tall with very prominent rings. The trunk was over 2 ft thick at the base and graduated in a bulging fashion to a 10-in. diameter at the crownshaft. The leaves were 7 ft long and 4 ft wide and carried leaflets seemingly more blue-green than other *Pseudophoenix* species. The fruit was not available.

  P. insignis is correctly *P. vinifera*.

Cultivation: Fairchild Tropical Garden lists all its species as hardy. De Leon reports seeds of *P. vinifera* began germinating after 33 days. U.S.P.I. Garden reports one batch of *P. vinifera* seeds began germinating in 23 days. *Pseudophoenix* palms grow so slowly that nurserymen generally refuse to stock them.

First discovered and named on Elliot Key in Florida, *Pseudophoenix sargentii* is here seen growing at Fairchild Tropical Garden.

PSEUDOPINANGA [1]

P. MACULATA

A species of monoecious, pinnate palm, not believed to have been introduced into the United States. The palm pictured is in Nassau, Bahamas.

Before 1936 this palm was known as *Pinanga maculata*, at which time Burret made a new genus of *Pseudopinanga*, in which genus the *Pinanga maculata* was then placed.

Fairchild spoke of this palm in his Occasional Paper No. 9. This paper was published in 1941 and Fairchild still uses the original name *Pinanga maculata*. He describes it as follows: "A slender, solitary, thin-stemmed palm bearing leaves that are mottled with patches of darker and lighter green. It may require special protection but as it only grows twenty feet tall it is suitable for tubs and large pots. Its fruits are salmon pink, turning to orange."

There are approximately 14 species of *Pseudopinanga* native to various islands from Borneo to Celebes. They are also found on Formosa and in the Philippines.

[1]Moore and Fosberg in *Gentes Herbarum*, vol. 8, page 451, give reasons for uniting *Pseudopinanga* with *Pinanga*. This action disagrees with Burret's conclusions. Burret's list of valid genera is reprinted in the Appendix of this book and it includes both *Pinanga* and *Pseudopinanga* as separate, valid genera.

Pseudopinanga maculata at the Retreat, garden of Mr. and Mrs. A. C. Langlois at Nassau, Bahamas.

PTYCHANDRA GLAUCA
Latin, *glauca*, bluish-gray

A monoecious, pinnate-leafed, single-trunked species indigenous to Malaya and the Moluccas. At least one nursery in southern Florida has grown seedlings recently and they seem to be prospering. Description of mature trees not available beyond what is revealed in the illustrations. This is usually considered to be a monotypic genus. Beccari writes of there being several other species of *Ptychandra* but does not name them. Certainly they are little known to cultivation.

PTYCHOCOCCUS

A genus of about 8 species, native to New Guinea and the Solomon Islands. The leaves are pinnate and the trunks range from medium height to tall. (Not illustrated.)

PTYCHORAPHIS
Greek, *ptychos*, a fold, and *rhaphis*, needle

A few species of Malayan and Indian palms somewhat similar in general appearance to *Ptychosperma* and *Rhopaloblaste*. They are characterized by a crown of perhaps a dozen long leaves drooping gracefully around a slender trunk with a prominent crownshaft.

Ptychandra glauca in Bogor Botanic Gardens, Java. Photo by T. Satake.

Looking up into the crown of *Ptychandra glauca*. Photo by T. Satake.

P. AUGUSTA
Latin, noble, majestic

Common name: None. **Origin:** Nicobar Islands. **Sex:** Monoecious. **Trunk:** 80–100 ft, usually much shorter; smooth; slender; 8 in. diameter or less; prominently ringed and topped by crownshaft. **Petiole:** Very short; bases clasping trunk to form crownshaft. **Leaf:** Pinnate; 8–12 ft long. **Leaflets:** Numerous; 2–3 ft long; narrow; long-pointed. **Flowerstalk:** Below crownshaft; 2½–3½ ft long. **Fruit:** 1 in. long; elliptic oblong; scarlet.

OTHER SPECIES

P. singaporensis (Singapore and India), a pocket edition of *P. augusta*, according to the proportions described by Blatter. Trunk 6–12 ft in height; clustering; 1½ in. diameter; black and ringed; petiole, 3 ft long; leaf only 4 ft long; leaflets ½ in. wide by 8–12 in. long (compared to 2–3 ft long in *P. augusta*); spadix, 1 ft long; fruit ⅔ in. long by ¼ in. thick; red. The black stems are said to make beautiful walking sticks.

Bailey describes *P. siebertiana* (Malaya) as being somewhat similar to *P. singaporiensis;* has copper-colored leaves when young.

Ridley describes *P. longiflora* (Malaya).

Brown describes 4 species in the Philippines: *P. microcarpa, P. intermedia, P. elmerii,* and *P. cagayanensis.*

Cultivation: U.S.P.I. Garden reports planting two batches of seeds of *P. augusta*. The first began germinating in 68 days, but the second began in 29 days. Johnston reports that small seeds germinate readily within two months. The plants are very susceptible to cold.

There are few, if any, mature plants in the United States, though seedlings are being tried. Found mostly in equatorial regions, suggesting the probable need for high temperatures and ample water.

Ptychoraphis augusta in Bogor Botanic Gardens, Java. Photo by T. Satake.

PTYCHOSPERMA*†

Greek, *Ptyche*, a fold, and *sperma*, seed, referring to the ruminate albumen

A genus whose name has been surrounded with confusion and whose history is too involved to be traced here. The confusion is due to honest mistakes made long ago and compounded when new genera were formed.

Ptychosperma elegans, until recently, was the only true *Ptychosperma* cultivated to any extent in the United States.

Now the genus *Actinophloeus* has been joined with *Ptychosperma*, so all former *Actinophloeus* species become *Ptychosperma* species, retaining their species names:

Actinophloeus macarthuri is correctly *Ptychosperma macarthuri*.

A. nicolai is correctly *P. nicolai*.

A. sanderianus is correctly *P. sanderianus*.

The name *Ptychosperma* in Greek means folded seed and probably was meant to indicate the ruminate albumen. At one time this was considered an important identifying characteristic in palms. The above newcomers to the genus (formerly *Actinophloeus*) *do not have* seeds with ruminate albumen, although the remaining original, *P. elegans*, does. Hence, there are in one genus species varying in this particular, indicating that the present authorities no longer feel strongly about ruminate albumen as a vital, distinguishing characteristic.

Ptychosperma elegans at Chapman Field in Florida. Photo by H. F. Loomis.

Many plants were raised in the United States for years under the name of *Seaforthia elegans*, a name now changed to *Ptychosperma elegans*. These plants were actually *Archonthophoenix cunninghamiana*. Hence, plants offered as *Seaforthia elegans*, or possibly as *Ptychosperma elegans*, must be suspected of being *Archonthophoenix*. See *Archonthophoenix*, *Loroma*, *Seaforthia*.

One outstanding characteristic of *Ptychosperma* is the appearance of its leaflets. They look as if they had been cut off at the end, leaving an oblique and jagged apex. Another is its very green ringed trunk, which turns gray with age but generally remains smooth and green throughout the several feet immediately below the crownshaft.

P. ELEGANS

Common name: Solitaire palm. **Origin:** Queensland, Australia. **Sex:** Monoecious. **Trunk:** To 20 ft in height, slender, up to 3–4 in. thick; very smooth and prominently ringed; surmounted by a rather short crownshaft; slightly enlarged at base. **Petiole:** Short. **Leaf:**

Ptychosperma macarthuri in Florida.

Pinnate; to 6½ ft long; recurved and arching; only 6 or 8 leaves on tree at one time; bases form crownshaft. **Leaflets:** 2 ft long, 1–3 in. broad; about 20 pairs to each leaf; cut off and jagged at apex; bright-green, paler beneath. **Flowerstalk:** Below crownshaft; 20 in. long; very bushy and branched. **Flowers:** White; fragrant. **Fruit:** Oblong globular; ¾ in. long; fleshy; bright-red. **Seed:** Globose; with 3 deep furrows and 2 faint ones; albumen ruminate.

P. MACARTHURI
Dedicated to Sir W. MacArthur of New South Wales
(Formerly *Actinophloeus macarthuri*)

A cluster palm, very popular in southern Florida and much used elsewhere as an indoor potted palm. It constantly develops additional slender stems with short leaves that remain within a fairly compact cluster.

Common name: MacArthur palm. **Origin:** New Guinea. **Sex:** Monoecious. **Trunk:** Usually to 10 ft tall, sometimes up to 20 ft; 1–3 in. thick; several to many; greenish-gray; strongly ringed and topped by crownshaft. **Petiole:** 1–1½ ft long; bases forming crownshaft. **Leaf:** Pinnate; 3–4 ft long; 40 or more leaflets. **Leaflets:** 6–15 in. long, up to 3½ in. wide; soft; sometimes transversely mottled; underside is lighter green, duller; jagged, square-ended, except for few pointed ones near base; several prominent nerves give leaflet a ridged feel. **Flowerstalk:** Below leaves; 8–12 in. long; pale yellow; short, but branched. **Flowers:** Yellow-green and white. **Fruit:** ½–¾ in.; cartridge-shaped, with point; first light-green, then yellow, then bright-red; wrinkled when dry. **Seed:** 1-seeded; wrinkled; albumen homogenous.

OTHER SPECIES

P. nicolai, formerly *Actinophloeus nicolai*, similar to *P. macarthuri*, but leaflets are usually not over 2 in. wide and have a very prominent midrib. Young leaves and spathe covering flowerstalk are purplish. A few young specimens are planted outdoors in southern Florida.

P. sanderianus (formerly *Actinophloeus sanderianus*), similar to *P. macarthuri*, but leaves are smaller and leaflets are much more narrow and delicate. Not known to be much in cultivation in the United States. Native to Australia.

There are many other species of *Ptychosperma* not described here and not cultivated in the United States.

Cultivation: Johnston reports that *Ptychosperma* seeds germinate readily within 2 months. He believes that the plants will not grow outdoors in the United States except in southern Florida. De Leon reports that seeds of *P. hosinoi* began germinating after 39 days, *P. ledermaniana*, after 60 days, and *P. augustifolium* after 43 days.

PYRENOGLYPHIS BALANOIDEA

This cluster palm, little-known in the United States, was photographed in the Retreat garden of Mr. and Mrs. A. C. Langlois in Nassau, Bahamas. Bailey described it in 1933 under the name of *Bactris balanoidea*. Burret retains it in the genus *Pyrenoglyphis*, which name is used by Mr. and Mrs. Langlois.

Bailey reported this genus from Guatemala, Costa Rica, and Panama. The brief description below is based on the description of *Bactris balanoidea* in *Gentes Herbarium*, vol. 3, fasc. 2, p. 97, and the Bailey Hortorium considers that to be its name, and *Pyrenoglyphis* a synonym.

Slender palms making a large thicket 15 ft tall; trunks 1–2 in. diameter; upright, but not rigidly erect; sometimes leaning and crossing each other; thickly beset with spines, particularly on the leaf sheaths; old trunks becoming almost bare. Leaves pinnate, 3–5 ft long. Petiole very slender, 18–24 in. long, and less than ½ in. thick; narrowly channeled underneath and convex above; armed with sharp, dark brown spines 1–3 in. long, which continue into the rachis. Leaflets 1–2 in. apart, giving the leaf an open look; grayish-green, lighter color underneath. Fruit, cream-colored, becoming purple; acornlike in shape; 1½ in. long, 1 in. broad. Seed, black and hairy.

This palm is not believed to have been cultivated in the United States and no information on cultivation is available.

Pyrenoglyphis sp. at the Retreat, the Nassau garden of Mr. and Mrs. A. C. Langlois.

Pyrenoglyphis sp. at the Retreat, the Nassau garden of Mr. and Mrs. A. C. Langlois.

RAPHIA*

A group of strange palms with some very unique characteristics. The leaves are the longest of all palm leaves, growing up to 65 ft long. Leaves 50 ft long and 10 ft wide are not uncommon. The flowerstalk (described below) is an enormous, strange-looking growth that will astonish the most blasé.

Each trunk of *Raphia* flowers only once and dies, but there are always new trunks coming along to continue the life of the plant, which suckers freely.

Some difference of opinion seems to exist as to the inflorescence in *Raphia*. Perrier de la Bathie, who studied it in its native land, states that it has a terminal inflorescence composed of 10–12 flowerstalks and that when these die, the plant dies. This would make it monocarpic, as is *Corypha*.

Beccari described it as polycarpic with large flowerstalks arising successively in the axis of the upper leaves.

Raphia was described years ago by Martius, by Beccari, and by Wallace. Peculiarly, none of these three speaks of the multiple trunks. All three speak of the trunk as if it were always single and rarely exceeded 10 ft. Blatter has seen a 30-ft trunk, but also speaks of it as single. Perrier de la Bathie speaks of *Raphia ruffia* as having a single trunk.

The figure in the foreground indicates the enormous size of these specimens of *Raphia ruffia*. The individual leaves are 60 feet long, the longest leaves among all palms. Photo courtesy of E. Johnston.

The *Raphia* plants in the U.S.P.I. Garden and in the private garden of the Jennings estate, both in southern Florida, grow in great clusters and are already composed of many trunks and are still suckering freely.

The famous raffia fiber is made from the leafbases or leaves of this remarkable plant.

R. RUFFIA

Common name: Raffia palm. **Origin:** Madagascar. **Sex:** Male and female flowers on same stalk; monocarpic. **Trunk:** Multiple; 6–30 ft in height, up to 3½ ft thick, but usually much less; throwing out many suckers. **Petiole:** Very stout; margins armed with teeth and bases carrying pale, ascending spines. **Leaf:** Pinnate; to 65 ft long, 10 ft wide, or considerably wider; standing nearly erect, but nodding a bit at ends; leaflets very numerous. **Leaflets:** 5 ft long, 1½ in. wide; those near base, long and narrow; armed on margins and on central nerve with spines; central leaflets wider, also armed, but with weaker spines; leaflets near apex, shorter and less wide, and almost, or entirely, unarmed; all are long, pointed, and rigid; dark-green above, whitish underneath. **Flowerstalk:** From among leaves; a curious and spectacular growth, bearing both male and female flowers. It is a long bulging cylinder, resembling a huge, stuffed stocking, 8 in. thick at the top, then diminishing gradually through a length of 7–11 ft and coming to a blunt point. At first erect, it eventually becomes pendulous. **Fruit:** Oblong ovoid; variable in size, up to 2½ in. long and 1½ in. broad; covered with large, overlapping, glossy, brown scales, with a very short conical point at one end. **Seed:** Wrinkled; albumen very hard.

R. VINIFERA

R. vinifera is similar to *R. ruffia.* Trunk usually shorter and leaves not quite as enormous. A pleasant wine is made from the juice obtained from this species by cutting off the flowerstalks when they first appear. Native to Nigeria.

A close-up of a huge specimen of *Raphia vinifera* showing the beginning of the long leaves. Raffia fiber is made from the leafbases. Note the long flowerstalk. Photo by T. Satake.

R. TAEDIGERA

This is the only species native to equatorial America. Although it has been suggested that it is really a variety of *R. vinifera*, Beccari considered it a separate species and Bailey took the same position.

It grows only in equatorial regions and there only near the coast. Bailey has described specimens in Panama.

The general appearance is much like that of *R. ruffia*, from which it seems to differ only by not being quite as enormous. It, too, is used to make raffia fiber.

Common name: None. **Origin:** Amazon region. **Sex:** Both on one spadix. **Trunk:** Multiple; to 30 ft in height, 1–2½ ft thick. **Petiole:** 4–6 in. diameter; rounded underneath, concave above; 12–15 ft long; base covered with long weak spines. **Leaf:** Pinnate; to 50 ft long, to 8 ft wide. **Leaflets:** 4–5 ft long, up to 2½ in. broad; midrib prominently elevated on upper side; armed with weak spines. **Flowerstalk:** Much as described in *R. ruffia*. **Fruit:** Much as described in *R. ruffia*. **Seed:** Much as described in *R. ruffia*. Great variety in size, from 2–3 in. long.

There are many other species of *Raphia*.

The spectacular long flower arms of *Raphia taedigera* sometimes reach 11 feet in length. Each trunk of *Raphia* flowers only once and then dies. Reprinted from *Gentes Herbarum*.

Cultivation: Johnston reports that in his experience the seeds are not easily obtainable and that only a small percentage of seeds will germinate. De Leon reports planting seeds of *R. gracilis;* germination began after 115 days. U.S.P.I. Garden reports planting seeds of *R. pedunculata;* germination began after 81 days. All *Raphia* palms need plenty of water.

RAVENEA

A genus of about 10 species of pinnate-leafed palms, all native to Madagascar. The species show great variety, the trunks ranging from 25 to 100 ft in height and from slender to robust. (Not illustrated.)

REHDEROPHOENIX

A monotypic genus from the Solomon Islands. The only species, *R. pachyclada*, has pinnate leaves. (Not illustrated.)

A close-up of fruits of *Raphia taedigera*. Fruits of this structure and appearance are called loricate (covered with scales). Reprinted from *Gentes Herbarum.*

Raphia fruit in cross section. Reprinted from *Gentes Herbarum.*

REINHARDTIA
(Including plants formerly in the genus *Malortiea*) [1]

Five species of small, graceful, shade-loving palms, usually found growing in deep woods where little or no direct sun reaches them. Native to southern Mexico and Central America, including Panama.

Several species have small, simple, undivided leaves, shaped rather unusually for palms. Others have leaves broken into only a few varied leaflets, each large leaflet having its ribbed sections divided by little openings near the stem. These are known as the palms "with windows in the leaves."

Only one species, *R. elegans*, is regularly pinnate, although all are pinnately nerved.

All reinhardtias are exotic and unusual, particularly suitable as potted plants for patios or small gardens. Their dainty, yet exotic, appearance would seem to warrant any special treatment necessary for their successful cultivation.

[1]Burret and Potztal still consider *Malortiea* as a separate, valid genus according to their list of valid genera as reprinted in the Appendix of this book. Moore united all *Malortiea* species with *Reinhardtia* in *Gentes Herbarum*, vol. 8, pages 541-576.

An unusually large specimen of *Reinhardtia* (formerly *Malortiea*) *latisecta*, a full-grown plant in the wilds of British Honduras. Photo by A. C. Langlois.

R. ELEGANS
Latin, elegant

Common name: None. **Origin:** Southern Mexico, at altitudes of 3,000 ft or more; in deep woods. **Sex:** Monoecious. **Trunk:** To 20 ft high, usually less; very slender; strongly ringed. **Petiole:** 1 ft long; brown; scurfy. **Leaf:** Pinnate; only 10–12 leaves on plant, 38–40 leaflets on each. **Leaflets:** Largest ones 16–17 in. long, ⅝ in. wide; those at base and top much smaller; all are split at apex and easily frayed; narrow, tapered; dark-green. **Flowerstalk:** From sheaths of older leaves; 3 ft long; branches are creamy white when in flower, but turn to orange-red as fruit matures. **Flowers:** Creamy white. **Fruit:** Ovoid; ¾ in. long; dark purple. **Seed:** Wrinkled; albumen ruminate.

R. LATISECTA
(Formerly *Malortica latisecta*)

The palm that has windows in its leaves. Probably the most interesting species of *Reinhardtia*, because of its leaf, composed of a few large odd-shaped leaflets, the leaflets being separated from each other only near the base by simple, tiny, open spaces, or windows.

Common name: Palm with windows. **Origin:** British Honduras, Central America; in deep forest shade. **Sex:** Monoecious. **Trunk:** Multiple; to 15–20 ft in height; slender; to 2½ in. diameter. **Petiole:** 16–20 in. long; rounded below; covered with red-brown scales; green and channeled above. **Leaf:** Pinnate; 30 in. long; 2 terminal, toothed leaflets, very large, and their leaflets separated only at the rachis by little open spaces. **Leaflets:** Varied; 2 terminal ones, each 6–7 in. wide, 24 in. long, toothed at tips; 2 basal leaflets, 3½ in. wide, 24 in. long; all these leaflets divided by pinnate nerves only, except for small open spaces at the rachis. The basal and terminal leaflets are 3 in. apart on the rachis and usually one or more narrow intermediate leaflets are inserted in this space. **Flowerstalk:** Among leaves; about 4 ft long, arching out beyond leaves; branched; white when flowering; bright-red when fruit is mature. **Fruit:** Bright red, black when ripe; obovoid; ¾ in. long. **Seed:** Ellipsoid; ⅓ in. long; wrinkled; albumen deeply ruminate.

Reinhardtia gracilis var. *rostrata*, a small plant from Costa Rica introduced by R. G. Wilson and growing in a tub at Longwood Gardens. Photo by G. Hampfler. Note the windows in the leaves. Reprinted from *Gentes Herbarum.*

OTHER SPECIES

The remaining species of *Reinhardtia* are still considered by Burret to comprise the genus *Malortiea*. They were also previously described by Bailey under the name *Malortiea*. There has been considerable difference of opinion on this subject among authorities.

Moore, in *Gentes Herbarum*, vol. 8, pages 541–576, unites these former *Malortiea* species with *Reinhardtia*. They are *R. gracilia*, *R. koschnyana* and *R. simplex*. He does, however, place these three species in a subgenus *Malortiea*. The three species in the subgenus *Malortiea* are distinguished from other Reinhardtias by having seeds with homogenous albumen (among other differences). [1]

R. gracilis, a species whose leaves are composed of very few varied leaflets, all with windows, or small spaces, separating strongly nerved segments of the leaflet. There are many varieties with variously shaped leaflets, always divided by little windows.

R. gracilis var. *gracilis*, *R. gracilis* var. *tenuissima*, *R. gracilis* var. *gracilior*, *R. gracilis* var. *rostrata;* are all from southern Mexico and Central America, and these too have windows in their leaves.

R. koschnyana (Costa Rica) and *R. simplex* (Honduras to Panama) do not have windows in their leaves, but they have very attractive, small, toothed, simple, undivided leaves. Both are very small cluster palms, with slender trunks which usually do not reach more than 3 ft in height. They grow at sea level in deep woods in equatorial areas.

Reinhardtias are rare in the United States. In spite of the proximity of their native countries, they have so far been little cultivated, if at all.

[1] *R. latisecta, R. elegans*=genus *Reinhardtia*, subgenus *Reinhardtia*. *R. gracilis, R. koschnyana, R. simplex*=genus *Reinhardtia*, subgenus *Malortiea*.

A close-up of the leaf of *Reinhardtia latisecta* with its windows near the base of each leaf. Photo by A. C. Langlois.

A large clump of the needle palm, *Rhapidophyllum hystrix*, growing at Huntington Botanical Gardens in California. This species is native to Florida, Georgia, and the Carolinas, but is surprisingly uncommon. Photo courtesy of Huntington Botanical Gardens.

RHAPIDOPHYLLUM*†
Greek, *rhaphis*, needle, and *phyllum*, leaf, referring to the long spines on leafbases

R. HYSTRIX
Greek, porcupine

One species of low, bushy, fan palm, noted for the masses of long, black spines that surround its base and for its deeply divided leaves.

Though native to a large area from South Carolina to southern Florida, *R. hystrix* is by no means common, being found only in low areas with rich soil. It is not usually available in nurseries. It occurs also in Mississippi.

Its comparative rarity is somewhat explained by the fact that the inflorescences are so deeply hidden in the crown that they are out of reach of animals and rarely drop to the ground, remaining hidden in the spike-protected crown of leaves without nourishment until they decay.

Common name: Needle palm. **Origin:** South Carolina to Florida. **Sex:** Hermaphrodite or polygamo-dioecious. **Trunk:** Sometimes erect, but usually creeping; covered with old leafbases; suckering freely to form heavy clusters. **Petiole:** Short; base covered with dark fibers and long, black spines, 6–8 in. long, which stick straight up toward the leaves. **Leaf:** Palmate; to 4 ft diameter; round; deeply divided almost to petiole. **Segments:** Long-pointed, but toothed at apex; dark glossy green, but powdery underneath. **Flowerstalk:** Short, 6–12 in. long; much branched; buried among leafbases or spines. **Flowers:** Minute; before opening the inflorescence cluster looks like a large white egg, sitting in among the spines; orange-colored when open. **Fruit:** Egg-shaped; 1 in. long. **Seed:** Smooth; albumen not ruminate. Huntington Gardens has one plant that has formed an almost impenetrable clump 10 ft square and 8 ft high.

RHAPIS*†
Greek, *rhapis*, a rod, perhaps alluding to the shape of the leaflets

A handsome group of clustering, but delicate, small palms, native to southern China. They have long been favorites as potted plants, having been introduced into England as early as 1774. They are grown in the open in southern Florida and California. They prefer shaded locations, the beautiful, dark-green foliage tending to turn yellow in full, hot summer sun.

The slender stems sucker easily, forming clumps of handsome small trunks, covered with curiously attractive woven fibers (from the adhering leafbases). The pattern of these fibers is often helpful in distinguishing one species from another.

Much of the charm of the "lady palms" is due to the shape and arrangement of the segments. Each gracefully tapered segment is cut almost to the petiole and stands well apart from the others; the 5–10 segments together form a beautiful design.

Because of frequent cross-pollination, the two species usually cultivated in the United States are sometimes difficult to distinguish. Authorities have pointed out the differences as to number of leaflets per leaf, the shape of the apex of leaflets, and the tendencies to grow taller or more slender. After examining hundreds of plants, the author hesitates to quote any authority as precisely correct or to draw any actual conclusions.

The two species widely grown here are *R. excelsa* and *R. humilis*. (*R. flabelliformis* is thought to be a synonym for *R. excelsa*.)

Bailey points out the great variety that exists in *R. excelsa*. Under this name he has seen plants with 5 segments to a leaf, and also some with as many as 27 segments.

Some of the so-called differences are here illustrated, but their dependability is not assured.

Four pictures of *Rhapis* palms growing in California.

Rhapis excelsa.

Rhapis humilis.

These palms seem to grow very differently under varying circumstances. No really complete and final study can be made from material in the United States, since there is no assurance that it bears the correct original name.

R. EXCELSA
Latin, lofty, high, elevated

Common name: Lady palm. **Origin:** Southern China. **Sex:** Dioecious. **Trunk:** Multiple; up to 15 ft tall; form delicate, graceful clusters; covered with leafbases, which eventually fall off the lower portion, revealing a very slender, smooth, green, canelike trunk with rings 1–3 in. apart. Sometimes these trunks remain for years no more than 3 ft high, and extremely slender. When leafbases are removed, these trunks are found to be no thicker than a goose quill. **Petiole:** 12–18 in. long, very slender; the bases are covered with woven fibers that vary greatly but generally are more coarse than those of *R. humilis*. (Description follows.) **Leaf:** Palmate; 5–10 segments, cut back to the petiole and spaced well apart. **Segments:** 9–12 in. long, ¾–1¼ in. wide; 2–4 strong ribs; margins of each segment are covered with teeth so fine that they are more easily felt than seen; dark-green, glossy. **Flower-stalk:** From upper leaf axils; 12 in. long; branched; not extending beyond leaves. **Fruit:** Short; oblong; ⅓ in. long; thinly fleshy. **Seed:** About ³⁄₁₆ in. diameter; glossy.

R. HUMILIS* AS CONTRASTED WITH *R. EXCELSA**

Bailey says the trunks of *R. humilis* (Latin, short stature) are more slender and do not reach

All photos courtesy of Huntington Botanical Gardens.

Leaf detail of *R. excelsa*.

Leaf detail of *R. humilis*.

as great a height. The fibrous covering of the trunks is more closely woven and less raveled looking. The leaves are smaller and are on shorter petioles. The segments are more deeply cut. The leaflet points are more pointed and less blunt. Flower stalks are longer.

Huntington reports that in southern California *R. humilis* grows much taller than *R. excelsa*.

OTHER SPECIES

Gentes Herbarum, vol. 4, page 199, also describes *R. filiformis*, *R. gracilis*, *R. laosensis*, *R. micrantha*, *R. multifida*, *R. robusta*, and *R. subtilis*. Bloom's Nursery, Fort Lauderdale, grows an unidentified species which it claims will grow in full sun. The leaves are a dark green and beautifully glossy. There are many other species, none of which are known to have been introduced into the United States.

Blatter states that *R. humilis* is adapted to room cultivation and may be kept at a great distance from the window. He also says that there are varieties with white and golden-yellow leaves.

Cultivation: *Rhapis* palms seldom seed in Florida. Propagation is mostly by suckers. Bailey states in his *Cyclopedia of Horticulture* that *Rhapis* palms are hardy in Florida and require moist soil and a shady place.

RHOPALOBLASTE

A genus of single-trunked, pinnate-leafed palms, native to Indonesia. *R. hexandra*, from the Moluccas and New Guinea, has a trunk only 4 ft tall at maturity and has been much cultivated in Europe as an indoor plant.

R. ceramica is a tall specimen with numerous, soft, drooping leaflets. It is illustrated growing in Bogor Gardens, Java.

RHOPALOSTYLIS†
Greek, *rhopalon*, club, and *stylos*, pillar, alluding to club-shaped flowerstalk

Crown of *Rhopaloblaste ceramica* in Bogor Garden, Java. Photo by T. Satake.

Rhopaloblaste ceramica, lower portion. Photo by T. Satake.

R. SAPIDA

R. sapida, the best-known of this genus, is one of the most handsome of the many palms with crownshafts, and one of the most hardy.

Its brisk, rather narrow crown of leaves twirls upward from a short and bulbous, glossy crownshaft formed by the leafbases.

The short petioles and erect leaves and the sharply ascending manner in which the leaflets leave the rachis combine to produce the upswept, feather-duster look from which the palm receives its common name.

Common name: Feather-duster palm, nikau palm. **Origin:** Norfolk Island, New Zealand. **Sex:** Monoecious. **Trunk:** Single; to 25 ft tall, usually less; strongly ringed; 4–8 in. diameter; topped by short, bulbous crownshaft. **Petiole:** Very short; bases form a short, fat crownshaft. **Leaf:** Pinnate; 4–8 ft long; 12–14 on tree; many leaflets set closely together; very erect; forming crownlike feather duster. **Leaflets:** 3 ft long, 1½–2 in. broad; ascending on rachis; very strong midrib and prominent intermediate veins; long, tapering to a narrow point. **Flowerstalk:** Below crownshaft; under 2 ft long; usually 2 or 3 on tree at one time. **Flower:** Purplish to lilac. **Fruit:** ½ in. long; elliptic; bright-red. **Seed:** Nearly filling the shell; light-colored; albumen homogenous.

OTHER SPECIES

Bailey describes *R. baueri* as growing to 50 ft tall, 12 in. thick, with longer leaves (6–9 ft) and with a longer spadix (3 ft) and larger seed (¾ in. long, dull brown). The flowers are white, the fruit scarlet. Native to Norfolk Island.

R. cheesemanii: Tall tree, to 60 ft; otherwise fairly similar to *R. sapida*. Native to Kermadec Islands north of New Zealand.

Characteristic feather-duster heads of nikau palms in the bush in northern New Zealand. *Rhopalostylis sapida.* Reprinted from *Gentes Herbarum.*

Close-up of feather-duster head of the *Rhopalostylis sapida.* Reprinted from *Gentes Herbarum.*

Cultivation: All species like cool weather, but are not particularly hardy to prolonged frost. If grown indoors, plants should be kept fairly cool in winter. They are said to prefer 42–46°F to any higher or lower temperatures.

U.S.P.I. Garden reports planting seeds of *R. sapida* which began germinating in 73 days. Johnston reports that his few efforts at germinating the small seeds of *R. sapida* in Florida have so far met with little success, although he realizes that in Miami there are several plants thriving and fruiting.

Huntington Gardens had large specimens of both *R. baueri* and *R. sapida* which were lost during the hard freeze of 1937.

RHYNCHOCARPA

(See *Burretiokentia*)

RHYTICOCOS*

One of the several genera separated from the genus *Cocos*.

The general appearance of this single-species palm much resembles the coconut. The crown of the tree usually has several boat-shaped spathes about 12 in. long suspended from its base.

Like the coconut, *Rhyticocos* seems to thrive close to salt water, the foliage unaffected by salt spray.

It has been recently introduced in Florida by several nurseries. Should it prove as tolerant of salt as the coconut, a greater variety of material will be available for seaside plantings.

Overtop palm, *Rhyticocos amara*, on the public square in Lamentin, Martinique. Reprinted from *Gentes Herbarum*.

R. AMARA
Latin, *amarus*, bitter
(The milk in the fruit is bitter)

Common name: Overtop palm. **Origin:** Dominica and French West Indies. **Sex:** Monoecious. **Trunk:** To 60 ft and more, 8 in. thick; swollen at base. **Petiole:** 3–6 ft long. **Leaf:** Pinnate; 6–9 ft, sometimes longer; 30 pairs of leaflets. **Leaflets:** 3 ft long, to 1½ in. wide; hanging; midrib prominent on upper side. **Flowerstalk:** Among leaves; 2–3 ft long; at first covered by spathe about 1 ft long that remains on tree for long period. **Fruit:** Egg-shaped; up to 2 in. long, 1½ in. thick; orange color at maturity. Looks like miniature coconut; contains a bitter milk when young. **Seed:** Albumen hard when mature.

Cultivation: U.S.P.I. Garden records show the first germination was on the 62d day after planting seeds of *R. amara*.

ROSCHERIA
Named for Albrecht Roscher, young traveler killed in Africa

One of the many unusual and interesting genera from the Seychelles Islands.

A second-story tree of the moist mountain forests of the Seychelles, where it grows above the underbrush, but below the canopy of taller trees; its aerial roots thrust into a unique, chestnut-colored, spongy soil, rich with organic materials.

Roscheria is sometimes included in the genus *Verschaffeltia*.

R. melanochaetes is the only recognized species of *Roscheria* and is not believed to be cultivated anywhere in the United States.

Crown of *Rhyticocos amara* showing the hanging spathes. Reprinted from *Gentes Herbarum.*

R. MELANOCHAETES
Means black, hairy or bristly

Common name: None. **Origin:** Seychelles Islands, at 1,500–2,500-ft elevation. **Sex:** Monoecious. **Trunk:** 15–25 ft high, 2–3 in. diameter; with aerial roots; a ring of spines beneath each leaf scar when young; topped by a short crownshaft. **Leaf:** Pinnate; 8–10 leaves on tree, each 4–6 ft long, 2–3 ft wide; pale green. **Leaflets:** Greatly varied in width and length, from 12–27 in. long, from ½–4 in. wide; the broad ones flare out from the rachis and round into a blunt apex; the narrow ones are pointed. **Flowerstalk:** 2–6 ft long; below crownshaft, but extending beyond leaves; covered by spathe 27 in. long. **Flowers:** Very small. **Fruit:** Globular; ¼ in. diameter; puckered; outside layers dry off leaving seed exposed. **Oddity:** Young plants have simple, bifid leaves. **Seed:** Smooth; very small; ruminate albumen.

Cultivation: Balfour states that *R. melanochaetes* grows in shaded forests in the Seychelles, about 1,000 ft elevation, where it is fairly common. Bailey's *Cyclopedia of Horticulture* states that, at the time of writing, young plants of *R. melanochaetes* were doing well in southern Florida in sheltered situations.

ROYSTONEA*
Named for General Roy-Stone (1836–1905) American engineer known for his work
in Puerto Rico
(Formerly known as *Oreodoxa*)

There is nothing in the palm family to quite equal the tall, majestic, stately appearance of the royal palm.

Roscheria melanochaetes in the Botanical Garden at Peradeniya. Reprinted from Blatter's *Palms of British India and Ceylon.*

Fruiting crown of *Roscheria melanochaetes* which displays the varied and attractive leaflets. Reprinted from *Gentes Herbarum.*

The smooth surface of the curiously bulged, whitish, stone-gray trunk gives the appearance of a strange marble column reaching straight up into the sky.

There are 4 species well known in the United States, one of which is indigenous, and although there is a difference between them, identification is difficult, because individual trees in one species will vary so greatly. All are monoecious.

It is not known that roystoneas hybridize among the species, but it is a possibility to be considered.

R. REGIA
Latin, royal

The most common species is *R. regia*, the royal palm of Cuba. It is probable that well over half of all the royals to be seen in the United States are of this species.

The trunks are usually enlarged at the base, then gradually reduced in girth, but swelling out again at about the middle, then diminishing gradually to the top. This bulging, however,

Rows of *Roystonea regia*, the Cuban royal palm, on Royal Palm Way, Palm Beach, Florida.

takes all kinds of forms and cannot be depended upon for identification. The trunks are of medium height (for royals), about 50–70 ft tall, with a very smooth surface of whitish, powdery gray. The leaves are 6–10 ft long, with a comparatively short petiole. The leaflets are attached to the rachis in four different rows, each at a different angle, giving a tousled, or cylindrical, look to the leaf. The leafbases join together at the top of the tree to form a glossy, smooth, tightly packed, green cylinder: the crownshaft. The flowers are borne on stalks 3 ft or more long, appearing below the crownshaft. Covered with a bright-green spathe, or envelope, this spadix is very erect, and stands out stiffly, looking almost like a green baseball bat. The fruit is small, about ⅝–½ in. long, and purplish.

R. ELATA
Latin, elevated

The next most common species is *R. elata* which is now generally considered to be native to Florida. Until recently *R. elata* was known as *R. regia* and was considered to be the same as that Cuban species.

In 1901 O. F. Cook decided that there was a species of *Roystonea* native to Florida. He described it as a new species and named it *R. floridana*, though he was not generally followed in this by other botanists.

In 1946 Francis Harper called attention to the fact that William Bartram in his *Travels* (1794) had written of a palm which he had discovered in central Florida in 1774 and which he called *Palma elata*. His description suggested that this was the royal palm.

After omitting mention of any species of *Roystonea* native to Florida in his famous *Standard Cyclopedia of Horticulture* and *Hortus Second*, L. H. Bailey recognized a Florida royal palm in 1949 (see *Gentes Herbarum*, vol. 8, pp. 114–134) and called it *R. elata*, honoring the species named by William Bartram in 1794. Bailey's *Manual of Cultivated Plants* (1954) states that *R. elata* is native to the Florida Everglades, where it grows in wet ground.

M. Bomhard in *Palm Trees in the United States* speaks of *R. elata* as native to Florida and illustrates a tall double row of this species growing in Fort Myers, Florida. Bomhard also says that the Florida royal palm once grew naturally at least as far north as De Land, Florida. It was once quite common in the wilds but was threatened with extermination because of removal for transplanting as ornamentals. The establishment of the Everglades National Park will preserve some of the fine old specimens.

Bailey in 1949 describes the following differences between the native *R. elata* and the Cuban *R. regia*.

R. elata	*R. regia*
Trunk, taller—to 100 ft	Trunk, 50–70 ft in height
Leaflets indifferently or not at all nerved lengthwise either side of the midrib	Leaflets stoutly nerved lengthwise either side of the midrib
Flowerstalk (spadix) long and loose	Spadix, shorter and as wide as long
Fruit almost round	Fruit slightly oblong
Grows in lowlands and swamps, Florida	Grows in middle elevations, Cuba

R. BORINQUENA

The next most common species of *Roystonea* is the Puerto Rican royal, *R. borinquena*, which varies from *R. regia* only in that it does not generally grow as tall, and the leaves and leaflets are usually a little shorter. The other differences are in details of flower and fruit. The fruit is about the same size as that of the Cuban royal, but is yellowish-brown. The leaflets are in four different ranks, as in *R. regia*. The swelling in the trunk is *usually* well above the middle.

R. OLERACEA

The Caribbean royal palm, *R. oleracea*, is the least common and for some reason is seldom available at nurseries. Its trunk grows the tallest (over 100 ft) and is usually enlarged only at

Roystonea oleracea, the Caribbean royal palm, in Panama. Reprinted from *Gentes Herbarum*.

the base, diminishing gradually to the crownshaft. Its leaves are very long, to 21 ft. Two characteristics definitely distinguish it from the other two species:

1. The leaflets are attached to the rachis in only two horizontal rows, one on each side of the rachis, giving a flat, or horizontal, look to the leaf. This is particularly true in the center of the leaf, and may vary a trifle at the base or apex.

2. The flowerstalk is packed into its envelope in such a way that the branches emerge in a wavy, undulating form, which they somewhat retain during flowering and fruiting.

The fruit is ½–¾ in. long and purplish-black. The large crown of leaves is less drooping than in the other species and, unlike them, usually leaves the flowers and crownshaft uncovered and plainly visible.

Fairchild, in his *The World Was My Garden*, tells of admiring a magnificent avenue of royal palms years ago in Rio. He failed to collect seeds because his mission was more concerned with economic plants. "That we have not yet brought it into common cultivation in the U.S. is an oversight for which I have no explanation."

The table on the opposite page shows comparative characteristics of these four species.

The undulating branches of the spadix of *R. oleracea*, a characteristic separating it from other roystoneas. Reprinted from *Gentes Herbarum*.

	R. regia	*R. borinquena*	*R. elata*	*R. oleracea*
Common name	Cuban royal palm	Puerto Rican royal palm	Florida royal palm	South American royal palm
Origin	Cuba	Puerto Rico	Low ground and swamps, Florida	South America
Sex	Monoecious	Monoecious	Monoecious	Monoecious
Trunk	Single, smooth; whitish; irregularly bulged; 50–70 ft; large glossy crownshaft	Single, smooth; whitish; to 55 ft; bulging well above middle; large glossy crownshaft	Single, smooth; whitish; to 100 ft and more; large glossy crownshaft	Single, smooth; to 120 ft or more; not bulging; large glossy crownshaft
Petiole	Short	Short	Short	Short
Leaf	To 10 ft long, 6 ft wide; leaflets in several ranks giving leaf cylindrical appearance	Much as *R. regia*	Much as *R. regia*	10–20 ft long, 6 ft wide; leaflets placed only in 2 horizontal directions giving leaf a flat look
Leaflets	3 ft long; stoutly nerved on either side of the midrib	Much as *R. regia*	As *R. regia*, but leaflets are indifferently (or not at all) nerved lengthwise on either side the midrib	As *R. regia*, except for placement mentioned above
Flowerstalk	3 ft long and nearly as wide; much branched; spathe, before opening, resembles baseball bat	Much as *R. regia*	Longer and more loose than *R. regia*	3 ft or more; branches emerge from spathe in marked undulating form which is retained through fruiting
Fruit	Oblong globose; ¼ in. long; purplish	Much as *R. regia* but yellowish brown	A trifle less oblong than in *R. regia;* purplish	Oblong cylindrical; ¾ in. long, ½ in. wide; purplish black

OTHER SPECIES

Bailey in "Palms Uncertain and New," *Gentes Herbarum,* vol. 8, pp. 118–134, names 8 other species which he found in various parts of the Caribbean, but since he does not mention them in his *Manual of Cultivated Plants,* they are omitted here.

Cultivation: Roystoneas are one of the fastest growing of all the palms, if their roots can reach the water. The more water they get, the faster they will grow. They are not very cold-hardy. Johnston reports that *Roystonea* seeds germinate readily without special treatment and well within 2 months.

Royal palms are not very hardy to cold. Their outdoor cultivation in the United States is limited to southern Florida. Attempts to grow them in southern California have been discouraging.

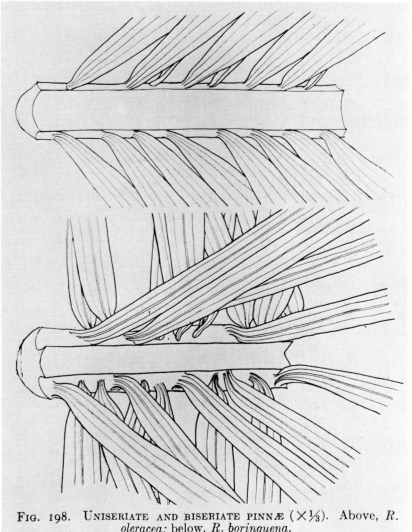

FIG. 198. UNISERIATE AND BISERIATE PINNÆ (×⅓). Above, *R. oleracea;* below, *R. borinquena.*

Illustrating the flat arrangement of the leaflets of *R. oleracea* compared to those of *R. borinquena. R. regia* and *R. elata* leaflets are arranged as are those of *R. borinquena.* Sketch reprinted from *Gentes Herbarum.*

SABAL*†
Said to be a native name in South America,
but originator gave no explanation

A perplexing genus, very common in cultivation and abundant in nature, yet very imperfectly understood.

Blatter, in his *Palms of British India and Ceylon*, says that this genus has survived from the time when palm trees abounded in North America and Europe. During the lower Miocene period, a large, Sabal-like tree has been proved to have inhabited Europe as far north as 56°, and others to have existed in Italy until the later Miocene period.

Many species have been established, including the famous *S. palmetto*, the common palmetto palm. This species is so variable in height, thickness, size of leaves, and even in fruits, that its extremes might answer the descriptions of almost any other species. Many other species are almost equally variable.

The dwarf palmetto, *S. minor*, and its short relative, *S. louisiana*, differ from all the other species in not having a costapalmate leaf. The petiole stops at the leaf and does not have an extension, or rib, protruding into the leaf itself. Usually a creeping, trunkless palm, *S. minor*, in a few instances, forms a short, upright trunk. Peculiarly, when this occurs, the leaf generally becomes slightly costapalmate, and a short rib extends from the petiole for a few inches into the leaf.

Historical note: On June 28, 1776, one hundred men on Sullivan's Island, in a rude fort made of *Palmetto* trunks, repulsed the British fleet. The state seal of South Carolina, commemorating this event, pictures the fort.

S. MINOR
Latin, smaller

Common name: Dwarf palmetto. **Origin:** Georgia to Florida and Texas. **Sex:** Monoecious. **Trunk:** Usually subterranean, but sometimes emerging into a short trunk up to 6 ft

Sabal minor in fruit in South Carolina. This plant is ordinarily trunkless and has no rib extending into the leaf. Reprinted from *Gentes Herbarum*.

tall or (rarely) 12 ft; usually covered with persistent leafbases, but eventually becoming bare. **Petiole:** ¾–1½ in. broad, about ½–⅓ as long as the leaf; no rib extending into the leaf, except on trees with trunks, and then rib is only from 1½ to several in. **Leaf:** Palmate; 24–60 in. diameter; divided ⅔ of way to base into 16–40 segments; few threads in sinuses. Sometimes a short rib extends from petiole into leaf for 1 or more in. **Segments:** Stiff; firm; long-pointed; split at apex; green, or slightly blue-green; central vein prominent on under surface. **Flowerstalk:** 18–80 in. long; very variable; erect at first and well exceeding the leaves, but eventually arching with weight of fruit. **Flowers:** White. **Fruit:** Globular; ⅓ in. diameter; black, shiny. **Seed:** ¼ in.; dark-brown to black; albumen very hard and homogenous.

S. *louisiana* is similar to S. *minor* but has a trunk usually to 7 ft in height. Leaf is not costa-palmate.

Sabal minor. In the few cases where this plant has an emergent trunk, it peculiarly develops an extension of the petiole, a rib which extends for a few inches into the leaf. Reprinted from *Gentes Herbarum.*

All other species of *Sabal* are conspicuously costapalmate, the petiole extending far into the leaf. This extension is strongly curved and arches toward the ground, giving the leaf a very twisted appearance.

The large leaves vary from bright-green to blue-green, depending almost as much on conditions as on species.

The fruit clusters are large and carry great numbers of fruits. The fruits are usually glossy and smooth and look like small or large blueberries, though sometimes they have a brownish cast.

The trunks are usually covered with old leafbases in a familiar criss-cross pattern, but these are sometimes unaccountably absent. This condition seems to depend more on the individual

Sabal viatoris, a species considered valid by L. H. Bailey, though he had originally included it under *S. palmetto*. This specimen at Huntington Garden is believed to be the only living specimen in the United States. Photo courtesy of Huntington Botanical Gardens.

vigor of the tree than on its species, though some species *tend* to have clean trunks more often than others.

S. PALMETTO

A tree of various statures and proportions, depending on conditions not yet understood as well as on age and soil conditions. Palmettoes sometimes bear fruit when tree is 3 ft tall, or

A *Sabal palmetto* in New Smyrna Beach, Florida, which has developed four heads instead of the usual one. This is certainly the result of an injury and possibly of repeated injuries and is highly unique. Photo by Dent Smith.

even much less. The trunks of some trees are almost bare; that of others of the same age may be completely covered with criss-cross leafbases. Even the fruit is exceedingly variable.

Common name: Palmetto palm, cabbage palm. **Origin:** Near the coast of the Carolinas and in many areas in Florida. **Sex:** Hermaphrodite. **Trunk:** 20–90 ft in height; very variable; often covered with familiar criss-cross pattern of old leafbases for years; sometimes losing leafbases quite early. **Petiole:** Variable; usually longer than leaf, sometimes as

A group of *Sabal palmettos* at Daytona Beach, Florida.
Photo by Dent Smith.

long as 9 ft; split at base; forms an extension which protrudes far into leaf, almost to outer margin. **Leaf:** Palmate; 3–6 ft long, a little broader than long; very conspicuously costapalmate; divided ⅓ of way to base; many threads in sinuses. **Segments:** Long, tapering, pointed; split at apex; green, sometimes slightly blue-green. **Flowerstalk:** 20–40 in. long; among leaves; as long as leaves or longer. **Fruit:** Globular; ⅓ in. diameter; shiny black. **Seed:** ¼ in. diameter; smooth; shiny dark-brown.

S. CAUSIARUM

S. causiarum is usually considered to be the most stocky of the sabals. To illustrate their variability one old 60-ft specimen of *Sabal causiarum* on the grounds of the University of Florida at Gainesville has a heavy trunk, but it is not as big around as several much younger, shorter specimens at Fairchild Tropical Garden, and at the U.S.P.I. Garden in Coconut Grove, Florida. If these trees are all properly named, it may be that the warmer climate of Coconut Grove creates a larger trunk.

A photograph emphasizing the extension of the petiole far into the leaf of *Sabal palmetto*.

The peculiar twisted look of a hanging leaf of *S. palmetto*. This is caused by the extra rib which projects into the leaf. This rib is curving and twists the leaf in a recognizable manner.

Common name: Puerto Rican hat palm. **Origin:** Puerto Rico and Virgin Islands. **Sex:** Hermaphrodite. **Trunk:** 30–50 ft tall, often much less; soon dropping leafbases and presenting a gray, smooth look. Diameter up to 40 in., perhaps more. **Petiole:** 6 ft or more; extending far into leaf, almost to far edge. **Leaf:** Palmate; to 6 ft or more; strongly costapalmate; many threads at sinuses; divided ⅔ of way to base. **Segments:** Firm; stiff; usually not drooping; usually bright-green, but sometimes dusty blue-green. **Flowerstalk:** From axils of leaves; usually projecting far beyond leaves. **Flowers:** White; slightly fragrant. **Fruit:** Globose; ⅓ in. diameter; dark-brown to black. **Seed:** ¼ in.; dark-brown.

Sabal causiarum, the Puerto Rican hat palm, with massive trunk, at the U.S.P.I. Garden at Coconut Grove, Florida.

Sabal causiarum at Huntington Gardens in California.

S. TEXANA

This species and *S. minor* are believed to be the only palms native to Texas. One tree in Cameron County, near the mouth of the Rio Grande, was mentioned by Cantino in 1502, supposedly the first written record of a United States native palm. A stocky tree with a substantial trunk.

Common name: Texas palmetto. **Origin:** Texas. **Sex:** Hermaphrodite. **Trunk:** To 50 ft in height, 24 in. thick without leafbases (which may, or may not, adhere); dead leaves sometimes adhere as in washingtonias; **Petiole:** reddish-brown. 3 ft or more; rib extending far into leaf. **Leaf:** Palmate; 3 ft or more; moderate amount of threads; divided ¾ of way to base; strongly costapalmate. **Segments:** Long; tapering; split at apex of long points; light-green. **Flowerstalk:** Shorter than leaves, or about equaling them. **Flowers:** White; fragrant. **Fruit:** Rounded; ¾ in. diameter; sometimes 2-lobed; flat on bottom; chocolate-brown.

S. UMBRACULIFERA
Latin, umbrella-bearing

According to Bailey, this is probably the most massive of the palmettos. In field studies of the sabals of Santo Domingo, he joins three species named by Beccari—*S. neglecta*, *S. domingensis*, and *S. haitensis*—with this species.

A large stand of *Sabal texana*. Photo by Dent Smith.

Its description is much like that of *S. causiarum* but (always allowing for variations) it is taller and not quite as stocky. Its flowerstalks do not project beyond the leaves and the fruit is very different, as described.

Common name: None. **Origin:** Santo Domingo. **Sex:** Hermaphrodite. **Trunk:** To 60 ft high; stocky; smooth; whitish; free of leafbases except at top, where a shag of dead leaves may adhere, as in *Washingtonia*. **Petiole:** 6 ft long; extending far into leaf. **Leaf:** Palmate; 6 ft long and a trifle more broad; very few threads; divided about halfway; strongly costapalmate. **Segments:** Stiff; midrib conspicuous underneath; bright gray-green; not glaucous. **Flowerstalk:** Shorter than leaves; usually hidden within head. **Fruit:** Oblate; $7/16$ in. long, $5/8$ in. broad; very dark-brown and shiny when ripe.

S. ETONIA

A trunkless species with costapalmate leaves.

Common name: Scrub palmetto. **Origin:** Peninsular Florida. **Sex:** Hermaphrodite. **Trunk:** Several ft long; subterranean. **Petiole:** About same length as leaf—3 ft or more long; slender; rib extended well into leaf. **Leaf:** Palmate; $2\frac{1}{2}$–4 ft long; 4 or 5 on trunk; definitely costapalmate; many hanging threads; divided $3/4$ or $7/8$ of distance to base. **Segments:** Central ones 30–36 in. long, 1–$1\frac{1}{2}$ in. broad; others much narrower; all long-pointed, deeply split at apex; prominent center rib; green. **Flowerstalk:** Shorter than leaves; much branched. **Fruit:** Depressed globular; $1/3$ in. broad, $1/6$ in. long; dark-brown.

The common *Sabal* of Hispaniola, *S. umbraculifera*, formerly *S. blackburnia*, growing in central Santo Domingo. Reprinted from *Gentes Herbarum*.

OTHER SABAL SPECIES

Bailey also mentions: *S. allenii* from Panama; *S. bahamensis* from the Bahamas; *S. black-burniana* = *S. umbraculifera*; *S. bermudana* of Bermuda; *S. deeringiana* = *S. louisiana*; *S. dugesii* from Mexico which has unusually large fruit; *S. exul* = *S. texana*; *S. glabra* = *S. minor*; *S. glaucescens* = *S. mauritiaeformis*; *S. mauritiaeformis* from Colombia: leaves bright-green above, blue-green beneath; segments deeply divided and drooping; spadix projecting beyond leaves; trunk self-cleaning; *S. mexicana*, from Mexico: spadix equaling or slightly exceeding leaves; *S. morrisana* from Guatemala: spadix much exceeding leaves; *S. parviflora* from Cuba: many threads; spadices shorter than leaves; foliage very stiff; the very stout trunks sometimes bulge variously; *S. peregrina*, nativity not determined; planted in Key West and West Indies; *S. pumila* = *S. minor*; *S. questeliana* from the Bahamas; *S. viatoris*, origin unknown; planted in southern California; *S. yapa:* flowerstalk projects well beyond leaves.

A specimen of *Sabal exul* in the garden of Mr. T. Satake in Saigo, Japan. Photo by T. Satake.

Sabal mauritiaeformis, at Bogor Botanic Gardens, Java. Photo by T. Satake.

Cultivation: Sabals are very hardy palms and are grown throughout South Carolina, Georgia, Florida, the Gulf States, and California. *S. palmetto* is the most common and probably the most hardy, although *S. minor* is also very hardy. *S. texana* is found mostly in southeastern Texas. A splendid collection of sabals can be seen at several botanical gardens. Even in these experienced hands, however, identification is usually not positive.

Johnston reports that *Sabal* seeds germinate readily and well within 2 months. The plants grow slowly. De Leon reports planting seeds of *S. glaucescens*, which began germinating on the 59th day.

Sabal mexicana planted in Huntington Gardens in 1943. This specimen has survived two severe freezes without evident damage. Similar in general size and outline to *S. umbraculifera*, this plant has not yet produced flowers and fruit, and identification is not positive. Photo courtesy of Huntington Botanical Gardens.

SALACCA
(Spelled *Zalacca* by some authorities)

A group of Malayan feather palms, young plants of which have recently been offered in southern Florida. In their native lands, they form large and very spiny clusters, usually in swampy ground.

S. EDULIS

Widely cultivated in Indonesia, and its very attractive fruits are sold in the markets. The trunks are multiple, but mostly subterranean. The mature plant is 15–20 ft tall and all its parts are covered with very sharp spines. The pinnate leaves stand erect, carrying leaflets 1½–2 ft long, 1½–2 in. broad, green above, whitish beneath. The pear-shaped fruit is 2½ in. long and is covered with overlapping orange-brown scales, under which there is pale-yellow edible flesh.

S. WALLICHIANA

Native to India, Burma, and Malaya. Forms large clusters not unlike *S. edulis*, but the

Salacca edulis. Photo courtesy A. Dilmy, Bogor Botanic Gardens, Java.

leaflets are much wider and are green on both sides. The fruit is 1½ in. long with overlapping brown scales.

S. CONFERTA

A trunkless palm, forming very large thickets and covered with very strong spines. Fruit is 1¼ in. long, ovoid, and covered with dull yellow scales.

OTHER SPECIES

Ridley, in his *Flora of the Malay Peninsula*, describes also *S. affinis* and *S. glabrescens*. *S. dubia* and *S. affinis* are growing in Bogor Gardens, Java.

There are other Malayan and Indonesian species of *Salacca*, none of which has been introduced into the United States.

Cultivation: Seedling plants have been raised and sold in southern Florida. Johnston reports *Salacca* seeds are not easy to obtain or to germinate. They are definitely tropical plants and require warm weather. De Leon reports seeds of *S. edulis* and of *S. wallichiana* germinating in 24 days.

Salacca affinis in Bogor, Java. Photo by T. Satake.

Salacca dubia in Bogor, Java. Photo by T. Satake.

SCHEELEA*

The genus consists of about 40 pinnate-leafed, South American palms, with long and very erect leaves. They differ from *Orbignya* and *Attalea* principally in details of the flowers. For a more complete description, see *Attalea*. The fruits of all three genera are much alike, and the plants are often misnamed among the genera.

SCHIPPIA CONCOLOR

The illustrations shown are by Mr. and Mrs. A. C. Langlois and were taken in the woods of British Honduras.

They sent the following description based on Standley's *Flora of British Honduras:* A tall unarmed palm about 33 ft high, the trunk 4 in. diameter, leaves fan-shaped, with long petioles, less than 3 ft broad, pale beneath. The inflorescences are 2 ft long, or more, and much branched; the flowers spirally arranged upon the branches; fruits globose, 7/8 in. or more in diameter. Monoecious. Indigenous to British Honduras alone.

Scheelea umbaniana, a specimen old enough to show some trunk, planted at Bogor Botanic Gardens, Java. Photo by T. Satake.

A typical *Scheelea* fruit cluster (*S. liebmanii*). Photo by Dent Smith.

SCHIZOSPATHA

A genus name published as a segregate from Calamus in Gardens Bulletin, Singapore, in 1955. It has not been recognized in Burret and Potztal's list of valid genera. (Not illustrated.)

SCLEROSPERMA

A genus of three species of pinnate-leafed palms, native to West Africa and little cultivated elsewhere. (Not illustrated.)

Schippia concolor specimen cut off in the woods of British Honduras and brought out for photographing. A rare and beautiful palm. Photo by A. C. Langlois.

SERENOA*

Named after Sereno Watson, American botanist (1826–1892)

The famous saw palmetto, which forms extensive dense colonies, often covering miles of territory with a continuous scrub.

The color range is surprising for one species. Often in the same field plants with bright yellow-green leaves are intermingled with others with leaves of very powdery blue-green. The causes of these variations are not known. If the blue-green leaves are cut off and dried in the sun, the blue-green color comes off in a waxy layer.

The deeply cut, small leaf of *S. repens* is one of the best-designed and most graceful of all palm leaves.

S. REPENS

Common name: Saw palmetto. **Origin:** South Carolina to Florida Keys. **Sex:** Hermaphrodite. **Trunk:** Usually subterranean and branching; sometimes forms erect or oblique trunk up to 10 ft or even more; forms huge colonies. **Petiole:** Slender, to 4–5 ft long; expanded base covered with woven brown fiber; margins finely toothed. **Leaf:** Palmate; orbicular; 3 ft across; deeply cut almost to base into 18–24 widely separated, very graceful segments. **Segments:** Firm; 2 ft long; midnerve prominent; very variable in color, from yellowish-green to blue-green. **Flowerstalk:** Among leaves; up to 3 ft long, or more; branched. **Fruit:** Variable from ovoid oblong to pyriform; ¾ in. long, ½ in. thick; black or bluish. **Seed:** ⅔ in. long, ⅓ in. thick; light brown.

SINDROA

A one-species genus native to Madagascar. *S. longisquama* has pinnate leaves. The trunk is 12–24 ft tall and 4–5 in. diameter. (Not illustrated.)

Serenoa repens in bloom in southern Florida. These plants often form large stands covering huge areas.

SIPHOKENTIA

A delicately beautiful palm, specimens of which have been thriving in a few private gardens in Miami, Florida, for about twenty years. Its pert, jaunty, pure white flowerstalk and its sleek, glossy trunk and crownshaft deserve wider attention.

Note: There is an entirely different genus, *Cyphokentia*, little-known in the United States, not to be confused with *Siphokentia*.

S. BEGUINII

Common name: None. **Origin:** Halmahera, one of the Molucca Islands. **Sex:** Monoecious. **Trunk:** Single; to 25 ft tall, usually less; 3–4 in. diameter; topped by crownshaft. **Petiole:** Short, 4 in. long; channeled above; bases form crownshaft. **Leaf:** Pinnate; 5–10 on

Siphokentia beguinii, photographed by Frank May in his own garden in Miami, Florida.

tree; 4–6 ft long; 17–18 pairs of leaflets. Young plants have simple, entire leaves. **Leaflets:** 24 in. long; basal and terminal ones 3 in. wide, with several nerves; intermediate ones 1½–2 in. wide; all leaflets have blunt, toothed ends; glossy green above, dull underneath. **Flower-stalk:** 12 in. long; under crownshaft; stalk and branches very white and strikingly attractive. **Flowers:** Creamy white. **Fruit:** Cylindrical; ¾ in. long, ¼ in. wide; reddish at maturity. **Seed:** Cylindrical; ⅜ in. long, 3⁄16 in. broad; albumen deeply ruminate; rosy red. **Oddities:** Flowers when trunk is only 1 ft tall. Young plants have simple, entire leaves.

Cultivation: De Leon reports seeds should germinate within 3 months. Plants like shade at all ages.

SOCRATEA

A rare tropical palm from Panama, which is closely related to, and sometimes included with, *Ireartea*, though it is separately a valid genus. It is not believed to be planted outdoors in the United States.

The tall, slender trunk is braced on stilt roots, sometimes as much as 10 ft tall, and topped by a long slender crownshaft.

The odd-shaped leaflets are attached to the leaves at various angles, and the leaf has a ruffled look.

The Panama species described below may possibly be a variety of *Ireartea exorrhiza*.

Details of *Siphokentia beguinii*. Left to right: outer and inner spathe, staminate and pistillate flowerstalks, young fruiting flowerstalk, leafbase. In the background, portions of the leaf. Reprinted from *Gentes Herbarum*.

Socratea durissima growing in Bogor Garden, Java, showing small stilt roots and large leaflets. Photo by T. Satake.

S. DURISSIMA

Common name: None. **Origin:** Panama Canal Zone. **Sex:** Monoecious. **Trunk:** Slender, to 70 ft in height, about 5 in. diameter; ringed; often leaning and swaying; produces many aerial roots as much as 10 ft high; topped by crownshaft. **Petiole:** 1 ft long; slender; grooved above; bases form crownshaft. **Leaf:** Pinnate; 5–6 ft long, 2–2½ ft wide; leaflets in four rows, two of which are in a horizontal plane, the other two are ascending. **Leaflets:** 1¼–2 ft long, about 1½ in. wide; blunt-ended; strongly ribbed and ridged; ruffly; the terminal pair united into one very large, rounded, ruffled leaflet; dark-green. **Flowerstalk:** Well beneath crownshaft; 20 in. long. **Flowers:** Large (for palms). **Fruit:** Oblong; 1¼ in. long, ¾ in. broad; with tiny point; dark-green, dull brown when ripe. **Seed:** Chalky white; albumen very hard. **Oddity:** Young trees have smaller leaves, with a few big, jagged leaflets.

Cultivation: Palms with stilt roots have the general reputation of being hard to grow in the United States. This may be no more than a superstition. In any case, there is quite a difference between the equatorial climate of Panama and that even of southern Florida. De Leon reports planting seeds of *S. durissima* which began germinating on the 55th day.

Close-up of the large stilt roots of a socratea. Photo by M. B. Foster.

SOLFIA

A little-known genus of pinnate-leafed palms indigenous to Samoa. (Not illustrated.)

SOMMIERIA

Three species of pinnate-leafed palms from New Guinea form this genus. They are little known to cultivation. (Not illustrated.)

STEVENSONIA
Named after a governor of Mauritius

According to the laws of nomenclature, this genus should be known as *Phoenicophorium*. It was first named for Stevenson, governor of Mauritius; the proper descriptions required by the rules were not published. Subsequently, when it was named *Phoenicophorium*, the proper procedure was employed. Since the name *Phoenicophorium*, however, commemorates the theft of one of these plants from Kew Gardens, both Bailey and Balfour prefer *Stevensonia*.

S. BORSIGIANA
(Formerly *S. grandifolia*)

A very attractive palm from the Seychelles Islands. It is curious that this one small group of islands should produce so many genera with unique and individual characteristics.

The leaves of *Stevensonia* are pinnately nerved, simple, solid leaves, the pinnately nerved segments being divided for a short distance at the outer edges. They are very impressive

Young specimen of *Stevensonia* sp. growing at the Retreat, garden of Mr. and Mrs. A. C. Langlois, at Nassau, Bahamas.

objects. Though *Stevensonia* is the most abundant of all the Seychelles palms in its native island, it is by no means common elsewhere.

Common name: None. **Origin:** Seychelles Islands, from sea level to 1,000 ft. **Sex:** Monoecious. **Trunk:** Slender, to 50 ft or more; spiny when young; smooth with age; ringed. **Petiole:** Short; 9–18 in. long; smooth; with short spines on base; young plants have spiny petioles. **Leaf:** Simple, entire, pinnately veined; 3–6 ft long, 1½–3 ft broad; arching strongly; indented about the outer edges. **Leaflets:** These are not really leaflets but divisions in a solid leaf which are separated on the outside 6 in. or more into leaflets (unless farther divided by the wind). **Flowerstalk:** From lower leaves; 3–6 ft long; much branched; not exceeding leaves. **Fruit:** Oblong ovoid; ⅓ in. long, ⅙ in. broad; greenish-yellow, becoming orange-red. **Seed:** Albumen ruminate.

Cultivation: The few attempts made at raising *Stevensonia* in Florida have not so far passed the seedling stage. Vero Beach Nursery had hundreds of seedlings, all of which failed to survive a temperature of 45°F.

Bailey's *Cyclopedia of Horticulture* states that *S. grandifolia* seems to be excessively tender in Florida but believes it might succeed if given protection until it reached considerable size.

STRONGYLOCARYUM

A genus of three species of pinnate-leafed palms native to the Solomon Islands. (Not illustrated.)

Young specimen of *Stevensonia* growing in a tub in a garden in Bombay, India. At this stage, the plant is very spiny, but will become smooth with age. Reproduced from Blatter's *Palms of British India and Ceylon.*

Photograph sent in by T. Satake, taken in Bogor Botanic Gardens, Java, where it is labeled *Stevensonia grandifolia.*

SYAGRUS*†
Greek, wild pig
(Formerly *Cocos*, also *Glaziova*)

A genus originally separated from the genus *Cocos*.
The four species described cover a wide variety.

S. WEDDELLIANA
Named for H. A. Weddell, collector in South America

This small graceful palm, the most common of the species, is generally seen as a potted plant for indoor use. In the juvenile state, the slim leaflets are only 3–6 in. long and the general appearance is very delicate. (Not illustrated.)
Common name: None. **Origin:** Rio de Janeiro, Brazil. **Sex:** Monoecious. **Trunk:** To 6–7 ft tall, slender, 2 in. thick; mostly covered with leafbases and dark network of fibers. **Petiole:** 2 ft long; base fibrous with dark-brown hair. **Leaf:** Pinnate; to 5 ft long, slender and graceful; arching; often touching the ground. **Leaflets:** 5 in. long; very slender and pointed;

Syagrus macrocarpa in California. Photo courtesy of Huntington Botanical Gardens.

green above, much paler beneath. **Flowerstalk:** From lower leaf axils; erect; 5 ft or more. **Flowers:** Yellowish; fragrant. **Fruit:** Globose oblong; ½ in. long; with abrupt short point; orange.

S. MACROCARPA
Latin, large-fruited
(Also known as *S. procopiana*)

A taller species, with attractive feathery leaves.
Common name: None. **Origin:** Brazil. **Sex:** Monoecious. **Trunk:** To 15 ft or more, diameter to 6 in.; ringed. **Petiole:** 2–3 ft long; covered with white, fuzzy wool. **Leaf:** Pinnate; 6–10 ft long; arched; leaflets set in various planes in clusters of four. **Leaflets:** In clusters of four; light-green. **Flowerstalk:** From lower leaf axils; 2–3 ft long. **Fruit:** Large, obloid; 3½ in. long, 1¾ in. thick; greenish-yellow; fibrous; 1-seeded.

S. CORONATA
Latin, crowned

An attractive species whose adhering leafbases form a compact, spiral pattern on the trunk. The leaves are erect and firmly arching.

Syagrus coronata at Fairchild Tropical Garden.

Common name: None. **Origin:** Brazil. **Sex:** Monoecious. **Trunk:** To 30 ft in height, to 10 in. diameter; covered by persistent leafbases arranged in an attractive, spiral pattern. **Petiole:** Short. **Leaf:** Pinnate; to 10 ft long; very erect and arching; leaflets arranged in clusters and at various angles. **Leaflets:** 1 ft long; thick and leathery; dark-green. **Flower-stalk:** To 3 ft long; much branched. **Flowers:** Yellow; very numerous. **Fruit:** 1 in. long; fleshy; orange-colored; edible.

S. INSIGNIS
Latin, distinguished

A small-growing palm with arching leaves and slim delicate leaflets.

Common name: None. **Origin:** Brazil. **Sex:** Monoecious. **Trunk:** 3–8 ft tall, 2 in. thick; rough-surfaced. **Petiole:** Short; base brown and hairy. **Leaf:** Pinnate; to 6 ft long; arching; recurved. **Leaflets:** Slender; pointed; dark-green above, silver beneath. **Flower-stalk:** Among leaves; 4 ft long; much branched. **Fruit:** Abundant; 1 in. long; abrupt short point; greenish with pink at apex.

Syagrus insignis.

OTHER SPECIES

Syagrus treubiana is somewhat similar to *S. coronata*.

Hortus Second also describes *S. petreae* of Brazil, a trunkless species not known to be cultivated in the United States.

Syagrus sancona was brought to Fairchild Tropical Garden from Molina, Colombia, by the Foster exhibition.

M. Michalowski tells of *Syagrus lilliputiana*, which is only 4 in. in height at maturity and has leaves 12–14 in. long. It grows only in the northeast corner of Paraguay.

Hawkes lists *S. campestris*, *S. cocoides*, *S. comosa*, *S. graminifolia*, *S. oleracea*, *S. picrophylla*, all of Brazil.

S. weddelliana and *S. insignis* are popular as house plants throughout the United States. They are grown outdoors in southern California and southern Florida but require shelter from the wind. Other *Syagrus* species are grown outdoors principally in southern Florida.

Cultivation: Huntington Gardens reports that the freeze of 1937 eliminated specimens of *S. insignis* and *S. macrocarpa*, leaving only *S. weddelliana*. U.S.P.I. Garden planted seeds of *S. comosa*, which began germinating on the 316th day; a second lot began germinating on the 99th day. Seeds of *S. campicola* were only planted once and did not germinate until the 293rd day.

Syagrus treubiana at U.S.P.I. Garden at Coconut Grove, Florida.

SYNECHANTHUS

A few small, shade-loving cluster palms, differing from *Chamaedorea* in being monoecious and in certain floral details. *Synechanthus* was separated from *Chamaedorea* in 1858 by Wendland. Only one of the species is known to have been cultivated in the United States.

S. WARSCEWICZIANUS

Common name: None. **Origin:** Panama, Costa Rica. **Sex:** Monoecious. **Trunk:** To 15 ft tall, 1 in. thick; ringed; sometimes found with few brace roots at base; green. **Petiole:** 2 ft long; slender; smooth; deeply channeled above. **Leaf:** Pinnate; 3–4 ft long; 8–10 on tree; greatly varied leaflets on each side. **Leaflets:** Greatly varied; from ½–4 in. broad; terminal ones still broader. **Flowerstalk:** From nodes on trunk; to 3 ft long or less. **Fruit:** Oblong; ⅝ by ¼ in.; sparse in cluster; yellow, drying black. **Seed:** Albumen ruminate.

OTHER SPECIES

S. angustifolia: similar to *S. warscewiczianus.*

Bailey describes *S. mexicanus*, a trunkless species from Mexico, and *S. fibrosus* from Costa Rica and Guatemala. These are not cultivated in the United States and are not described here.

Synechanthus warscewiczianus in Panama.
Photo by A. C. Langlois.

Cultivation: De Leon reports seeds of *S. warscewiczianus* germinated within 2 months. Plants require shade and good drainage.

TAENIANTHERA

A little-known genus of pinnate-leafed South American palms, native to Brazil, Colombia and Peru. (Not illustrated.)

TAVEUNIA

A monotypic genus of pinnate-leafed palm. Its one species is native only in the Fiji Islands and is rarely encountered elsewhere. (Not illustrated.)

TESSMANNIODOXA

A little-known genus of pinnate-leafed palms native to Brazil. (Not illustrated.)

Top of another *Synechanthus warscewiczianus* with flower cluster. Reprinted from *Gentes Herbarum*.

TEYSMANNIA
Named for S. E. Teysmann

T. ALTIFRONS
Latin, tall-fronded

This one species from Sumatra is unique because of its large, simple, undivided, paddle-shaped leaves. The great leaves of this palm were much valued for roofing huts, because they are large, solid, and durable, and easily arranged for rainproofing. It is not cultivated in the United States, unless in special collections.

Common name: None. **Origin:** Sumatra. **Sex:** Hermaphrodite. **Trunk:** 7 ft tall, usually much shorter; thick; sometimes completely subterranean. **Petiole:** 2½–3 ft long; spines on base. **Leaf:** Simple and undivided; 8 ft long, 2 ft wide; rigid; leathery; notched along edge; pinnately nerved. **Leaflets:** None. **Flowerstalk:** 6 in. long; down-curved; branched; fuzzy, red. **Fruit:** Globose; 1½ in. thick; brown; warts on surface.

Teysmannia altifrons. Photograph sent in from Johore, Malaya, and loaned by N. de Leon.

Leaf of *Teysmannia altifrons.* Photograph courtesy of N. de Leon.

Thrinax parviflora in Florida.

Thrinax parviflora in Florida.
Photo by H. F. Loomis.

THRINAX*
Greek, fan

A genus of handsome, slender, fan palms, native to southern Florida and the West Indies. They grow abundantly on some of the Florida Keys.

Thrinax palms have slender graceful trunks; the leaves of some species are almost perfectly round. The glossy green leaflets are divided about halfway to the base and are fastened together with strong, bright-yellow ribs. These ribs surround the leaf center, and the whole leaf shimmers with a gay, golden-green luster.

The shiny, white, pea-sized fruits are on long stalks that reach out about as far as the leaves, or sometimes a little beyond.

The leaflets of some species are green on both sides, as in *T. parviflora;* other species have leaflets with silvery backs, as *T. microcarpa.*

Many species have been named and described over the years and the confusion in the nomenclature is almost beyond repair. To quote Blatter, "but with regard to their names . . .

it is difficult to imagine a greater confusion."

Beccari said "A critical revision of the literature of the *Thrinax* would be a bold, if not an impossible, undertaking."

Under the circumstances, only a few very old, established species are described and mentioned here.

Sargent in 1899 established two new species: *T. floridana* and *T. keyensis;* but these names are not generally accepted as valid by botanists today. Many plants are still offered under these names, but they should be under their older, original names as listed at the end of this article.

T. PARVIFLORA
(*T. floridana*)

Common name: Peaberry or thatch palm. **Origin:** Florida Keys, Bahama Islands, Cuba, Jamaica, Haiti. **Sex:** Hermaphrodite. **Trunk:** 9–27 ft tall, and probably more; 4–6 in. thick; enlarged at base by mass of tight rootlike growths. **Petiole:** 2–3 ft long; bases reddish and enclosed in hairy fiber. **Leaf:** Palmate; 3 ft across; cut halfway to base into about 50 segments forming almost a complete circle around the petiole. Segments are joined together by yellow ribs which are very prominent on the upper side. Short hastula protrudes from leaf center. **Segments:** 1 in. broad; points rather short, not long and narrow; green on both sides, under side usually a little paler. **Flowerstalk:** Among leaves; 3 ft long or more; equals or exceeds leaves; branched. **Flowers:** Very small. **Fruit:** Almost perfectly globular, ¼ in. diameter; white when ripe; attached to branches of flowerstalk by short pedicel. **Seed:** ³⁄₁₆ in. diameter; globular; albumen not ruminate but having a central cavity.

T. MICROCARPA
Latin, small-fruited

The differences from *T. parviflora* are printed in italics.

Common name: Peaberry or thatch palm. **Origin:** Southern Florida, Panama, West Indies. **Sex:** Hermaphrodite. **Trunk:** To 30 ft tall, *but usually 9–12 ft, generally shorter than T. parviflora and thicker, 8–12 in. diameter.* Base enlarged by masses of tight, rootlike growths. **Petiole:** 2–3 ft long; base reddish, covered with woolly webbing. **Leaf:** Palmate; 2–3 ft across, divided for about half their length. The leaf is usually less completely round than in *T. parviflora*, the segments *describing approximately a semicircle around the petiole, or, if segments continue beyond the 180°*, they are inclined to be quite small and to stand off at more of a right angle to the petiole than the other segments. Short hastula protrudes from leaf center. **Segments:** 1 in. broad; shiny *gray green above, light gray beneath.* **Flowerstalk:** Among leaves; 3 ft long or more; projecting as far as leaves, or beyond them. **Flowers:** Very small. **Fruit:** *Globular; ⅛ in. diameter;* albumen homogenous, but containing a central cavity.

OTHER SPECIES

Hortus Second describes: *T. excelsa* (Jamaica), trunk to 20 ft in height; leaflets with silvery backs; *T. morrisii* (Anguilla), low trunk, 2–6 ft in height; leaflets green both sides, sometimes slightly glaucous beneath.

T. floridana is correctly = *T. parviflora.*
T. keyensis is correctly = *T. microcarpa.*
T. wendlandiana is correctly = *T. parviflora.*

Cultivation: *Thrinax* palms grow very slowly but require little special care. The small seeds germinate readily within a few weeks.

Thrinax microcarpa. The leaves of this species are silvery underneath, distinguishing them from those of *T. parviflora.* Photo by H. F. Loomis.

An unusually tall specimen of *T. microcarpa.* Photo by H. F. Loomis.

TRACHYCARPUS*†
Greek, rough fruit

Several species of hardy fan palms native to China, Japan, and the Himalayas, in regions where trees are often covered with snow.

They are widely planted on the west coast of the United States, in California, and even occasionally as far north as Oregon. On the east coast, they are grown as far north as North Carolina, and a few have been successful in Georgia, withstanding temperatures as low as 10°F.

T. FORTUNEI
(Sometimes still found in nurseries as *Chamerops excelsa*)

The most widely planted species of the genus.
Common name: Chinese windmill palm. **Origin:** Central and eastern China. **Sex:**

Trachycarpus fortunei, the windmill palm, grown in San Marino, California. Old leafbases with their long, dark-brown fibers adhere to the trunk for years. Photo courtesy of Huntington Botanical Gardens.

Monoecious. **Trunk:** Single; slender, 10–40 ft high; leafbases adhere for long periods, covering the trunk with a mat of their dark-brown fibers. **Petiole:** 1½ ft long; toothed; base densely covered with long brown fibers. **Leaf:** Palmate; 3 ft diameter; fan-shaped; divided almost to base. **Segments:** Stiff, glaucous underneath; dark-green above. **Flowerstalk:** Small; inconspicuous. **Flowers:** Yellow; fragrant. **Fruit:** 3-lobed; kidney-shaped; ½ in. long; blue when ripe.

T. MARTIANUS
(Also known as *T. khasianus*.)

Common name: None. **Origin:** Eastern Himalayas, northern Burma, Assam. **Sex:** Monoecious. **Trunk:** To 50 ft; single; slender; mostly naked, with some leafbases adhering at top. **Petiole:** 3 ft long; toothed; base covered with reddish brown hair. **Leaf:** Palmate; 3 ft diameter. **Segments:** Dark, shiny green. **Flowerstalk:** 1½ ft long; branched. **Flowers:** White. **Fruit:** Obloid; ½ in. long; glossy blue. **Seed:** Deeply furrowed.

Trachycarpus martianus grows more slowly than *T. fortunei* and leaf fibers do not generally adhere except at the top of the trunk. Photo courtesy of Huntington Botanical Gardens.

OTHER SPECIES

T. caespitosus (China): a species with multiple trunks, rare in the United States.

T. takil (Western Himalayas): a species with short, robust trunk slow-growing.

Huntington Gardens has *T. caespitosus, T. fortunei, T. martianus, T. nana, T. takil,* and *T. wagnerianus.*

Hortus Second mentions *T. wagnerianus.*

T. excelsus is correctly = *T. fortunei.*

T. khasianus is correctly = *T. martianus.*

Cultivation: Plants are very hardy to cold. One specimen of *T. fortunei* has been growing for years in the open in the Royal Botanical Gardens at Edinburgh, Scotland. Seeds are readily obtainable and germinate within 2 months. Plants grow poorly in southern Florida compared to those in California, perhaps because of temperature or rainfall. *T. martianus* grows more slowly than *T. fortunei.*

TRITHRINAX*†
Greek, triple-pronged palm, probably alluding to leaf division

Three species of stiff-leafed palms from Brazil and Argentina. Their most distinctive characteristic is the beautifully intricate fibrous pattern that covers the trunk. This pattern is formed of the woven webbing and long slender spines that grow out of the adherent leaf-bases.

Trachycarpus takil in San Marino, California. Grows the most slowly and has the most robust trunk. Photo courtesy of Huntington Botanical Gardens.

T. ACANTHOCOMA

Common name: None. **Origin:** Brazil. **Sex:** Hermaphrodite. **Trunk:** Single; to 12 ft tall, 3–4 in. thick; covered with leafbases, forming a spiral pattern of webbing and long spines. **Petiole:** Short; base covered with webbing and slender spines 3–6 in. long. **Leaf:** Palmate; to 3 ft across; deeply cleft into about 40 segments. **Segments:** Rigid; long-pointed; split at apex; central segments long, side ones shorter; basal ones very short; gray-green above, paler green beneath. **Flowerstalk:** From lower leaf axils; 2 ft long; much branched. **Flowers:** Creamy white. **Fruit:** ¾ in. thick; globular; yellow-green. **Oddity:** Fruits when very young.

OTHER SPECIES

T. brasiliensis (Southern Brazil to Paraguay), similar to above; fruit smaller, ½ in. diameter. In this species, flowering may begin when trunk is a few feet high. The creamy white, compact inflorescences, at first covered by a pure white spathe, often appear several at a time and create a strikingly beautiful effect.

T. campestris (Argentina), a dwarf, compact palm, with multiple stems and unique leaflets, the upper surfaces of which are covered with a white woolly fuzz, the undersides being glossy. Huntington Gardens report that the leaves on their plant are almost white. Fruit is 1 in. diameter.

Cultivation: All species of *Trithrinax* are considered reasonably hardy to cold, *T. brasiliensis* being considered the most hardy. The plants grow slowly.

The interesting trunk pattern formed by the leafbases (and their fibers) of *Trithrinax acanthocoma* and its rather spectacular flower cluster. Photo courtesy of Huntington Botanical Gardens.

VEITCHIA*
Named for James Veitch, British nurseryman (1792–1863)
(Including plants formerly known as *Adonidia* and *Vitiphoenix*)

Veitchia is a large genus of moderate to tall, single-trunked, pinnate-leafed palms, whose slender trunks are topped by glossy green crownshafts under which are borne clusters of attractive red fruits.

There are 18 species which are native to the Philippine Islands, New Hebrides, New Caledonia, and the Fiji Islands.

The 5 species described below are believed to be the most widely cultivated and are all known to be in cultivation in the United States.

V. MERRILLII
Species name dedicated to E. D. Merrill
(Formerly *Adonidia merrillii*)

A medium-sized palm, whose prominent, smooth crownshaft, and stiffly arching leaves have a well-groomed, formal appearance, at times enhanced by large clusters of very ornamental bright-red fruits.

Small enough for most gardens, its popularity has greatly increased in the last decade, particularly in southern Florida.

Veitchia (formerly *Adonidia*) *merrillii* at Fairchild Tropical Garden.

Adonidia merrillii was officially joined with the genus *Veitchia merrillii* by an article by Moore published in *Gentes Herbarum*, vol. 8, August, 1957, page 501ff.

Common name: Manila palm. **Origin:** Philippine Islands. **Sex:** Monoecious. **Trunk:** 15–20 ft, usually much less; smooth; tapering to crownshaft; closely but faintly ringed. **Petiole:** Short; smooth. **Leaf:** Pinnate; to 6 ft, usually less; rigidly arched; 50 pairs of leaflets, pointing stiffly upward. **Leaflets:** Sword-shaped; 18–30 in. long; broad; bright-green. **Flowerstalk:** From trunk, below crownshaft; much branched; stems almost white. **Flowers:** Yellow-green and white. **Fruit:** Egg-shaped; 1¼ in. long; with point; bright-red; smooth; glossy; very attractive. **Seed:** Oblong; ⅞ in. long; germination period short, 3–4 weeks in Florida.

V. JOANNIS

A species growing at Fairchild Tropical Garden, but not generally much found in private gardens in the United States. According to descriptions in *Gentes Herbarum*, vol. 8, this tree is very variable, reaching a height of 100 ft in the wild state and "in cultivation to 37 ft or more."

The trunk is 10–11 in. through and slightly thickened at the base. The petiole is short. The new leaves, 6–10 ft long, are ascending, the old ones horizontal. The 70–80 pairs of lustrous, dark-green leaflets droop at an angle of 45° and vary in length from 1–2½ ft. They are 2 in. broad, or less, and are cut off squarely or obliquely at the apex. The flowerstalk

Veitchia joannis at Fairchild Tropical Garden in Florida.

Veitchia joannis. A tall specimen at the Botanical Garden, Rio de Janeiro, Brazil. Photo by A. C. Langlois.

grows from below the crownshaft, is much branched, and bears beautiful red fruit, about 1–1½ in. long and ¾ in. through. Native to the Fiji Islands.

V. MONTGOMERYANA
(Formerly *V. joannis*)

This species is much like *V. joannis*, but grows to 40 ft high. It has been stated that the leaves and petioles are more ascending and less horizontal and that the leaflets are less drooping in *V. montgomeryana* than in *V. joannis*. These are conditions that must vary in individual trees and are difficult to use for identification. The fruit is about the same size as in *V. joannis*. Origin unknown, possibly New Hebrides.

Plants of *V. montgomeryana* have been cultivated for many years under the name of *V. joannis*, in private collections and in various botanical gardens, including Fairchild Tropical Garden. *V. montgomeryana* was separated from *V. joannis* by Moore in an article in *Gentes Herbarum*, vol. 8, pages 494–495.

V. WININ

This is a palm similar to *V. montgomeryana* but is said to grow to 65 ft in height. The fruit is smaller—about ½ in. long. The angles of the petioles and leaflets are said to be like *V. montgomeryana* instead of horizontal and drooping as in *V. joannis*. Commences to fruit when 4–6 years old. Native to Malekula Island, New Hebrides.

V. SESSILIFOLIA [1]
(Formerly *Vitiphoenix sessilifolia*)

This species is rare in cultivation and is included here because the genus *Vitiphoenix* has been united with *Veitchia* by an article published in *Gentes Herbarum*, vol. 8, page 487. Native to Fiji.

Cultivation: *V. merrillii* grows rapidly and fruits readily. Seeds germinate quickly, usually within 1 month. Not a good plant for locations colder than southern Florida. Each frost seems to spoil their appearance, though they usually survive.

V. joannis seeds, as reported by Johnston, germinate easily without special attention. The plants are fast growers and seem reasonably hardy to cold.

U.S.P.I. Gardens reports planting seeds of *V. joannis* that began germinating in 82 days; *V. montgomeryana*, much as *V. joannis*; *V. winin*, much as *V. joannis*, except that early reports suggest that *V. winin* may be by far the fastest growing of all the veitchias.

All veitchias at Fairchild Tropical Garden are listed as hardy.

---

[1]Burret and Potztal still list *Vitiphoenix* as a valid genus and would consider this plant to be *Vitiphoenix sessilifolia*.

Veitchia montgomeryana at Mrs. Jennings' garden in Florida. A new species recently separated from *Veitchia joannis*.

VERSCHAFFELTIA
Dedicated to Ambrose Verschaffelt, Belgian horticulturist, 1825–1886

V. SPLENDIDA
Latin, splendid

V. splendida is perhaps the most beautiful of the many unique palms, native only to the Seychelles Islands.

The unusually broad, deep-green, entire leaves and spectacularly prominent stilt roots are strikingly beautiful.

Young plants have spiny trunks and petioles and troughlike, entire leaves.

In mature trees, the spines gradually disappear and the simple leaves are split or frayed into pinnate segments, retaining, nevertheless, much of the original outline.

Common name: None. **Origin:** Seychelles Islands. **Sex:** Monoecious. **Trunk:** To 80 ft in height, usually much less; 6 in. diameter; tapering to top; spiny when young; vaguely ringed; set on long aerial roots. **Petiole:** 6–12 in. long; pale-green; deeply grooved on face; spiny when young; base white granular. **Leaf:** 5–8 ft long, 4 ft wide; simple; pinnately veined; divided by wind and time into irregular, pinnate leaflets; but entire when young, or sheltered; deep-green. **Leaflets:** Partial irregular leaflets formed with age; deep-green. **Flower-stalk:** 3–6 ft long; among leaves. **Fruit:** Globular; 1 in. diameter; green. **Seed:** Very hard; ridged endwise; albumen much ruminate.

Cultivation: Bailey, in *Gentes Herbarum*, vol. 7, page 48, states that on the islands of Mahe

Verschaffeltia splendida, group of trees. Reprinted from Blatter's *Palms of British India and Ceylon*.

and Silhouette in the Seychelles, *Verschaffeltia* is found as a frequent tree between 1,000 and 2,000 ft elevation and that it is most frequently found propped on steep hillsides. Bailey's *Standard Cyclopedia* says that *Verschaffeltia* does not thrive in Florida.

Balfour, in *Flora of Mauritius and the Seychelles*, states that it is "very common amongst rocks in all the islands."

Many other palms, native to Mauritius and the Seychelles Islands, are well established in southern Florida (*Latania*, *Mascarena*, *Dictyosperma*, *Nephrosperma*). It is to be hoped that attempts will be made to plant *Verschaffeltia* among some rocks in southern Florida. It is one of the most impressive of all palms and well worth any special care it may require.

VITIPHOENIX*
(See *Veitchia*)

This genus still appears as a valid genus on Max Burret's 1956 list. *Vitiphoenix* has recently been transferred to *Veitchia* by H. E. Moore Jr. of the Bailey Hortorium. In this book, it is included with *Veitchia*.

VONITRA

A genus of pinnate-leafed palms, native to Madagascar. The 5 species show great variety. Some have single, some multiple trunks. In some species, the trunks are smooth; in others they are covered with adhering leafbases and hairy fibers. They vary from 6–50 ft in height. (Not illustrated.)

Verschaffeltia splendida in Bogor Botanic Gardens, Java. Photo by T. Satake.

Verschaffeltia sp. in Bogor Botanic Gardens, Java. Photo by T. Satake.

Verschaffeltia splendida, small tree showing close-up of large simple leaf. Photo by T. Satake.

WALLICHIA
Named after Nathaniel Wallich, superintendent of Botanical Gardens, Calcutta

A genus of very exotic palms from India and Malaya.
One of the few pinnate genera in which leaves are induplicate. [1]
Most species are low, pinnate-leafed cluster palms, distinguished by their odd-shaped leaflets.

W. DISTICHA
Latin, having two rows

One species, *W. disticha*, is distinguished by the unusual (distichous) arrangement of the leaves and petioles. They project in two vertical rows on diametrically opposite sides of the single trunk. This creates the weird and striking effect of a flat tree. (See illustration.)

[1]The other genera are *Arenga, Caryota, Didymosperma, Phoenix.*

Wallichia disticha with leaves forming two distinct vertical rows on two diametrically opposite sides of the trunk. Reprinted from Blatter's *Palms of British India and Ceylon.*

W. disticha is the only species of *Wallichia* with a single trunk, or with a trunk of any size.

Common name: None. **Origin:** Himalayas (between 2,000–4,000 ft alt.). **Sex:** Monoecious. **Trunk:** Single; 10–20 ft tall, 6–12 in. diameter. **Petiole:** 2 ft long; scurfy. **Leaf:** Pinnate; 7–9 ft long; distichous; erect. **Leaflets:** 1–2 ft long, 2–3 in. broad; stiff and ribbed; green above, somewhat glaucous beneath; narrow at base; cut off and jagged at wide apex, with a little lobe about the middle of each side. **Flowerstalk:** 6–8 ft long; pendulous. **Fruit:** Obloid; ½ in. long; top obscurely lobed; reddish.

W. CARYOTOIDES

A certain few plants of *Arenga wightii* have been mistakenly distributed in southern Florida under the name of *W. caryotoides*.

Common name: None. **Origin:** Bengal, Burma. **Sex:** Monoecious. **Trunk:** Clustered; with little or no trunk above ground. **Petiole:** 4 ft long; roundish. **Leaf:** Pinnate; 8–9 ft long; curving or arching; oblong in outline; only about a dozen leaflets. **Leaflets:** Very irregularly shaped; long oblong, with sides indented and toothed; green above, white beneath. **Flowerstalk:** Shorter than leaves. **Fruit:** Ovoid oblong; 1 in. long; size of nutmeg; dull purple.

Wallichia caryotoides in the Botanic Garden at Peradeniya, Ceylon. Reproduced from Blatter's *Palms of British India and Ceylon.*

W. DENSIFLORA
Latin, dense flowers

From Assam and the tropical Himalayas; grows up to 4,000 ft, in shady, moist valleys.

A cluster palm, not unlike *W. caryotoides*, but with many more leaflets, bright-green above, white beneath. The terminal leaflets are wedge-shaped and three-lobed; and the tiny flowers are both purple and yellow.

Not known to be cultivated in the United States.

W. oblongifolia is believed to be a synonym for *W. densiflora*.

Cultivation: Bailey's *Standard Cyclopedia of Horticulture* states that *W. caryotoides* thrives in shady positions in southern Florida. Associates tell the author that wallichias have been grown in southern Florida gardens for years. They are by no means commonplace, however, and there are no wallichias listed at Fairchild Tropical Garden, at U.S.P.I. Garden, or at Huntington Gardens.

Wallichia densiflora (sometimes found as *W. oblongifolia*). Photograph courtesy A. Dilmy, Bogor Botanic Gardens, Java.

A variety of *Wallichia densiflora* in bloom at Bogor Botanic Gardens, Java. Photo courtesy A. Dilmy, Bogor Botanic Gardens, Java.

Washingtonia filifera in its native habitat of Palm Springs Canyon. Washingtonias are the only palms indigenous to California. Photo courtesy of Huntington Botanical Gardens.

WASHINGTONIA*†

Named for George Washington

The only genus indigenous to California, the *Washingtonia* palms have, in a comparatively short time, become one of the most widely planted of all palms. They have been known to horticulturists only since 1879, when Herman Wendland published a botanical account and established the generic name, *Washingtonia*.

Their most distinguishing characteristic is the shag, or petticoat of dead leaves that adheres to the trunk for many years. If not removed, these dead leaves form a solid column, as thick as 8 ft, reaching from the ground 40–50 ft to the top of the trunk.

Washingtonias are much used for street planting, and a boulevard, both sides of which are lined with these strange haystacks, is a sight to be remembered.

There have been other species of *Washingtonia*, but the two species mentioned below are now generally considered to be the only two valid species. *W. filifera* is the northern species, native to California, and *W. robusta* is the southern species, native to Mexico.

W. FILIFERA
Latin, bearing filaments, or threads

Common name: Petticoat palm. **Origin:** Southern California, western Arizona, north-western Mexico. **Sex:** Hermaphrodite. **Trunk:** To 50 ft tall; thick, to 3 ft diameter; not enlarged at base; upper part, or sometimes all the trunk, covered with a huge shag or petti-coat of dead leaves. If leaves are cut off, the leafbases form a covering for the trunk, compact, but with no regular pattern. The gray surface of trunk, if exposed, is marked with vertical chinks or ridges that are more prominent than the rings. **Petiole:** Long, to 6 ft; 6 in. broad near base; margins armed with prominent teeth; green in color; leafbases are sometimes brown or reddish. **Leaf:** To 6 ft or more across; divided more than halfway to base; many long threads attached to segments and sinuses throughout life of tree. **Segments:** 50 or more gray-green; not glaucous. **Flowerstalk:** From lower leaves; 9–12 ft long; erect at first, then hanging with fruit, and eventually becoming involved in the shag of dead leaves, of which it becomes a part. **Flowers:** Small; numerous; white. **Fruit:** ⅓ in. long, ¼ in. broad; ovoid; lightly wrinkled. **Seed:** Single; same shape as fruit, but trifle smaller.

W. ROBUSTA
Latin, robust
(Generally known as the southern *Washingtonia*)

A species native to northwest Mexico, with flowers and fruits very similar to *W. filifera*, but differing in the following particulars:

Washingtonia sp. in Palm Beach, Florida.

Trunk: Brownish, instead of grayish. Rings more conspicuous, less vertical chinks. Grows to greater height—to 80 ft. More slender, except at expanded base. If shag is removed, adhering leafbases form criss-cross pattern, similar to the palmettos. **Petiole:** Reddish-brown, instead of green; conspicuously brown at base. Usually more toothed than *W. filifera*, in young trees; less toothed in mature trees. Not as long, to 4 ft. **Leaf:** Bright-green, and usually not as wide as in *W. filifera*. Many long threads only in youth, disappearing with age. **Segments:** Bright-green, instead of gray-green. **Oddity:** The species named *robusta* is really not as robust as *W. filifera*.

Because different trees of any one species vary considerably, these differences are not always clear cut and recognizable. Except in very typical cases, identification is not easy.

Cultivation: Both species are hardy and are cultivated in California, Arizona, Texas, and the Gulf states, and along the east coast as far north as South Carolina. *W. robusta* is said to be better adapted for planting near the coast than is the desert variety.

Mr. Bert Wheeler, a palm fancier in Houston, Texas, reports that during a severe freeze period in the Houston area, in the winter of 1950, so far as he could learn not many *W. filiferas* were lost, while the *W. robustas* were practically wiped out.

Hume says that *W. filifera* is much hardier but often suffers during periods of excessive rainfall from too much water. He says in severe winters leaves of *W. robusta* are destroyed but that the plants come back rapidly.

Johnston reports *Washingtonia* seeds germinate readily and well within 2 months. The plants are hardy and easy to grow in any palm area of the United States.

Well-grown tree of *W. filifera* with lower part of shag removed. *W. filifera* usually has a more robust trunk than *W. robusta*. Reprinted from *Gentes Herbarum*.

Row of perfect *Washingtonia* palms lining a thoroughfare in Riverside, California. Reprinted from *Gentes Herbarum*.

WELFIA

Tall, pinnate-leafed palms from Central America, not generally cultivated in the United States. Plants are not available for study and the description is from written records.

W. GEORGII

Common name: None. **Origin:** Panama, Costa Rica. **Sex:** Monoecious. **Trunk:** To 70 ft in height; ringed; 1 ft thick. **Petiole:** Short; firm. **Leaf:** Pinnate; to 20 ft in height; arching; leaflets drooping; glossy. **Leaflets:** Numerous; leathery; narrowed at base; many-nerved; unequal in size; green above, whitish underneath. **Flowerstalk:** 2 ft long; branched; stout; pendulous. **Fruit:** Almond-shaped; 2 in. long; dark violet.

Welfia georgii in a valley in Costa Rica. Photo by A. C. Langlois.

WENDLANDIELLA

A little-known genus of pinnate-leafed palms, native to Brazil.

WETTINIA

A genus of pinnate-leafed palms, native to tropical America and distinguished by its large and unusual fruit. (See illustration.)

WETTINIICARPUS

A genus of pinnate-leafed palms, native to Colombia, noted for its strange fruit and the unusual way it grows from the tree. (See illustration.)

WISSMANNIA

A genus of palmate-leafed palms from North Africa. (Not illustrated.)

YUYBA
Pronounced you-ee-bah

A group of delicate, slender palms, with small, pinnate leaves, divided into two or more broad, odd-shaped segments.

The genus is not known to be cultivated in the United States. Its miniature proportions make it particularly suitable for indoor planting anywhere or for protected outdoor areas in southern Florida. Its unusual leaflets would be sure to attract favorable attention.

Unusual fruit of *Wettinia maynensis*. Photo by M. B. Foster.

Fruit of *Wettiniicarpus fascicularis*. Photo by Eva Potztal.

Y. SIMPLICIFRONS
Latin, simple-leafed
(Formerly *Y. trinitensis*)

Common name: Yu-yu palm. **Origin:** Trinidad. **Sex:** Monoecious. **Trunk:** Clustered; to 3 ft high, less than ½ in. thick; reedlike. **Petiole:** 8–12 in. long. **Leaf:** Pinnate; 2-lobed. **Leaflets:** Each lobe about 12 in. long, 2 in. broad at base; curving out to a central breadth of 3–4 in., then down to a short point; dull green; 6 or 7 main ribs. **Flowerstalk:** Short, 1½ in. long; simple. **Fruit:** Globular; ⅓ in. long; red. **Seed:** Single; ¼ in. long; albumen homogenous.

OTHER SPECIES

Gentes Herbarum, vol. 8, page 173–176 also describes *Y. gleasonii* (British Guiana) and *Y. schultesii* (Colombia).

ZALACCELLA

A little-known genus of pinnate-leafed palms, native to Cochin China. Almost unknown to cultivation. (Not illustrated.)

Yuyba simplicifrons (formerly *Y. trinitensis*) with its simple two-lobed leaves. Growing in Trinidad. Photo by A. C. Langlois.

ZOMBIA*
(Formerly *Oothrinax*)

Z. ANTILLARUM
Latin, of the Antilles

A strange cluster palm introduced to this country by the U.S.P.I. Garden at Coconut Grove, Florida, in 1927, from seed collected by O. F. Cook in Haiti.

Each slender trunk is covered with an unbelievably intricate pattern of woven fabric, combined with rings of long, downward-pointing spines. The trunk is actually enveloped by the old leafbases, whose fibers and spines weave themselves into this complex and beautifully fashioned effect as they grow.

One tree at Chapman Field, which already has over a dozen trunks, has fruited, and seeds have been distributed to a few enthusiasts. A few young plants are beginning to appear in southern Florida nurseries.

Common name: None. **Origin:** Haiti, on high or dry land. **Sex:** Monoecious. **Trunk:** Multiple; to 10 ft high, 2 in. thick; covered with fibers of adhering leafbases. **Petiole:** 2–3 ft long, ⅓ in. thick; base much expanded and completely encircling trunk; covered with two-directional fibers which are interwoven; the leftover ends of these fibers project as spines. **Leaf:** Palmate; fan-shaped; 24 in. long, 34 in. wide; cut ½ or ⅔ of the way to base into 30–40 segments. **Segments:** 24 in. long; center ones 2 in. broad, outer ones very narrow; dull-green

A close look at a *Zombia antillarum* with a glimpse at the tree's attractively marked trunk. Photo by H. F. Loomis.

above, silvery underneath. **Flowerstalk:** Among leaves; 18 in. long; branched. **Flowers:** Small; white. **Fruit:** Globular; ¾ in. diameter; white. **Seed:** ⅓ in. diameter; irregularly creased and veined; albumen homogenous.

There is only one species of *Zombia*.

Cultivation: *Zombia* seeds germinate readily within 2 months. The plants grow very slowly. U.S.P.I. Garden reports planting seeds of *Z. antillarum*, the first germination appearing in 48 days.

The attractive pattern formed by old leafbases and their surrounding fabric and spines on the trunk of *Zombia antillarum*.

Close-up of the details of the trunk of *Zombia antillarum*. Reprinted from *Gentes Herbarum*.

APPENDIX

AN OFFICIAL LIST OF
THE WORLD'S VALID PALM GENERA
AND SOME SYNONYMS

This list was published by Max Burret and Eva Potztal in February, 1956, in Willdenowia and reprinted as Bulletin XXI. The list was brought up to date with a few corrections by Burret and Potztal in September, 1959, and is reprinted here with their permission, and exactly as prepared by them.

The valid names are in roman type; the synonyms are in italics. The first word is always the genus name; the second word indicates the originator of the name.

Liste der Palmengattungen
einschlieglich der Synonyma

A

Acanthococos Barb. Rodr.

Acanthophoenix Wendl.

Acanthorrhiza Wendl. = Cryosophila Blume

Acanthosabal Prochowsky = Paurotis Cook

Acoelorrhaphe Wendl. = Paurotis Cook

Acrista Cook = Euterpe Gaertn.

Acrocomia Mart. = *Gastrococcus* Morales

Acrostigma Cook = Catostigma Cook et Doyle

Actinokentia Dammer

Actinophloeus Becc. = Ptychosperma Labill.

Actinorhytis Wendl. (? *Opsicocos* Wendl.)

Adelodypsis Becc. = Dypsis Noronha

Adelonenga Becc. = Hydriastele Wendl. et Drude

Adonidia Becc. = Veitchia Wendl.

Aeria Cook = Gaussia Wendl.

Aiphanes Willd. = *Curima* Cook = *Marara* Karst. = *Martinezia* R. et P. = *Tilmia* Cook

Alfonsia H. B. K. = Elaeis Jacq.

Allagoptera Nees = Diplothemium Mart.

Ammandra Cook ? = Phytelephas R. et P.

Amylocarpus Barb. Rodr. = Yuyba L. H. Bailey

Anaclasmus Griff. = Nenga Wendl. et Drude

Ancistrophyllum Mann et Wendl. = *Laccosperma* Mann et Wendl.

Anoosperma Kunze = Oncosperma Blume

Antongilia Jum. in Mus. Col. Marseille (1928) Ser. IV, VI, II 17, 19; nomen

Araucasia Benth. et Hook. = Orania Zipp.

Arausiaca Blume = Orania Zipp.

Archontophoenix Wendl. et Drude = *Loroma* Cook

Areca L. = *Mischophloeus* Scheff.

Arecastrum Becc.

Arenga Labill. = *Gomutus* Correa = *Gumutus* Spr. = *Saguerus* Rumph., Blume

Arikury Becc. = Arikuryroba Barb. Rodr.

Arikuryroba Barb. Rodr. = *Arikury* Becc.

Asterogyne Wendl.

Astrocaryum G. F. W. Meyer = *Toxophoenix* Schott.

Atitara O. Ktze. = Desmoncus Mart.

Attalea H. B. K. = *Lithocarpus* Targioni-Tozetti = *Pindarea* Barb. Rodr.

Augustinea Karst. = Pyrenoglyphis Karst.

B

Bactris Jacq.

Bacularia F. v. Muell. = Linospadix Becc.

Balaka Becc.

Barbosa Becc. = *Langsdorffia* Raddi

Barcella Drude

Barkerwebbia Becc. = Heterospathe Scheff. ex cl. Beccari

Basselinia Vieill. = *Microkentia* Wendl. = *Nephrocarpus* Dammer

Beccariophoenix Jum. et Perr.

Beethovenia Engel = Ceroxylon H. B. K.

Bejaudia Gagnep.

Bentinckia Berry = *Keppleria* Mart.

Bentinckiopsis Becc.

Bessia Raf. = Corypha L.

Bismarckia Hildebr. et Wendl.

Blancoa Blume = Didymosperma Wendl. et Drude

Blancoa O. Ktze. = Didymosperma Wendl. et Drude

Blumea Zipp. ex Miq. = Didymosperma Wendl. et Drude

Borassodendron Becc.

Borassus L. = *Lontanus* Gaertn. = *Lontarus* Adans.

Brahea Mart.

Brassiophoenix Burret

Brongniartikentia Becc.

Burretiokentia Pic. Ser.

Butia Becc.

C

Calamosagus Griff. = Korthalsia Blume

Calamus L. = *Palmijuncus* O. Ktze.

Calospathe Becc.

Calycodon Wendl. nomen = Hyospathe Mart.

Calyptrocalyx Blume = *Laccospadix* Wendl. et Drude

Calyptrogyne Wendl. = *Cocops* Cook = ? *Roebelia* Engel

Calyptronoma Griseb. (Vgl. Burret in Willdenowia I, 1 [1953] 57–58)

Campecarpus Wendl.

Carpentaria Becc. in Ann. Jard. Buitenzorg II (1885) 128; nomen

Carpoxylon Wendl. et Drude = *Kajewskia* Guillaumin

Caryota L. = *Thuessinkia* Korth. ex Miq.

Catis Cook = Euterpe Gaertn.

Catoblastus Wendl.

Catostigma Cook et Doyle = *Acrostigma* Cook

Ceratolobus Blume

Ceroxylon H. B. K. = *Beethoveniana* Engel = *Klopstockia* Karst.

Chamaedorea Willd. = *Kinetostigma* Dammer = *Nunnezharoa* O. Ktze. = *Nunnezharia* R. et P. = *Nunnezia* Willd. = *Psilostachys* Oerst. = *Spathoscaphe* Oerst. = *Stephanostachys* Klotzsch = *Stachyophorba* Liebm.

Chamaephoenix A. H. Curtiss = Pseudophoenix Wendl.

Chamaeriphes (Dill.) O. Ktze. = Hyphaene Gaertn.

Chamaeriphes (Oerst.) Gaertn. = Chamaerops L.

Chamaerops L. = *Chamaeriphes* (Oerst.) Gaertn.

Chamaethrinax Wendl. = Trithrinax Mart.

Chambeyronia Vieill.

Chelyocarpus Dammer = *Tessmanniophoenix* Burret

Chrysalidocarpus Wendl. = *Phlogella* Baill.

Chuniophoenix Burret

Cladosperma Griff. = Pinanga Blume

Cleophora Gaertn. = Latania Comm. ex Juss.

Clinosperma Becc.

Clinostigma Wendl.

Clinostigmopsis Becc. = Exorrhiza Becc.

Coccos L. (1736) = Cocos L.

Coccothrinax Sargent = *Thringis* Cook = *Thrincoma* Cook

Cocops Cook = Calyptrogyne Wendl.

Cocos L. = *Coccos* L.

Codda-Pana Adans. = Corypha L.

Coelococcus Wendl. = Metroxylon Rottb.

Coleospadix Becc.

Collinia Liebm.

Colpothrinax Griseb. et Wendl. = Pritchardia Seem. et Wendl.

Copernicia Mart.

Corozo Gis.

Corypha L. = *Bessia* Raf. = *Codda-Pana* Adans. = *Dendrema* Raf. = *Elate* L. = *Gembanga* Blume = *Kodda-Pana* Adans. = *Taliera* Mart.

Cryosophila Blume = *Acanthorrhiza* Wendl.

Cuatrecasea Dugand

Curima Cook = Aiphanes Willd.

Cyclospathe Cook = Pseudophoenix Wendl.

Cyphokentia Brongn.

Cyphophoenix Wendl.

Cyphosperma Wendl.

Cyrtostachys Blume

D

Dachel Adans. = Phoenix L.

Daemonorops Blume

Dammera K. Schum. et Lauterb. = Licuala Wurmb

Dasystachys Oerst.

Deckenia Wendl.

Deckeria Karst. = Iriartea R. et P.

Dendrema Raf. = Corypha L.

Desmoncus Mart. = *Atitara* O. Ktze. = *Jatitara* Marcgr.

Dictyocaryum Wendl.

Dictyosperma Wendl. et Drude

Didymosperma Wendl. et Drude = *Blancoa* Blume = *Blancoa* O. Ktze. = *Blumea* Zipp. ex Miq.

Diglossophyllum Wendl. et Drude = Serenoa Hook f.

Diodosperma Wendl. = Trithrinax Mart.

Diplorhipis Drude = Mauritia L. f.

Diplothemium Mart. = *Allagoptera* Nees

Dolichokentia Becc.

Doma Lam. = Hyphaene Gaertn.

Douma Poir. = Hyphaene Gaertn.

Drymophloeus Zipp.

Drypsis Duch. = Dypsis Noronha

Dypsidium Baill. = Neophloga Baill.

Dypsis Noronha = *Adelodypsis* Becc. = *Drypsis* Duch. = *Trichodypsis* Baill.

E

Elaeis Jacq. = *Alfonsia* H. B. K.

Elate L. = Corypha L.

Eleiodoxa (Becc.) Burret

Elephantusia Willd. = Phytelephas R. et P.

Eleutheropetalum (Wendl.) Oerst.

Englerophoenix O. Ktze. = Maximiliana Mart.

Eremospatha Mann et Wendl.

Erythea S. Watson = *Glaucotheca* Cook

Ethnora Cook = ? Maximiliana Mart.

Eugeissona Griff.

Euterpe Gaertn. = *Acrista* Cook = *Catis* Cook = *Prestoea* Hook. f.

Exorrhiza Becc. = *Clinostigmopsis* Becc.

F

Fulchironia Lesch. ex Desfont. = Phoenix L.

G

Gastrococcos Morales = Acrocomia Mart.

Gaussia Wendl. = *Aeria* Cook

Gembanga Blume = Corypha L.

Geonoma Willd. = *Gynestum* Poit.

Gigliolia Becc.

Glaucotheca Cook = Erythea Wats.

Glaziova Mart. = Syagrus Mart. p. pte.

Gomutus Correa = Arenga Labill.

Goniocladus Burret

Goniosperma Burret

Grisebachia Wendl. = Howea Becc.
Gronophyllum Scheff.
Guilielma Mart.
Gulubia Becc.
Gulubiopsis Becc.
Gumutus Spr. = Arenga Labill.
Gynestum Poit. = Geonoma Willd.

H

Haitiella L. H. Bailey
Haplodypsis Baill. = Neophloga Baill.
Haplophloga Baill. = Neophloga Baill.
Harina Buch. Ham. = Wallichia Roxb.
Hedyscepe Wendl.
Hemithrinax Hook. f.
Heterospathe Scheff. = *Barkerwebbia* Becc. ex cl. Beccari
Hexopetion Burret
Howea Becc. = *Grisebachia* Wendl.
Hydriastele Wendl. et Drude = *Adelonenga* Becc.
Hyophorbe Gaertn. = *Sublimia* Comm. ex Mart.
Hyospathe Mart. = *Calycodon* Wendl. nomen
Hyphaene Gaertn. = *Chamaeriphes* (Dill.) O. Ktze. = *Doma* Lam. = *Douma* Poir.

I

Iguanura Blume = *Slackia* Griff.
Inodes Cook = Sabal Adans.
Iriartea R. et P. = *Deckeria* Karst.
Iriartella Wendl.

J

Jatitara Marcgr. = Desmoncus Mart.
Jessenia Karst.
Juania Drude
Jubaea H. B. K. = *Micrococos* Phil. = *Molinaea* Bert.
Jubaeopsis Becc.

K

Kajewskia Guillaumin = Carpoxylon Wendl. et Drude

Kalbreyera Burret
Kentia Blume
Kentiopsis Brongn.
Keppleria Mart. = Bentinckia Berry
Keppleria Meissn. = Oncosperma Blume
Kinetostigma Dammer = Chamaedorea Willd.
Klopstockia Karst. = Ceroxylon H. B. K.
Kodda-Pana Adans. = Corypha L.
Korthalsia Blume = *Calamosagus* Griff.
Kunthia H. et B. = Morenia R. et P.

L

Laccospadix Wendl. et Drude = Calyptro-calyx Blume
Laccosperma Mann et Wendl. = Ancistro-phyllum Mann et Wendl.
Lacuala Blume = Licuala Wurmb
Ladoicea Miq. = Lodoicea Comm.
Langsdorffia Raddi = Barbosa Becc.
Latania Comm. ex Juss. = *Cleophora* Gaertn.
Leopoldinia Mart.
Lepidocaryon Spreng. = Lepidocaryum Mart.
Lepidocaryum Mart. = *Lepidocaryon* Spreng.
Lepidococcus Wendl. et Drude, nomen = Mauritiella Burret
Lepidorrhachis (Wendl.) Burret
Leptophoenix Becc. = Nengella Becc.
Liberbaileya Furtado = *Symphyogyne* Burret p. pte.
Licuala Wurmb = *Dammera* K. Schum. et Lauterb. = *Lacuala* Blume = *Pericycla* Blume
Linospadix Becc. = *Bacularia* F. Muell.
Lithocarpus Targioni-Tozetti = Attalea H. B. K.
Livistona R. Br. = *Saribus* Rumph in Blume
Lodoicea Comm. = *Ladoicea* Miq.
Lontanus Gaertn. = Borassus L.
Lontarus Adans. = Borassus L.
Lophospatha Burret
Loroma Cook = Archontophoenix Wendl. et Drude
Louvelia Jum. et Perr.
Loxococcus Wendl. et Drude
Lytocaryum Toledo

M

Macrocladus Griff. = Orania Zipp.
Macrophloga Becc.
Malortiea Wendl.
Manicaria Gaertn. = *Pilophora* Jacq.
Marara Karst. = Aiphanes Willd.
Martinezia R. et P. = Aiphanes Willd.
Masoala Jum.
Mascarena L. H. Bailey
Mauritia L. f. = *Diplorhipis* Drude = *Orophoma* Drude
Mauritiella Burret = *Lepidococcus* Wendl. et Drude, nomen
Maxburretia Furtado = *Symphyogyne* Burret p. pte.
Maximiliana Mart. = *Englerophoenix* O. Ktze. = ? *Ethnora* Cook
Medemia P. G. de Württemb.
Menalia Noronha = Wallichia Roxb.
Metasocratea Dugand
Metroxylon Rottb. = *Coelococcus* Wendl.
Micrococos Phil. = Jubaea H. B. K.
Microcoelum Burret et Potztal
Microkentia Wendl. = Basselinia Vieill.
Micronoma Wendl. ex Benth. et Hook. ?
Microphoenix Carriere = Phoenix L. Bastard ?
Mischolitzia Wendl. inedita
Mischophloeus Scheff. = Areca L.
Molinaea Bert. = Jubaea H. B. K.
Morenia R. et P. = *Kunthia* H. et B.
Myrialepis Becc.

N

Nannorrhops Wendl.
Nenga Wendl. = *Anaclasmus* Griff.
Nengella Becc. = *Leptophoenix* Becc.
Neodypsis Baill.
Neonicholsonia Dammer = *Woodsonia* Bailey
Neowashingtonia Sudw. = Washingtonia Wendl.
Neophloga Baill. = *Dypsidium* Baill. = *Haplodypsis* Baill. = *Haplophloga* Baill.
Neoveitchia Becc.
Nephrocarpus Dammer = Basselinia Vieill.
Nephrosperma Balf. f.

Nipa Thunb. = Nypa Wurmb
Normanbya F. Muell.
Nunnezharia R. et P. = Chamaedorea Willd.
Nunnezharoa O. Ktze. = Chamaedorea Willd.
Nunnezia Willd. = Chamaedorea Willd.
Nypa Wurmb = *Nipa* Thunb.

O

Oenocarpus Mart.
Oncocalamus Mann et Wendl.
Oncosperma Blume = *Anoosperma* Kunze = *Keppleria* Meissn.
Oniscophora Wendl. inedita, cfr. *Macrophloga*
Ophiria Becc. = Pinanga Blume
Opsiandra Cook
Opsicocos Wendl. ? = Actinorhytis Wendl.
Orania Zipp. = *Araucasia* Benth. et Hook. = *Arausiaca* Blume = *Macrocladus* Griff.
Orbignya Mart.
Oreodoxa Willd. = Roystonea Cook
Orophoma Drude = Mauritia L. f.

P

Palandra Cook = Phytelephas R. et P.
Palmijuncus O. Ktze. = Calamus L.
Paragulubia Burret
Parajubaea Burret
Paralinospadix Burret
Parascheelea Dugand
Paurotis Cook = *Acanthosabal* Prochowsky = *Acoelorrhaphe* Wendl.
Pelagodoxa Becc.
Pericycla Blume = Licuala Wurmb
Phaenix Hill = Phoenix L.
Phloga Noronha
Phlogella Baill. = Chrysalidocarpus Wendl.
Phoenicophorium Wendl. = *Stevensonia* Duncan
Phoenix L. = *Dachel* Adans. = *Fulchironia* Lesch. ex Desfont. = *Microphoenix* Carriere = *Phaenix* Hill = *Phoniphora* Neck. = *Zelonops* Raf.
Pholidocarpus Blume
Pholidostachys Wendl.
Phoniphora Neck. = Phoenix L.

Physokentia Becc.

Phytelephas R. et P. = *Ammandra* Cook = *Elephantusia* Willd. = *Palandra* Cook = *Yarina* Cook

Pigafetta Mart., Benth. et Hook. = Pigafetta Becc.

Pigafettaea Post et O. Ktze. = Pigafetta Becc.

Pigafetta Becc. = *Pigafetta* Mart., Benth. et Hook. = *Pigafettaea* Post et O. Ktze.

Pilophora Jacq. = Manicaria Gaertn.

Pinanga Blume = *Cladosperma* Griff. = *Ophiria* Becc.

Pindarea Barb. Rodr. = Attalea H. B. K.

Platenia Karst. = Syagrus Mart.

Plectis Cook

Plectocomia Mart.

Plectocomiopsis Becc.

Podococcus Mann et Wendl.

Polyandrococos Barb. Rodr.

Ponapea Becc.

Porothrinax Wendl. ex Griseb. = Thrinax Wendl.

Prestoea Hook. f. = Euterpe Gaertn.

Pritchardia Seem. et Wendl. = *Colpothrinax* Griseb. et Wendl.

Pritchardiopsis Becc.

Pseudophoenix Wendl. = *Chamaephoenix* A. H. Curtiss = *Cyclospathe* Cook = *Sargentia* Wendl. nomen

Pseudopinanga Burret

Psilostachys Oerst. = Chamaedorea Willd.

Ptychandra Scheff.

Ptychococcus Becc.

Ptychoraphis Becc.

Ptychosperma Labill. = *Actinophloeus* Becc. = *Saguaster* Rumph. = *Seaforthia* R. Br.

Pyrenoglyphis Karst. = *Augustinea* Karst.

R

Raphia P. de B. = *Sagus* Gaertn.

Rathea Karst. = Synechanthus Wendl.

Ravenea Wendl. = *Ravenia* Bouché

Ravenia Bouché = Ravenea Wendl.

Rehderophoenix Burret

Reineckia Karst. = Synechanthus Wendl.

Reinhardtia Liebm.

Rhaphis Walp. errore = Rhapis L. f.

Rhapidophyllum Wendl. et Drude

Rhapis L. f. = *Rhaphis* Walp., errore

Regelia hort. ex Wendl. = Verschaffeltia Wendl.

Rhopaloblaste Scheff.

Rhopalostylis Wendl.

Rhyticocos Becc.

Roebelia Engel ? = Calyptrogyne Wendl. oder Welfia Wendl.

Roscheria Wendl.

Roystonea O. F. Cook = *Oreodoxa* Willd.

S

Sabal Adans. = *Inodes* Cook

Saguaster Rumph. = Ptychosperma Labill.

Saguerus Rumph., Blume = Arenga Labill.

Sagus Gaertn. = Raphia P. de B.

Salacca Reinw. = *Zalacca* Reinw. ex Blume

Sargentia Wendl. nomen = Pseudophoenix Wendl.

Saribus Rumph. in Blume = Livistona R. Br.

Scheelea Karst.

Schippia Burret

Sclerosperma Mann et Wendl.

Seaforthia R. Br. = Ptychosperma Labill.

Serenaea Hook. f. = Serenoa Hook. f.

Serenoa Hook. f. = *Diglossophyllum* Wendl. et Drude = *Serenaea* Hook. f.

Sindroa Jum.

Siphokentia Burret

Slackia Griff. = Iguanura Blume

Socratea Karst.

Solfia Rechinger

Sommieria Becc.

Spathoscaphe Oerst. = Chamaedorea Willd.

Stachyophorbe Liebm. = Chamaedorea Willd.

Stephanostachys Klotzsch = Chamaedorea Willd.

Stevensonia Duncan = Phoenicophorium Wendl.

Strongylocaryum Burret

Sublimia Comm. ex Mart. = Hyophorbe Gaertn.

Syagrus Mart. p. pte. = *Glaziova* Mart. = *Platenia* Karst.

Symphyogyne Burret = Liberbaileya Furtado und Maxburretia Furtado

Synechanthus Wendl. = *Rathea* Karst. = *Reineckia* Karst.

T

Taenianthera Burret

Taliera Mart. = Corypha L.

Taveunia Burret

Tessmanniodoxa Burret

Tessmanniophoenix Burret = Chelyocarpus Dammer

Teysmannia Reichenb. et Zoll.

Thrinax L. f. = *Porothrinax* Wendl. ex Griseb.

Thrincoma Cook = Coccothrinax Sargent

Thringis Cook = Coccothrinax Sargent

Thuessinkia Korth. ex Miq. = Caryota L.

Tilmia Cook = Aiphanes Willd.

Toxophoenix Schott. = Astrocaryum G. F. W. Meyer

Trachycarpus Wendl.

Trichodypsis Baill. = Dypsis Noronha

Trithrinax Mart. = *Chamaethrinax* Wendl. = *Diodosperma* Wendl.

V

Veitchia Wendl. = *Adonidia* Becc.

Verschaffeltia Wendl. = *Regelia* hort. ex Wendl.

Vitiphoenix Becc.

Vonitra Becc.

W

Wallichia Roxb. = *Harina* Buch. Ham. = *Menalia* Noronha = *Wrightea* Roxb.

Washingtonia Wendl. = *Neowashingtonia* Sudw.

Welfia Wendl. = ? *Roebelia* Engel

Wendlandiella Dammer

Wettiniella Cook et Doyle = Wettinia Poepp. et Endl.

Wettinia Poepp. et Endl. = *Wettiniella* Cook et Doyle

Wettiniicarpus Burret

Wissmannia Burret

Woodsonia Bailey = Neonicholsonia Dammer

Wrightea Roxb. = Wallichia Roxb.

Y

Yarina Cook ? = Phytelephas R. et P.

Yuyba L. H. Bailey = *Amylocarpus* Barb. Rodr.

Z

Zalacca Reinw. ex Blume = Salacca Reinw.

Zalaccella Becc.

Zelonops Raf. = Phoenix L.

Zombia L. H. Bailey

Total valid genera: 235

LISTS OF PALMS TO BE FOUND GROWING OUTDOORS IN CERTAIN FAMOUS BOTANICAL GARDENS (REPRINTED FROM THE VARIOUS GARDEN LISTS)

FAIRCHILD TROPICAL GARDEN, COCONUT GROVE, FLORIDA

* This mark on any genus heading in this book indicates that at least one species of this genus can be found growing outdoors in southern Florida, either at this garden or at Chapman Field.

More species of palms can be seen growing outdoors in this garden than in any other place in the United States. There are 214 determined species and 89 undetermined. A good many of the palms are centered in one area and most of them are labeled.

The following list is reprinted from *Fairchild Tropical Garden Bulletin*, Winter Issue, 1958.

Acrocomia aculeata
A. armentalis
A. fusiformis
A. mexicana
A. sclerocarpa
A. totai
Actinorhytis calapparia
Aiphanes acanthophylla
A. caryotaefolia
A. erosa
A. flavispina
A. lindeniana
A. truncata
Archontophoenix
    alexandrae
Archontophoenix
    cunninghamiana

Areca cathecu
Arecastrum
    romanzoffianum
Arenga ambong
A. engleri
A. pinnata
A. tremula
A. undulatifolia
A. westerhoutii
A. wightii (?)
Arikuryroba schizophylla
Astrocaryum mexicanum
A. segregatum
A. standleyanum
Attalea amygdalina
A. indaya
Bactris major

Bismarckia nobilis
Borassus flabellifer
Butia bonnetii
B. braziliensis (?)
B. capitata
B. capitata var.
    nehrlingiana
B. entre -rios (?)
B. eriospatha
B. yatay
Calamus sp.
    (D.F. No. 437)
Caryota cumingii (?)
C. griffithii
C. mitis
C. ochlandra (?)
C. plumosa

C. urens
Chamaedorea elatior
C. erumpens
C. erumpens var.
    fairchildii
C. geonomaeformis
C. glaucifolia
C. c. pacaya (?)
C. radicalis
C. seifrizii
C. stolonifera
C. tepijilote
C. wendlandiana
Chamaerops canariensis
C. humilis
C. humilis var. *elegans*
C. macrocarpa

280

Chrysalidocarpus
   lucubensis
C. lutescens
C. madagascariensis
C. sp. c. "Cabada
   palm"
Coccothrinax acuminata
C. alta
C. argentata
C. dussiana
C. fragrans
C. martii
C. miraguama
Cocos nucifera
C. mucifera var. dwarf
   orange malay
C. nucifera var. dwarf
   yellow malay
C. nucifera var. dwarf
   green malay
C. nucifera var. king
   No. 1
C. nucifera var. king
   No. 2
C. nucifera var. nina
C. nucifera var. nawassi
Copernicia australis
C. baileyana
C. burretiana
C. cerifera
C. curbeloi
C. fallaense
C. gigas
C. glabrescens
C. holguinensis
C. hospita
C. pauciflora
C. rigida
C. seuroana (rigida x
   hospita)
C. torreana

C. yarey
C. yarey var. robusta
Corozo oleifera
Corypha elata
C. talliera
C. umbraculifera
Cryosophila nana
C. warscewiczii
Desmoncus polycanthus
Dictyosperma album
D. album var. rubrum
D. aureum
Drymophloeus beguinii
Elaeis guineensis
Eleutheropetalum sartorii
Erythea armata
Gaussia princeps (?)
Guilielma gasipaes
Heterospathe elata
Howeia forsteriana
H. belmoreana
Hyphaene coriacea
H. shatan
Jubaea spectabilis
Latania borbonica
L. loddigesii
L. verschaffeltii
Licuala grandis
L. spinosa
Livistona australis
L. chinensis
L. chinensis var.
   subglobosa
L. decipiens
L. hoogendorpii
L. mariae
L. muellerii
L. olivaeformis
L. ovalifolia
L. robinsoniana
L. rotundifolia var.

   luzonensis
Mascarena lagenicaulis
M. verschaffeltii
Nannorrhops ritchieana
Neanthe bella
Neodypsis decaryi
Normanbya (?) sp.
Nypa fruticans
Opsiandra maya
Orbignya barbosiana
O. cohune
O. guacayule
O. lydiae
Paurotis wrightii
Phoenix canariensis
P. dactylifera
P. humilis var. hanceana
P. macrocarpa
P. ouseleyana
P. pumila
P. reclinata
P. roebelenii
P. rupicola
P. senegalensis
P. sylvestris
P. tenuis
P. tomentosa
P. zeylanica
Pinanga kuhlii
Pritchardia affinis
P. pacifica
P. thurstonii
Pseudophoenix saonae
P. sargenti
P. vinifera
Ptychosperma
   augustifolia (?)
P. elegans
P. macarthuri
P. sanderianus
P. sp. 1 "taksi palm"

Rhapidophyllum hystrix
Rhapis excelsa
R. humilis
Roystonea oleracea (?)
R. regia
Sabal adansonii
S. causiarum
S. exul
S. glaucescens (?)
S. havenensis (?)
S. jamaicensis
S. longipedunculata (?)
S. mauritaeformis
S. mexicana
S. minor
S. nematoclada
S. palmetto
S. parviflora
S. umbraculifera
S. yapa
Scheelea butryracea
S. leandroana
S. liebmanii
S. urbaniana
Serenoa repens
S. repens var. cinerea (?)
Syagrus coronata
S. flexuosa
S. sancona
Thrinax microcarpa
T. morrisii
T. parviflora
Trithrinax acanthocoma
Veitchia joannis
V. merrillii
V. montgomeryana
V. winin
Washingtonia filifera
W. robusta
Zombia antillarum

U.S. PLANT INTRODUCTION GARDEN LOCATED AT COCONUT GROVE, FLORIDA, OFTEN KNOWN AS CHAPMAN FIELD

*This mark on any genus heading in this book indicates that some species of this genus can be found growing outdoors in southern Florida, either at this garden or at Fairchild Tropical Garden.

This long-established garden contains many mature palm specimens, including some very uncommon varieties. It is an experimental station and is open to the public; but there are no attendants or guides and the plants are not labeled.

The following list of palms definitely established in this garden as of August 15, 1956 is reproduced from *Principes*, the journal of the Palm Society, Vol. 1, No. 1, October 1956.

Acrocomia armentalis
A. sclerocarpa
Adonidia merrillii
Aiphanes caryotaefolia
A. lindeniana
Archontophoenix
    alexandrae
Areca cathecu
Arecastrum
    romanzoffianum
Arenga ambong
A. saccharifera
A. wightii
Arikuryroba schizophylla
Astrocaryum alatum
A. murumuru
A. standleyanum
Attalea crassispatha
Bactris balanoidea
Bentinckia nicobarica
Bismarckia nobilis
Borassus flabellifer
Brahea dulcis
Butia bonnetii
B. capitata
Caryota cumingii
C. mitis
C. plumosa
C. urens
Chamaedorea
    arenbergiana
C. concolor
C. erumpens

C. oblongata
C. tepejilote
Chamaerops humilis
Chrysalidocarpus
    lucubensis
C. lutescens
C. madagascariensis
Coccothrinax argentata
C. argentea
C. crinita
C. dussiana
C. martii
Cocos nucifera
Copernicia burretiana
C. cerifera
C. curbeloi
C. gigas
C. torreana
C. yarey
Corozo oleifera
Corypha elata
C. talliera
C. umbraculifera
Cryosophila warscewiczii
Daemonorops niger
Desmoncus oxyacanthos
Dictyosperma album
D. album var. rubrum
D. aureum
Diplothemium caudescens
Drymophloeus beguinii
D. olivaeformis
Elaeis guineensis

Eleutheropetalum ernesti-
    augustii
E. sartori
Erythea aculeata
E. armata
E. pimo
Eupritchardia affinis
E. lowreyana
E. pacifica
E. thurstonii
Gaussia attenuata
Geonoma sp.
    (Colombian)
Glaziova treubiana
Guilielma gasipaes
Heterospathe elata
Hexopetion mexicanum
Hyphaene turbinata
Latania borbonica
L. loddigesii
Licuala grandis
L. spinosa
Livistona altissima
L. chinensis
L. decipiens
L. hoogendorpii
L. mariae
L. Saribus
Mascarena lagenicaulis
M. verschaffeltii
Mauritia flexuosa
Nannorrhops ritchieana
Nypa fruticans

Oothrinax anomala
Opsiandra maya
Orbignya cohune
O. speciosa
O. spectabilis
Paurotis wrightii
Phoenix abyssinica
P. acaulis
P. canariensis
P. dactylifera
P. farinifera
P. pusilla
P. reclinata
P. roebelenii
P. rupicola
P. sylvestris
P. tomentosa
P. zeylanica
Pinanga kuhlii
Pseudophoenix saonae
P. sargentii
P. vinifera
Ptychosperma elegans
Raphia vinifera
Rhapis excelsa
Rhyticocos amara
Roystonea borinquena
R. elata
R. regia
Sabal beccariana
S. causiarum
S. glaucescens
S. mauritiaeformis

S. mexicana	*Scheelea butyracea*	*S. orinocensis*	*Trachycarpus martianus*
S. nematoclada	*S. gomphococca*	*Thrinax microcarpa*	*Trithrinax acanthocoma*
S. palmetto	*S. humboldtiana*	*T. morrisii*	*T. brasiliensis*
S. minor	*S. lauromuelleriana*	*T. parviflora*	*Vitiphoenix* sp.
S. texana	*Siphokentia beguinii*	*T. punctulata*	*Washingtonia robusta*
S. umbraculifera	*Syagrus coronata*		

HUNTINGTON BOTANICAL GARDENS, SAN MARINO, CALIFORNIA

† This mark on any genus described in this book indicates that some species of this genus can be found growing outdoors in this California garden.

This list of palms was compiled by the author from *Palms and Cycads* (1951) written by William Hertrich, curator of the Huntington Botanical Gardens near Pasadena.

There are some points in the southern end of California that have milder winters than Pasadena and whose climate might be a little more encouraging to certain tender species of palms.

Archonthophoenix alexandrae	*species*	*P. dactylifera*	*S. mexicana*
A. cunninghamiana	*Chamaerops humilis*	*P. glauca* (hybrid)	*S. minor*
Arecastrum romanzoffianum	*Chrysalidocarpus lutescens*	*P. humilis* (hybrid)	*S. palmetto*
A. romanzoffianum var. *australis*	*Collinia elegans*	*P. jubae* (hybrid)	*S. texana*
A. romanzoffianum var. *botryophorum*	*Erythea armata*	*P. loureiri* (hybrid)	*S. umbraculifera*
Arenga engleri	*E. brandegeei*	*P. paludosa*	*S. viatoris*
Brahea dulcis	*E. edulis*	*P. reclinata*	*S. yapa*
Butia bonnetii	*E. elegans*	*P. roebelenii*	*Syagrus insignis*
B. capitata	*Hedyscepe canterburyana*	*P. rupicola*	*S. macrocarpa*
B. eriospatha	*Howea belmoreana*	*P. sylvestris*	*S. weddelliana*
B. yatay	*H. forsteriana*	*P. zeylanica* (hybrid)	*Trachycarpus caespitosus*
Chamaedorea ernesti-augustii	*Jubaea spectabilis*	*Ptychosperma elegans*	*T. fortunei*
C. graminifolia	*Livistona australis*	*Rhapidophyllum hystrix*	*T. martianus*
C. pringlei	*L. chinensis*	*Rhapis excelsa*	*T. nana*
C. sartori	*L. decipiens*	*R. humilis*	*Trachycarpus takil*
C. stolonifera	*L. mariae*	*Rhopalostylis sapida*	*T. wagnerianus*
C. several unnamed	*Mascarena lagenicaulis*	*Sabal causiarum*	*Trithrinax acanthocoma*
	M. verschaffeltii	*S. deeringiana*	*T. campestris*
	Paurotis wrightii	*S. exul*	*Washingtonia filifera*
	Phoenix canariensis	*S. guatemalensis*	*W. robusta*
	P. cycadifolia (hybrid)	*S. louisiana*	*W. robusta* var. *gracilis*
		S. mauritaeformis	

BOGOR BOTANIC GARDENS, BOGOR, JAVA

This list was published in 1957 by the gardens and supplied by Mr. Anwara Dilmy, Director of the Herbarium Bogoriense of the Bogor Botanic Gardens. Only the names of the genera are given, as compiled on page 262 of the catalogue. A full list of all species and varieties at this garden would be too lengthy. This list is printed exactly as published.

These famous gardens, established in 1817, have been described as the most beautiful in the world. There is little doubt that the variety of palms to be found here is greater than in any other garden. The total annual rainfall of Bogor is 180–200 inches, or about four times that of Miami, Florida, and ten times that of southern California.

PALMAE

Acanthophoenix	*Cocos*	*Kentia*	*Pigafetta*
Acanthorrhiza	*Coelococcus*	*Kentiopsis*	*Pinanga*
Acoelorraphe	*Corypha*	*Korthalsia*	*Plectocomia*
Actinophloeus	*Cyrtostachys*	*Latania*	*Plectocomiopsis*
Actinorhytis	*Daemonorops*	*Licuala*	*Pritchardia*
Adelonenga	*Deckenia*	*Linospadix*	*Ptychandra*
Ancistrophyllum	*Desmoncus*	*Livistona*	*Ptychococcus*
Archontophoenix	*Dictyosperma*	*Lodoicea*	*Ptychoraphis*
Areca	*Didymosperma*	*Loxococcus*	*Ptychosperma*
Arecastrum	*Drymophloeus*	*Martinezia*	*Raphia*
Arenga	*Elaeis*	*Maximiliana*	*Rhapis*
Astrocaryum	*Eremospatha*	*Medemia*	*Rhopaloblaste*
Attalea	*Erythea*	*Metroxylon*	*Rhopalostylis*
Bactris	*Eugeissona*	*Nenga*	*Sabal*
Barbosa	*Euterpe*	*Nephrosperma*	*Scheelea*
Bentinckia	*Gaussia*	*Nypa*	*Socratea*
Borassus	*Geonoma*	*Normanbya*	*Stevensonia*
Brahea	*Glaziova*	*Oenocarpus*	*Syagrus*
Butia	*Gronophyllum*	*Oncosperma*	*Thrinax*
Calamus	*Gulubia*	*Opsiandra*	*Trachycarpus*
Calyptrocalyx	*Heterospathe*	*Orania*	*Trithrinax*
Calyptrogyne	*Hyophorbe*	*Orbignya*	*Veitchia*
Caryota	*Hyphaene*	*Oreodoxa*	*Verschaffeltia*
Ceratolobus	*Iguanura*	*Pelagodoxa*	*Vitiphoenix*
Chamaedorea	*Inodes*	*Phoenix*	*Wallichia*
Chamaerops	*Iriartea*	*Pholidocarpus*	*Washingtonia*
Chrysalidocarpus	*Jubaea*	*Phytelephas*	*Zalacca*

BOTANICAL GARDEN, RIO DE JANEIRO, BRAZIL

One of the world's greatest botanical gardens, the Botanical Garden contains a great number and variety of palm species.

This special list was sent to the author by the director, P. Campos Porto, on July 9, 1958. The words following the species name are the sources of origin of the names. The names following the dashes are evidently common names. The list is reproduced as received.

Acanthophoenix rubra H. Wendl.

Acrocomia intumescens Drude—Macauba

A. sclerocarpa Mart.

Aiphanes acanthophylla (Mart.) Burret

A. caryotifolia (H.B.K.) Wendel.—Paxiuba majerona

A. elegans (Linden and Wendl.)

A. erosa (Linden) Burret

A. lindeniana Wendl.

Archontophoenix alexandrae Wendl. and Drude

A. cunninghamiana (Wendl. and Drude) Burret

Areca catechu Linn.

A. triandra Roxb.

Arecastrum romanzoffianum (Cham.) Becc.— Geriva, Baba de Bei

A. Becc. var. *australe* (Mart.) Becc.

Arenga engleri Becc.

A. saccharifera Labill.

A. undulatifolia Becc.

Arikuriroba schizophylla (Mart.) Bailey—Aricuriroba, Nicuriroba, Urucuriroba

Astrocaryum acaule Mart.

A. aculeatissimum (Schott) Burret

A. jauari Mart.—Jauari

A. munbaca Mart.—Mumbaca

A. murumuru Mart.—Murumuru

Attalea dubia (Mart.) Burret—Indaia

A. concinna (Barb. Rodr.) Burret—Coco de Indaia

A. funifera Mart.—Piacaba

A. humilis Mart.—Pindoba

Bactris caryotaefolia Mart.

B. setosa Mart.—Tucum de Brejo

B. utilis Benth et Hook

B. vulgaris Barb. Rodr.—Airi, Airi-mirim, Iri-mirim

Balaka seemanii Becc.

Barbosa pseudo-cocos Becc.—Palmito amargoso

Borassus flabellifer Linn.

Butia capitata (Mart.) Becc.—Coqueiro cabeludo

B. capitata var. *odorata* (B.R.)—Beccari, Butia

B. eriospatha (Mart.) Becc.—Butia do Campa

Calamus dealbatus Hort.

C. ornatus Blume

Caryota mitis Lour.

C. plumosa Hort.

C. rumphiana Mart.

C. urens Linn.

Chamaedorea oblongata Mart.

C. tepejilote Liebm.

Chamaerops humilis Linn.

C. humilis L. var. *dachylocarpa* Becc.

C. humilis L. var. *macrocarpa*

Chrysalidocarpus lucubensis Becc.

C. lutescens H. Wendl.—Palmeira bambu

Coccothrinax argentea K. Sch.

C. martii Becc.

Collinia elegans (Mart.) Liebm.

Copernicia australis Becc.—Caranda

C. cerifera (Arruda Camara) Mart.—Carnauba

Corozo oelifera (H.B.K.) Bailey—Caisue

Corypha gebanga Blume

C. taliera Roxb.

C. umbraculifera Linn.

Cryosophila nana (H.B.K.) Blume ex Jacks

C. warscewiczii (Wendl.) Bartlett

Cyphosperma vieillardi Benth.

Cyrtostachys renda Blume—Palmeira lacca

Daemonorops grandis Mart.

Desmoncus horridus Splitg. ex Mart.

D. polyacanthos Mart.—Jacitara

D. pycnacanthos Mart.

Dictyosperma album H. Wendl. et Drude

D. furfuraceum H. Wendl. et Drude

Didymosperma distichum Hort.

Diplothemium maritimum Mart.—Coco da praia, guriri

Elaeis guineensis Jacq.—Coco de dende

E. quineensis Jacq. var. *communis* Chev.— Palmeira dende

Erythea roezlii (Linden) Becc.

Euterpe badiocarpa Barb. Rodr.—Acai Pardo

E. catinga Wallace—Açai chumbo

E. oleracea Mart.—Açai, palmiteiro, pina, Tucaniei, Jussara

Geonoma princeps Linden—Uakanga

G. pumila H. Wendl.—Uricana

Guilielma gasipaes (H.B.K.) Bailey—Pupunha verde amarela

G. gasipaes (H.B.K.) Bailey var. *coccinea* (Barb. Rodgr.) Bailey—Pupunha

Howea forsteriana Becc.

Hyophorbe amaricaulis Mart.

H. verschaffeltii H. Wendl.

Iriartea ventricosa Mart.—Paxiuba barriguda

Kentia kersteniana Hort.

Kentiopsis macrocarpa Brongn.

Latania commersonii Gmel.

L. verschaffeltii Lem.

Leopoldinia piassaba Wallace—Palmeira piassava

L. pulchra Mart.—Jara, Mucuri

Licuala amplifrons Miq.

L. elegans Blume.

L. grandis H. Wendl.

L. jeannenceyi Hort.

L. rumphii Blume

L. spinosa Thunb.

Linospadix petrickiana Hort.

Livistona australis Mart.

L. decipiens Becc.

L. geninghei Hort.

L. hoogendorpii Hort.

L. olivaeformis Mart. var. *albo striata* Hort.

L. rotundifolia Mart.

L. subglobosa Mart.

Manicaria saccifera Gaertn.—Byçu, Ubuçu, Tucuri

Mauritia aculeata H.K.K.—Carana-i

M. flexuosa Linn. f.—Meriti, Arvore da vida, Buriti do brejo, Muriti

M. vinifera Mart.—Buriti

Maximiliana regia Mart.—Inajai

Microcoelum insigne (Drude) Burret and Potztal—Palmerinha da Serra

Microcoelum martianum (Glaz. ex Drude) Burret and Potztal—Palmeira de Petropolis

Nenga wendlandiana Scheff.

Neonicholsonia georgei Damm.

Oenocarpus bacaba Mart.—Bacaba

O. distichus Mart.—Bacaba de azeite

Oncosperma filamentosum Blume.

Opsiandra maya O. F. Cook

Orania philippinensis Scheff.

Orbignya barbosiana Burret—Babaçu

O. cohune (Mart.) Dahlgr.

O. spectabilis (Mart.) Burret—Curua piranga, Uauçu

Phoenix dactylifera Linn.

P. farinifera Roxb.

P. humilis Royle.

P. porphyrococcos Vasc. et Franc.

P. pumila Hort.—Tamara

P. rupicola T. Anders.

P. sylvestris Roxb.

P. tomentosam Hort.

P. zeylanica Hort.

Phytelephas macrocarpa Ruiz et Pav.—Marfim vegetal

Pinanga kuhlii Blume.

P. spectabilis Bull.

Plectocomia elongata Mart. and Blume

Pritchardia aurea Hort. ex Hook.

P. pacifica Seem and Wendl.

P. thurstoni F. Muell. and Dr.

Ptychococcus paradoxus Becc.

Ptychosperma elegans Blume.

P. macarthurii H. Wendl.

Pyrenoglyphis balanoidea (Oerst.) Karst.

P. concinna (Mart.) Burret

P. maraja (Mart.) Burret

P. ottostapfeana (Barb. Rodr.) Burret—Maraja-açu

Rhapis flabelliformis L*Herit.—Jupati

R. humilis Blume

Roystonea oleracea (Mart.) Cook—Palmeira real

R. regia (H.B.K.) Cook

Sabal blackburnianum Glazebrook

S. causiarum Becc.—Iarai

S. ghiesbrechtii Hort.

S. glaucescens Lodd.

S. havanensis Lodd.

S. palmetto Lodd.

S. texana (Cook) Becc.

Serenoa repens (Bartr.) Small

Scheelea amylacea Barb. Rodr.—Anaja

S. huebneri Burret *Urucuri*

S. lauromulleriana Barb. Rodr. Baguaçu

S. leandreana Barb. Rodr.

S. macrocarpa Karst.

S. osmantha Barb. Rodr.

S. urbaniana Burret

S. wallisii (Hub.) Burret—Jaci

Socratea exhorrhiza (Mart.) Wendl.—Paxiuba

Stevensonia grandifolia J. Dunc.

Syagrus campos-porteana (Sond.) Burret—Licuri-assu

S. catechucarpa (Barb. Rodr.) Becc.

S. chloroleuca (Barb. Rodr.) Burret

S. coronata (Mart.) Becc.—Aricuri, Nicuri

S. edulis (B. R.) Fromb. Dahler apud.

S. inajai Becc.—Pupunha de Porco, Inaja-y-Jara

S. quinquefaria (Barb. Rodr.) Burret

Thrinax floridana Sarg.

T. punctulata Becc.

T. sapida Lodd.

T. wendlandiana Becc.

Trachycarpus takil Becc.

T. excelsus (Thunb.) Wendl.

T. wagnerianus Hort.

Trithrinax acanthocoma Drude—Buriti palito

T. brasiliensis Mart.—Carandai

Veitchia joannis H. Wendl.

Washingtonia sonorae S. Wats.

W. robusta Wendl.

Wallichia densiflora Mart.

W. macrophylla ?

Zalacca edulis Blume

HOPE BOTANIC GARDEN, KINGSTON, JAMAICA, WEST INDIES
(From list printed in 1954, printed as original)

Acanthorriza aculeata

Acrocomia lasiospatha

Archontophoenix cunninghamiana

Areca aliciae

A. catechu

A. glandiformis

A. triandra

Astrocaryum vulgare

Attalea cohune

Caryota mitis

C. sobolifera

C. urens

Chrysalidocarpus lutescens

Cocos bitryophora

C. flexuosa

C. plumosa

C. romanzoffiana

Copernicia cerifera

Corypha umbraculifera

Dictyosperma album

D. rubrum

Dypsis madagascariensis

Elaeis guineensis

Euterpe edulis

Geonoma swartizii

Heterospathe elata

Hydriastele wendlandiana

Licuala elegans

L. peltata

L. spinosa

L. grandis

Livistona australis

L. chinensis

L. olivaeformis

L. rotundifolia

L. subglobosa

Oncosperma fasciculatum

Oreodoxa oleracea

O. regia

Phoenix acaulis

Pinanga kuhlii

Pritchardia thurstonii

P. pacifica

Sabal umbraculifera

S. andansoni

Stevensonia grandifolia

Thrinax argentea

T. excelsa

BOTANIC GARDEN OF ADELAIDE, AUSTRALIA
(From list sent to the author by the director, F. R. H. Lothian, April 16, 1958)

Actinophloeus macarthuri

Archontophoenix alexandrae

A. cunninghamiana

Areca cathecu

A. triandra

Arecastrum romanzoffianum

Arenga pinnata

Bentinckia nicobarica

Butia capitata

B. capitata var.

odorata

Caryota mitis

C. urens

Chamaerops humilis

Chrysalidocarpus lutescens
Coccothrinax argentea
Cryosophila nana
Daemonorops grandis
Dictyosperma album
Elaeis guineensis
Erythea armata
E. edulis

Howeia forsteriana
Jubaea spectabilis
Livistona cochinchinensis
L. mariae
Phoenix canariensis
P. dactylifera
P. humilis

P. reclinata
P. roebelinii
Raphia pedunculata
Rhopalostylis sapida
Roystonea oleracea
R. regia
Sabal bermudana

S. minor
S. palmetto
Syagrus campestris
S. weddelliana
Trachycarpus fortunei
Washingtonia filifera
W. robusta

BOTANIC GARDENS, SINGAPORE
(From a list published in 1939)

Acanthorrhiza aculeata
Actinorhytis calapparia
Archontophoenix
   alexandrae
Areca catechu
A. glandiformis
A. triandra
Arecastrum romanzoffianum
Arenga saccharifera
A. undulatifolia
A. westerhoutii
Astrocaryum tucumoides
Attalea cohune
Bactris utilis
B. major
Bentinckia nicobarica
Borassus machadonis
Calamus scipionum
Calyptrocalyx spicatus
Caryota mitis
Chrysalidocarpus
   decipiens

C. lutescens
C. madagascariensis
Cocos nucifera
Coelococcus carolinensis
Cyrtostachys lakka
Daemonorops
   angustifolius
D. grandis
Didymosperma
   porphyrocarpon
Elaeis guineensis
Euterpe oleracea
Heterospathe elata
Korthalsia scaphigera
Licuala ferruginea
L. grandis
L. horrida
L. rumphii
L. spinosa
Livistona chinensis
L. cochinchinensis

L. rotundifolia
Loxococcus rupicola
Martinezia caryotaefolia
M. erosa
Nenga wendlandiana
Nypa fruticans
Normanbya muellerii
Oncosperma horridum
O. tigillarium
Orania macrocladus
O. philippinensis
O. regalis
Oreodoxa oleracea
O. regia
Paurotis wrightii
Phoenix sylvestris
Pholidocarpus
   macrocarpa
Pinanga coronata
P. disticha
P. furfuracea

P. kuhlii
Plectocomia elongata
Ptychococcus paradoxus
Ptychoraphis
   singaporensis
Ptychosperma elegans
P. macarthuri
P. sanderianum
Raphia ruffia
R. hookeri
Rhopaloblaste hexandra
Sabal adansonii
S. causiarum
S. palmetto
Sagus laevis
Scheelea kewensis
Stevensonia grandifolia
Thrinax argentea
T. parviflora
Verschaffeltia splendida
Zalacca edulis

BIBLIOGRAPHY

Bailey Hortorium, *Gentes Herbarum*, vols. 2, 3, 4, 6, 7, 8.

Bailey, L. H., *Hortus Second*, compiled by L. H. Bailey and Ethel Zoe Bailey, The Macmillan Company, New York, 1930.

——, *Manual of Cultivated Plants*, by L. H. Bailey and the Staff of the Bailey Hortorium at Cornell University, The Macmillan Company, New York, 1924.

——, *The Standard Cyclopedia of Horticulture*, 3 vol. The Macmillan Company, New York, 1914.

Baker, J. G., *Flora of Mauritius and the Seychelles;* Palm Section by Dr. I. B. Balfour, Lovell Reeve & Company, Ltd., London, 1877.

Beccari, O., and R. E. G. Pichi-Sermolli, *Subfamiliae Arecoidearum Palmae Gerontogeae* (Reprinted from *Webbia*, vol. XI, pp. 1–187, 1955).

Blatter, Ethelburt, *The Palms of British India and Ceylon*, Oxford University Press, London and New York, 1926.

Bomhard, Miriam L., *Palm Trees in the United States* (Agricultural Information Bulletin No. 22, undated).

Brown, William H., *Useful Plants of the Philippines*, Technical Bulletin 10, vol. 1, Department of Agriculture, Republic of the Philippines, 1951.

Burret, Max, and Eva Potztal, *Systematische Übersicht über die Palmen* (Fortsetzung), Paper No. XXI, 1956; reprinted from *Willdenowia*. Berlin Dahlen, 1956.

Dahlgren, B. E., *Index of American Palms*, Field Museum of Natural History, Chicago, 1936.

Fairchild, David, *Exploring for Plants*, The Macmillan Company, New York, 1931.

——, *Garden Islands of the Great East*, Charles Scribner's Sons, New York, 1948.

——, *Occasional Papers*, No. 7, 15, 17, Fairchild Tropical Garden, 1940–1948.

——, *The World Grows Round My Door*, Charles Scribner's Sons, New York, 1947.

——, *The World Was My Garden*, Charles Scribner's Sons, New York, 1948.

Hawkes, Alex D., *The Major Kinds of Palms* (Botanical Papers 1–8, Fairchild Tropical Garden, Coral Gables, Florida, 1950–1952).

Hertrich, William, *Palms and Cycads, Their Culture in Southern California*, Henry E. Huntington Library and Art Gallery, San Marino, California, 1951.

Humbert, H., *Flore de Madagascar*, Palm Section by H. Jumelle and H. Perrier de la Bathie, L'Imprimerie Officielle, Tananarive, Madagascar, 1945.

289

Humbert, H., *Flore General de l' Indo-China*, vol. VI, Palm Section by Gagnepain and Conrard, Masson et Cie, Paris, 1937.

Kuck, Loraine E. and Tongg, Richard C., *The Modern Tropical Garden*, Tongg Publishing Company, Honolulu, Hawaii, 1955.

Leon, Hermano, *Flora de Cuba*, Cultural, S. A., Havana, Cuba, 1946.

Loomis, H. F., *The Nipa Palm of the Orient*, reprinted from *National Horticultural Magazine*, January, 1949.

MacMillan, H. F., *Tropical Planting and Gardening with Special Reference to Ceylon*, The Macmillan Company, Ltd., London, 1949.

Martius, Karl F. P. von, *Historia Naturalis Palmarum*, 1823–1850.

Mowry, Harold, *Native and Exotic Palms of Florida*, Agricultural Extension Service Bulletin 152, Gainesville, Florida, February, 1955.

Ridley, Henry N., *Flora of the Malay Peninsula*, vol. V, Lovell Reeve & Company, Ltd., London, 1925.

Rodrigues, Barbosa, *Surtum Palmarum Braziliensis*,

Saakov, S. G., *Palms and Their Culture in U.S.S.R.*, Academy of Science, Moscow, U.S.S.R., 1954.

Seemann, Berthold, *Popular History of the Palms and Their Allies*, Lovell Reeve & Company, Ltd., London, 1856.

Standley and Steyermark, *Flora of Guatemala*, Field Museum of Natural History, Chicago, 1958.

Thistelton-Dyer, Sir W. T., *Flora of Tropical Africa*, vol. VIII, Lovell Reeve & Company, Ltd., Ashford, Kent, 1902.

Wallace, Alfred Russel, *Palm Trees of the Amazon*, J. Van Voorst, London, 1853.

Williams, R. O., *The Useful and Ornamental Plants in Trinidad and Tobago*, Guardian Commercial Printery, Trinidad, 1951.